SUPERTHERAPIES

SUPERTHERAPIES
JANE ALEXANDER

BANTAM BOOKS

TORONTO • NEW YORK • LONDON • SYDNEY • AUCKLAND

SUPERTHERAPIES
A BANTAM BOOK : 0 553 40997 2

First publication in Great Britain

PRINTING HISTORY
Bantam edition published 1996

The author of this book is not a physician, and the ideas,
procedures, and suggestions in this book are intended to supplement,
not replace, the medical and legal advice of trained professionals.
All matters regarding your health require medical supervision.
Consult your medical practitioner before adopting the suggestions in
this book, as well as about any condition that may require
diagnosis or medical attention.

Set in 10 on 12pt Linotype Palatino by
Phoenix Typesetting, Ilkley, West Yorkshire

Bantam Books are published by Transworld Publishers Ltd,
61–63 Uxbridge Road, London W5 5SA,
in Australia by Transworld Publishers (Australia) Pty Ltd,
15–25 Helles Avenue, Moorebank, NSW 2170
and in New Zealand by Transworld Publishers (NZ) Ltd,
3 William Pickering Drive, Albany, Auckland.

Reproduced, printed and bound in Great Britain by
Cox & Wyman Ltd, Reading, Berks.

For Rosemary and Erik – my original supertherapists

ACKNOWLEDGEMENTS

I hope you find this book a helpful friend. It would not be sitting in your hands now without the following people whose help and support have been an inspiration.

My family who brought me up with alternative health: my mother the homeopath and my father the wonder-masseur. My brother who wound me into yoga positions when I was young and supple enough to bend; my sister who took me chanting and meditating. My wonderful husband for always managing to drum up (undoubtedly feigned) interest when I enthuse about yet another weird and wonderful therapy.

My agent Judy Chilcote for persuading me to write this book. My editor Francesca Liversidge for her enthusiasm and for making the process such fun.

And a huge thank you to all the amazing supertherapists I have met who have fed me herbs and made me pop vitamins; who have bent and twisted and manipulated me in every which way. Many was the time I walked off the streets into your clinics feeling shattered and walked out after a couple of hours floating on cloud nine. You are too many to mention, but you will find your wisdom in these pages. Bless you all and thank you.

CONTENTS

INTRODUCTION

Why this book – and why me?

I'm not a doctor and I'm not a therapist. I'm just an ordinary person who became fed up with feeling permanently under par and luckily stumbled on a way to do something about it. My interest in the supertherapies began when I was in my early twenties. I always seemed to be sick, permanently going down with colds and flu, bouts of bronchitis and strep throat. Then by some lucky chance, I stumbled across homeopathy and acupuncture, herbalism and aromatherapy. I tried them, started to feel better and became hooked. Natural health has been a way of life for me for most of my life now.

As a journalist, I had written, on and off, about natural therapies for many years, but around three years ago the *Daily Mail* asked me to write for a new weekly column called 'Self'. The aim of 'Self' was to provide an insight into the best ways – whether ancient or ultra-modern – to keep fit and healthy in body and mind. Each method had to be tried and tested – and I was the guinea pig. My friends fondly imagine I spend my entire working life lying on a massage table but, sadly, it's not an endless round of aromatherapy and facials. I've been crunched and cracked, twisted and trodden on, hypnotized and regressed. One week I subsisted on a detoxification diet of orange juice and garlic (and was promptly put into solitary confinement by my husband); another week I spent gnawing my fingernails and chewing Biros on a water fast. I've passed out in steam cabinets, tramped over burning coals, sat submerged up to my ears in mud. I have endured needles stuck in places that even gynaecologists haven't discovered. Sometimes I think I must be mad.

However, I have now tried virtually every therapy under the sun, and I think I'm in a position to give you an idea of what's out there. I'm sure plenty of people don't venture into natural health because they simply don't know what to expect. After all, Zero Balancing sounds less than reassuring and Manual Lymph Drainage sounds like some kind of sewer system. Hopefully, *Supertherapies* will help you sort out your Bowen from your Bach flower remedies, and radionics from Rolfing. It's not a clinical textbook and it won't tell you how to treat individual illnesses and ailments. I'm not qualified to do that, and it's not something any mere book can or should do. What it does do, however, is tell you what's out there and how it might help you. And instead of getting the opinion of just one expert, you'll be able to read the wisdom of scores of them.

All the practitioners I interviewed while researching this book are renowned in their fields; many have been practising for decades. Between them they boast hundreds of years of healing expertise. Hopefully, *Supertherapies* will allow you to choose a therapy that suits you. Where space allows, I've included my personal experiences of each therapy purely because the one thing most books and leaflets don't ever tell you is the nitty-gritty: do you have to take your clothes off; will you be asked all kinds of embarrassing questions; will you be prodded and poked in weird places; and, above all, will it hurt? Personally, I think those things are important. *Supertherapies* will, I hope, make all crystal clear.

WHY SUPERTHERAPIES?

Imagine waking up every morning and feeling as if you were literally bursting with life. Imagine having all the energy you need and much, much more. Imagine looking in the mirror and seeing a smiling face grinning back at you: eyes bright, skin clear, the expression calm and relaxed. Imagine dealing with all the strains and tensions of everyday life with consummate ease. By now you're probably thinking 'dream on', but good health and positive wellbeing are not some impossible quest for hidden treasure – they should be our birthright. It's simply up to us to claim them.

The problem is we have become accustomed to feeling ill, run-down, depressed and low. It's hardly surprising when you look around you: switch on the television and the news is full of disasters, death and decay; flick open a paper and you'll read about rising figures for cancer, terrifying new diseases, the frightening escalation in mental illness. Financial advisers give grim warnings: get private health insurance, because who knows when you'll need that operation; and you'll need insurance in case you fall so ill you won't be able to work; and while you're at it, you'd better grab life insurance because you're sure to meet with a mishap which will plunge your family into financial ruin. No wonder we spend so much of our lives ill or under par – it's as if the whole of society expects it of us. But it doesn't have to be that way.

Unless we have had the misfortune to be born with a disability or congenital illness, we start off OK; it's just what we do to ourselves that causes the rot. We live surrounded by pollution, breathing in a toxic cocktail of car fumes, cigarette smoke and chemicals. We eat food that has been so tampered with that it isn't just lacking in essential nutrients, it is often potentially damaging. We sit all day in front of screens and in cars that force us to contort our posture. We lead lives so full of anxiety and anguish that it affects not only our minds but also our bodies. Our lives are so toxic that it's a surprise we function at all.

So, doom and gloom? No, not at all. I'm not saying you can cure everything in one fell swoop, but you can make your life better, much better. I'm not a health fascist and there's no way I'm going to suggest anything draconian or unfeasible. Frankly, what's the point in swapping a miserable life of indulgence for a miserable life of abstinence? To be healthy, you have to be happy too and there's no way I, for one, could devote every waking hour to my health. So this book won't ask you to eat seaweed for breakfast or to spend six hours a day exercising. I wouldn't dream of telling you to kiss goodbye to chocolate for ever and I certainly won't object if you knock back the odd glass of wine or gobble the stray bacon sandwich.

Admittedly, this book does contain some seemingly bizarre tips for health – but they are the views of the individual practitioners. If you like the sound of them, try them and see how you feel. If not, forget it. Truly, there's no point in forcing yourself to do anything you don't want to. Almost all the supertherapists would agree that *you* are the one who heals your body; they only act as catalysts. And, most importantly, if you throw yourself hook, line and sinker into a wonderful new healthy lifestyle, please don't bully your family and friends into following your new-found zeal for health. If they want to join in, great, but remember that marriages have broken up over a steak sandwich or a packet of cigarettes.

I'm not promising you instant and everlasting perfect health either. Natural healthcare certainly doesn't mean you won't ever get another cold or dose of flu. Being ill is the body's way of telling us something needs changing. Sometimes we're running round so fast that the only way our bodies can get a rest is by totally incapacitating us with a cold. But what do we do? We stuff ourselves with cold remedies to suppress the symptoms, or we race off for flu jabs to prevent it happening again. The net result is that our immune systems are prevented from doing their work; they don't get a chance to build up their natural defences. The odd cold does wonders for your immune system, and if you take to your bed it allows your whole body the rest it probably craves. But then again, once you get your body in tip-top working condition, immune system happily chugging along, you'll find you get less minor colds and flu. And when you do, don't expect your practitioner to automatically give you something to cure it. He or she might suggest a remedy to help relieve the worst symptoms, but generally the advice will be to let it run its course.

A large part of this book is simple good commonsense. Get your diet right, your exercise right and your mind set right, and you shouldn't really need much more. But that can be tough to do all on your own, which is where the supertherapies come in. A good natural healthcare practitioner should be able to put you on the right track and keep you there.

On skimming through this book, you might think the therapies are all completely different. But what they do have in common is that they all work *with* your body, coaxing and encouraging it back to health. In addition, they are all totally holistic. In other words, they aim to treat your *whole* self – your body *and* your mind – not just your immediate symptoms. This is a really important point and it's where natural health and orthodox medicine really diverge.

Don't ditch your doctor

Please don't think I'm advising you to ditch your GP tomorrow – or, indeed, at all. We have a lot for which to thank orthodox medicine, and powerful modern drugs most certainly play an essential role in the treatment of serious illnesses. I myself might not be here were it not for the antibiotics that pulled me through pneumonia many years ago. Orthodox medicine is great at racing in when the situation gets really dire. Doctors and surgeons are like the cavalry – they sweep in and save the day. But what they aren't so good at is preventing illness in the first place. A few are now catching on: some health centres offer specialists in nutrition to guide patients towards healthier eating; a rare few prescribe the gym for their patients, and the truly enlightened enrol their stressed patients on a course in meditation, instead of packing them off with a prescription. But those are exceptions and, for the time being, if you want to safeguard your health you have to do it for yourself.

Take responsibility

The single most important thing we can do towards a happier, healthier life is to realize that we can make choices and take responsibility for our own wellbeing. It's a tough one, because all our lives we've been taught that the doctor knows best. We've sat patiently while consultants talked over our heads and nurses muttered over charts. We've obediently swallowed powerful drugs without even questioning what they do and what their side effects might be.

We've so abnegated responsibility that we no longer know how to listen to our bodies. We've been on so many diets that we no longer know when we're hungry; we take so many stimulants (yes, coffee and tea do count) that we hardly know when to sleep. And the pressures of work and family are so great that even when we're virtually fainting on our feet with tiredness or flu, we ignore our bodies' plaintive pleas to take to our beds: we just keep going regardless.

Natural medicine helps us get back in tune with our bodies. Practised properly, it doesn't just attack the symptom; it roots around for the cause. This is the reason why natural therapies are not generally a quick fix. Although an osteopath will often be able to give you swift relief from a twisted muscle or a painful joint, his or her real aim will be to balance your whole body, to coax you back to optimum strength and vitality and to prevent the problem recurring. And although acupuncturists may have gained a reputation for being able to stop you smoking or bingeing by sticking a needle in your ear, their true way of working would be to treat the whole person, by slowly ironing out the reasons behind your smoking or overeating, so that the cure will be permanent.

What to expect; what not to expect

Don't expect an instant cure. Sometimes miraculous things do happen very quickly, but that is not usually the case. Beware of any practitioner who swears he or she can 'cure' serious diseases. No-one can promise to cure cancer, or AIDS, or multiple sclerosis just like that. Even orthodox doctors with all those powerful drugs and highly refined surgery can't do that. Cures do happen, miracles do occur, but please don't pin all your hopes on the claims of anyone who promises them as a matter of course. Sadly, not everyone in natural medicine is totally trustworthy: some are merely misguided; others are total charlatans. Two things ring warning bells in my head: anyone claiming cast-iron 'cures' and anyone charging extortionate amounts of money. Which brings me on to a very important issue . . .

How to choose a therapist

Personal recommendation is obviously the best way of all. If some-one has had wonderful results with a therapist, then that therapist must be doing something right. But bear in mind that what suits your best friend or your mother might not suit you. Most good, well-qualified, ethical therapists belong to societies and organizations that monitor standards, and when such organizations exist, I have listed them at the back of this book. Sometimes there are several organizations for each discipline and this rather confusing situation is likely to continue until complementary medicine brings everyone into line. Umbrella organizations such as the Institute for Complementary Medicine also hold lists of qualified practitioners.

Sometimes, however, there is no controlling organization, as is generally the case when there are only a few therapists in a particular discipline. In these instances, I have listed individual contacts who are willing to pass on the names of qualified practitioners.

Having tracked down a practitioner in your area, phone up and have a chat. Anyone worth their salt will be happy to discuss their therapy and answer any of your queries. You can gauge a lot from a short conversation: if it makes you feel uneasy and uncomfortable, forget it – this isn't the practitioner for you. On the other hand, if you feel relaxed and think you could work with him or her (remember this is a partnership, not a doctor-patient relationship), then go ahead and book an appointment. And, if, after the first appointment you aren't happy with that practitioner, then try someone else. It's perfectly permissible to try out a few practitioners before you make your final choice, and no-one will think it strange.

How to choose your supertherapy

I have personally tried all the therapies outlined in this book. Some of them I have been using for years and I can positively swear by their efficacy. Others, naturally, haven't had the opportunity to be given the full grilling, and in these cases I have talked to people who have used them over months, and sometimes years, and all seem to be pretty valid.

Making your choice can be tricky. I am always asked which are the best supertherapies but, to be honest, there is no such thing as a 'best'. What's easy going for me might prove a tough ride for you, and my best advice to you is to skim through this book and see what appeals to you. If you loathe needles, then don't choose acupuncture simply because your best friend says you must. And if you can't get your head round the idea of taking a pill that contains not even a molecule of its original substance, then forget homeopathy.

Dangers, warnings and reassurances

If you pick a good practitioner there really is no danger in any of these therapies. However, they are powerful and they do deserve respect, which is why, as a general principle, you should always consult a qualified practitioner rather than rely solely on a DIY book. For example, aromatherapy is a beautiful therapy, highly relaxing and utterly divine. But the oils used are very strong, very potent, and some of them are highly toxic if taken in the wrong amounts or if given to the wrong person. Some can even induce miscarriage. So don't just pull nice-smelling bottles off the chemist's shelf and ladle them onto your skin – consult the experts.

There has been a lot of fuss about herbs in recent years with reports that herbal products are toxic or that Chinese preparations

22

could damage the liver. Frankly, there is very little substance in these. It's a sad fact, but many of the rumours are spread by people with highly vested interests: doctors scared of losing their customers and the large pharmaceutical companies who are alarmed at the thought of seeing their profits drop. One particular herb, valerian, came under attack with claims that it was toxic to the liver. A report was filed in the medical press and, years later, doctors still point the finger accusingly and use it as an excuse to try to ban herbal medicines. Yet extensive research showed that the report was far from conclusive, and valerian has been totally exonerated. What I find rather ironical about cases like this is that the doctors who point their fingers in dire warning against natural medicines seem to forget what their own drugs do. Flip through any handbook of drugs and just look at the side-effects. From the horrors of thalidomide, to everyday drugs like antihistamines which make you drowsy and confused, and cortisones which make skin paper-thin.

Let it be said that, in the hands of a qualified practitioner, herbs, oils and homeopathic preparations are totally totally safe. And one more reassurance: if you have a serious medical condition and need to take medical drugs, there is absolutely no way a qualified therapist will take you off those drugs. What could happen is that, as treatment progresses, you might be able to reduce your dose and eventually not need the drugs at all. But this would only happen under strictly controlled conditions, and in close consultation with your doctor. No good therapist will shun orthodox medicine. Sometimes drastic measures are called for – your condition might be too extreme and need urgent medical help. Then it would be a case of having the operation or taking the drugs – but your therapist will be able to help minimize the shock to your body and help you recover far more quickly. Many therapists now work in enlightened hospitals, helping with patients' post-operative care, and the medical staff have been amazed and very impressed with their results.

Warning over – now it's up to you. Simply deciding to try a new kind of diet, taking up walking or booking an appointment with a therapist is the beginning of a new life. It indicates that you're starting to take charge of your own health and take responsibility for your own life.

How to use this book

The first part of this book is all about what you can do for yourself: good basic stuff, some of which may already be familiar to you, but which is well worth another look to remind yourself. It's a brief overview on how to eat, exercise, breathe and sleep for health and how to combat that demon stress. Alongside the standard information, I've included a few fresh things to think about or maybe try. Some are pretty ancient; some are sparkling new.

Then we launch into the supertherapies. These are roughly grouped into sections according to their focus. In actual fact, the distinctions are often pretty spurious. For example, most of the 'bodywork' therapies also work on energy and, likewise, many of the 'energy' systems also work on the body. However, it seemed more natural to group them according to their broad focus rather than simply run through them in alphabetical order.

The information included at the beginning of each therapy should give you a quick idea about what that particular therapy does best and how long it takes. Again, it's very difficult to be specific, because all these therapies will affect your whole body, rather than deal with a specific symptom. Equally, how long it takes to see results will largely depend on you.

As far as cost is concerned, I have not given specific figures, because rates vary according to the area. However, as a broad guide, *low* is generally under £25; *medium* ranges from around £25 to £45, and *high* is over £45 per session. But I would recommend you always ask your potential therapist precisely how much your treatment will cost when you book the appointment, i.e. *before* you go. Also, check if there are likely to be extra costs, for example, X-rays or medical tests, supplements or medication.

At the back of the book is an information section which lists the relevant organizations and shows you how to get in touch with the therapists mentioned in this book or ones in your area.

The Basics

Get the basics right, and you might find you don't even need a supertherapy. Well, maybe just the odd massage – for the sheer joy of it. Simply speaking, to enjoy rude good health you need four simple ingredients: good food, enough exercise, good breathing and the right mental attitude.

GOOD FOOD

The hunt for food that feeds

Remember when tomatoes used to taste like tomatoes? Somehow they seemed sweeter and juicier and tastier, didn't they? It might sound a bit like the 'good old days' chant, but there really is more than a kernel of truth in this. Nowadays, our food is so processed, so tampered with that you would be surprised to learn how little goodness it actually contains. We shop in supermarkets, buying produce that was grown and packaged often hundreds or even thousands of miles away. It has to look good – we have grown to like the look of perfectly shaped fruit and vegetables and smooth plump meat. And it has to last – often it is forced to undergo a long journey from where it was produced to the shop shelf. Many of us

25

don't even bother with the raw ingredients of food any more; we simply buy bundles of ready-cooked meals, stack the freezer full of convenience foods and snatch a hamburger or microwave meal for lunch.

But food doesn't naturally come in perfect shapes and it doesn't have an endless shelf-life. It needs to be pumped full of chemicals, pesticides and preservatives to look perfect, grow large and last long. Some of these additives are undoubtedly harmless: others are potentially more worrying. Remember the scares about the chemicals used on apples that rendered them potentially carcinogenic? This is just one example that came to light.

But even if the chemicals we pump into vegetables or the hormones we pump into livestock aren't directly harmful, we are nonetheless eating food that is lacking in essential vitamins and minerals most of the time. So, first and foremost, take the trouble to find the freshest, least processed food possible. Few of us have the time or inclination to grow our own fruit and vegetables, so you'll have to find a good shop. If you're a meat-eater, for heaven's sake please ferret out a supplier of free-range organic meat. Not only is it a far more ethical way of raising and killing animals, but your health will also benefit as much as your conscience. There are sheer horror stories about what happens in non-organic farming with animals being pumped full of hormones and antibiotics, not to mention the scares of BSE (bovine spongiform encephalopathy) in cattle.

Buy food as fresh as you can and as untampered with as you can. Try to buy your food as you need it, rather than stocking up on large supplies and leaving it lying around for several days before eating it. Rediscover cooking with fresh ingredients: yes, it takes more time than throwing something in the oven or microwave, but you'll be doing your health a favour – and also your pocket (convenience foods cost a small fortune). It doesn't have to take that long either. Cookery writers like Nigel Slater have devised new super-fast recipes using high-quality, fresh ingredients. Sniff out his books – no recipe takes longer than half an hour to prepare and they are simply delicious.

The right stuff

We're fed so much conflicting advice on diet that it's hard to sort the facts from the big fat fiction. It seems that every day we read that we should be eating more protein or less protein; that we should give up all fat or that we should cut down on certain kinds. In truth, even the supertherapies sometimes contradict each other in this respect. However, the World Health Organisation have come up with some very simple guidelines based on universally agreed scientific principles. Here are a few golden rules:

1.   Around half your daily intake of calories should come from complex carbohydrates (the solid starchy foods such as bread, pasta, potatoes, rice and cereals). In the past, we tended to avoid large amounts of these, thinking they were fattening, but now it's clear that *complex* carbohydrates are actually great for our health. It's no real hardship: bowls of warming pasta, delicious risottos and pilaus, doorstep sandwiches of wholemeal bread, filling jacket potatoes. Another key word here is 'wholefoods' – the less refined and processed these staple foods are the better. Make friends with your local health-food shop – they're not all full of nut-roasts and lentils – many have wonderful breads. Or make your own. Soda bread, in particular, is simplicity itself and isn't stuffed full of flour-improvers and preservatives.

2.   Eat more fresh fruit and vegetables – at least five portions a day. The recommended amount per day is 400 g/14 oz, but the more you eat, the better for your health. Fresh (and yes – the fresher, the better) fruit and vegetables are packed full of essential vitamins and minerals including the highly important antioxidants (which I'll discuss later). But don't boil them to death – light steaming or stir-frying keeps nutrients locked inside. Use fruit as a healthy and filling snack.

3.   Cut down on sugar. Simple carbohydrates are the 'bad' carbohydrates and the ones to avoid – these include sugar, syrups, fructose and sucrose. Sugar simply isn't needed in a healthy diet. If you can't give up sugar (or sweet things) altogether, then do try to cut down and have cakes or chocolate as a special treat only rather than as a daily snack. And if you can't avoid buying processed foods check the labels – simple carbohydrates lurk in the most unsuspected places.

4. Cut down on fat. Some fat is essential – and it's pretty tough to avoid it altogether anyway. But saturated fat, in particular, is perilous to our health, putting us at risk of heart disease and some cancers. The main culprits here are most red meat and dairy produce – even so-called 'low-fat' varieties are stuffed full of harmful fat. Still, switching to low-fat milk and cheese will make a difference in the right direction. Again, check the labels on pre-prepared foods – the fat content is often way up high.

5. Cut down on salt. This is a tough one if, like me, you are addicted to salty, savoury foods. But too much sodium is bad for your heart and your general health.

Meat or two veg?

Some people swear the only truly healthy diet is to forgo flesh altogether, and vegetarianism, veganism and even the stringent macrobiotics are on the increase. Most supertherapists would certainly suggest you cut down on meat – many would say cut it out altogether. I've been a complete vegetarian, and I've also been a meat-eater. I must say that during my vegetarian phase I lost weight, felt much healthier and had more energy. However, it's perfectly possible to eat healthily without giving up meat and, indeed, meat does have some benefits for a healthy diet. In Chinese medicine, meat is even prescribed for certain problems: one practitioner I know who is predominantly vegetarian always has a lamb stew every month after her period to fortify her system.

If you feel happy without meat, then that's great. Do, however, make sure you eat plenty of dark green vegetables, dried fruit, nuts and wholegrains to ensure you don't miss out on essential minerals and vitamins. If, however, you don't want to give up meat or your family makes it tricky for you to do so, then my advice would be to cut down on the amount of red meat you eat and, when you do eat it, make sure you are eating meat, not fat. Choose lean cuts and trim off excess fat. Burgers, sausages, pies and pâtés are chock full of saturated fat: if you can't give them up, have them once in a while as a treat.

Chicken and other poultry generally contain less fat than red meat but again, do choose free-range birds wherever possible. Fish, as you're probably aware, is also a healthy option (provided it hasn't swum in polluted waters). The fats it contains are un-saturated and some are even positively healthy, helping prevent the blood clots that lead to heart attacks.

The diet dilemma

Don't talk to me about diets. I've been dieting since I was fourteen years old, and guess what? In twenty years of diet shakes and calorie counting I haven't actually lost a pound. In fact, I've put on over two stone. I'm in good company – experts reckon that by the year 2,000, 25 per cent of the UK population will be obese.

I've used every excuse over the years: slow metabolism, mal-functioning hormones, even starvation in a past life, but I know, at heart, I'm kidding myself. A very few people have a real medical problem, such as a malfunctioning thyroid or other hormonal problem. Most of us don't, and the key to losing weight is basically quite simple.

Here are some pointers:

• Most people who think they are overweight actually aren't. When I was in my teens I was the perfect weight for my height. I had a bit of a tummy, but I could have solved that with exercise. Instead, I dieted and starved myself and threw my body into panic, into yo-yo dieting – and into a real problem. I was doing what most of us do: judging myself against models, actresses and all the other beanpole role models we're given. So, if you're within the target weight bracket for your height, please don't diet. If you want a firmer, leaner body, take up exercise instead.
• Once you get into a diet mentality, you will tend to launch into yo-yo dieting – losing weight on a diet, then putting it back on when you come off. The solution is to stop dieting and start re-educating your body back into normal, healthy eating. Follow the guidelines above: cut down on fat and sugars, fill up on complex carbohydrates and fruit and vegetables. Reduce your alcohol intake – alcohol taken in excess can really pile on empty calories. Eat when you're hungry and eat until you're full – then stop. Drink plenty of water to help fill you up and to flush out toxins.
• Allergies and food intolerances might be the root of your problem. If certain foods make you feel bloated, give you

headaches or make you tired, you could well be intolerant to them. And food intolerances can also be a factor in weight retention. A good nutritionist or naturopath will be able to test you for allergies and advise on how to deal with them.

• If you've tried all the above and you're still piling on the pounds then, sadly, you're probably just eating too much. Scientists reckon this is the simple reason why so many of us are overweight: we underestimate what we eat or we kid ourselves about our food intake. In 1955, the American *Better Homes and Gardens Diet Book* gave this simple message: 'You're fat because you eat too much. There *isn't* any other reason.' Thirty years and thousands of diets later, scientists have turned full circle. Although we are actually eating fewer calories than in 1955, we are apparently eating too many for our new sedentary lifestyles. Depressing, isn't it? However, if like me, you know all this and *still* put on weight, there is one more factor that most diets and scientists ignore altogether . . .

• The mind factor. If we accept that we overeat, we have to ask ourselves why? It could be simple ignorance – and if you're not sure what constitutes 'normal' portions, then I'd advise you check it out with a nutritionist. But, if you know what you *should* be eating but still find yourself bingeing at midnight, then the problem might lie deeper. Some of us use food as a weapon: we eat to punish ourselves, to take control, to keep people at arm's (or stomach's) length. We might eat out of self-pity, out of fear, out of intense self-dislike. If food is so important to you that you simply can't get it back into proportion and if dieting is taking over your life, then you need to look at the reasons why. Many psychotherapists are skilled in the treatment of eating disorders – and *any* obsession with food is an eating disorder; it's not confined to serious conditions such an anorexia or bulimia.

Ten to one you will find that you automatically lose weight once you start to follow one of the supertherapies. If you particularly want to focus on weight loss, then investigate one of the following as your first port of call: NUTRITIONAL THERAPY; AYURVEDA; NATUROPATHY; ACUPUNCTURE (*see* TRADITIONAL CHINESE MEDICINE).

Superfoods

So, you're eating a good healthy diet – full of energy-packed wholefood and nutrient-rich fruit and vegetables. You've swapped the burgers and microwave suppers for freshly cooked pastas and soups. You've cut down on your fat, sugar and salt intake. Hopefully, you are being moderate with your alcohol intake. (The odd glass of wine won't hurt and may even help your heart according to recent studies. However, alcohol is fattening and sucks nutrients from the body, so keep your units down.) And you are trying to cut down on stimulants like coffee and tea – again, these strip nutrients from the body. So isn't all this enough?

It's certainly a step in the right direction. You're now eating a diet that isn't harmful and which, hopefully, won't make you put on weight. However, if you want to eat the optimum diet, it's necessary to flesh out the guidelines a little, and this is where the superfoods come in.

Superfoods are nothing new. In fact recent renewed interest in the diet of wartime Britain has shown that, although the war years were associated with deprivation and poor nutrition, in fact the ration-book diet was very healthy. The government at that time spoke of 'foods for protection against ill-health' and advised people to take foods containing vitamins A, B and C on a daily basis. Scientists today have much the same message, since they are now finding out what ancient systems of natural medicine have known for years: certain foods can actively help your health.

The Chinese have followed this teaching for thousands of years and, in fact, the first 'medicine' that is generally prescribed by practitioners of traditional Chinese medicine (TCM) is food. Sun Ssu-mo, an ancient Chinese physician in the Tang Dynasty, correctly diagnosed and cured beriberi, the nutritional-deficiency disease – one thousand years before European doctors. He wrote: 'A truly good physician first finds out the cause of the illness, and having found that, he first tries to cure it with food. Only when food fails does he prescribe medication.'

This principle holds good today and in the Far East it is not unusual to come across medicinal restaurants. There are no menus; you simply tell the waiter/doctor your ailments, he examines your tongue and takes your pulses and then the kitchen will provide a tailor-made therapeutic meal, guaranteed to banish your cold alongside your hunger, to ease bronchial pain or simply to lift a bad mood. Some can even prepare an aphrodisiac feast, but the ingredients might prove less than alluring.

Alice Lyon, a London-based Chinese herbalist, describes one such meal: 'In Taiwan we were offered fallopian tubes, testicles . . . everything – the whole meal was geared towards sexual organs and we could hardly touch the food. But in Hong Kong it's quite different – here, we were offered food that's good for your health and tasty as well.'

So far, British restaurateurs have not followed suit, but it is quite simple to follow a DIY home regime with most herbalists happy to advise on a diet specifically tailored to your requirements and advise on herbs which can be used to give your cooking an extra boost.

'Using food for health has a long tradition in China,' says Alice Lyon. 'You can boost your energy, tonify your body, help your memory and even give your sex life a kick-start.'

THE CHINESE KITCHEN MEDICINE CABINET

The following is just a taster of the healing properties of common foodstuffs that are probably sitting in your kitchen cupboards.

Barley meal helps the digestion and drains what the Chinese call 'damp heat', moving away foods that are stagnant in the system. To cook barley meal, boil it with rice for two hours.

Brussels sprouts (best lightly steamed) are rich in alkalizing elements and particularly good for the pancreas.

Cherries are detoxifying, laxative and stimulate the nervous system. The darker the cherries, the more therapeutic their value.

Chicken raises *chi* (energy) and is generally uplifting.

Cucumber is rich in potassium, sodium and phosphorus, which is good for the nails and hair as well as for promoting excretion of waste through the kidneys.

Grapes are frequently used to cure constipation and gastritis and as general detoxifiers. They also alkalize the digestive tract and bloodstream. Dark grapes are best.

Horseradish and lemon juice (*see* Juicing for health in POLARITY THERAPY) provides quick relief from mucus congestion – useful in coughs, colds, flu, asthma and pneumonia.

Raw beetroot juice is a natural kidney cleanser, dissolving and eliminating any gravel.

Raw carrot and spinach juice detoxifies the digestive tract and helps normal bowel function. It is also used to treat tonsillitis and pneumonia; can help with rheumatism and colitis and is believed to strengthen the heart and ease menstrual problems.

Raw tomato is believed to reduce inflammation of the liver.

Raw crushed garlic contains allicin, a powerful natural antibiotic and fungicide, which helps prevent colds and flu and is said to raise libido.

Red meat is helpful for the blood. Although red meat is eaten very rarely by the Chinese, some practitioners recommend that women consume it after their periods to make up for lost blood. A typical recipe is to cook lamb with Chinese Angelica and Lycii berries.

For more information and more intriguing insights into just how precisely food can work as medicine, take a look at *Chinese Systems of Food Cures* by Henry C. Lu (Sterling Publishing).

THE WESTERN APPROACH

For a Western approach, Michael Van Straten and Barbara Griggs' *Superfoods* (Dorling Kindersley) provides excellent, clear and informative advice and is packed with recipes for individual complaints and problems. The information is too complex to condense here but, broadly speaking, the foods you need to boost in your diet are:

Fruits   The more the merrier. Apples and pears, citrus and soft, homegrown and exotic.

Vegetables   Again, you can't go far wrong if you bulk up on as many fresh vegetables as you can.

Grains   Barley, brown rice, millet and oats, buckwheat and wholewheat are all great for health. Strangely enough, many people who are intolerant of processed wheat can tolerate it in its whole unrefined form.

33

Nuts, seeds and pulses These are often dismissed as vegetarian fare, but everyone (vegetarian or meat-eater) should eat more.

Dairy products A short list here – only goat's milk and live yoghurt really help your health.

Meat, fish and poultry Oily fish like herrings, mackerel and sardines are good for the heart. Game is surprisingly healthy (generally very low in cholesterol) and beef, lamb and chicken are recommended only if free-range and hormone-free.

Herbs and spices Fresh herbs and spices often have wonderful health-giving properties (more about these in the chapters on herbalism and aromatherapy). Add as much garlic and ginger to your food as your friends and family can bear, plus plenty of parsley, sage, rosemary and thyme.

Keep a mental checklist of these superfoods when you go shopping and use as many of them as possible on a regular basis – in every meal. After all, why settle for a diet that is simply not doing you any harm when you could be eating food that positively enhances your health?

Supersupplements: do we really need all those extra vitamins?

Take a look at any health-food shop, chemist or even the local supermarket and you'll find shelves brimming with pots of vitamins, minerals and other arcane supplements. But are they really necessary? Surely, if we eat a good diet, based on all the foods already mentioned we have no need for extra nutrients?

Sadly, many nutritionists now believe that this is no longer the case. Few of us have the luxury of eating completely fresh, organic, additive-free food all the time. And even organic food can't be protected from the increased pollution that filters through from the air (via factories, car fumes and aircraft fuel) or in the water (from chemical dumping, boat fuel and sewage). In addition, our lifestyle nowadays tends to strip away vitamins and minerals from our bodies. Stress, pollution, smoking and alcohol can all scupper our best intentions.

Many experts now recommend taking a good quality multi-vitamin and mineral supplement as an additional safeguard against deficiencies. Look for one which contains both vitamins and minerals. This is important because vitamins and minerals work in tandem: too much of one and you could end up deficient in another; equally some vitamins and minerals are dependent on others in order to work within the body.

Exactly how much of each vitamin and mineral we need each day is a continuing source of debate. Britain now has a new set of standards, drawn up by COMA (Committee on Medical Aspects of Food Policy). The average amount of a nutrient needed by almost everyone, even those with high needs, is known as the Reference Nutrient Intake (RNI). This is roughly equivalent to the old measure, the RDA (Recommended Daily Amount), which is still often quoted on labels. RNIs are given in either milligrams (mg), micrograms (mcg) or international units (iu). However, some experts still think many RNIs are set too low.

THE CURRENT RNI GUIDELINES

Vitamins

Vitamin A	800 mcg
Vitamin C	60 mg
Vitamin D	5 mcg
Vitamin E	10 mg
Thiamin (vitamin B_1)	1.4 mg
Riboflavin (vitamin B_2)	1.6 mg
Niacin (vitamin B_3)	18 mg
Vitamin B_6	2 mg
Biotin	0.15 mg
Vitamin B_{12}	1 mcg
Pantothenic Acid	6 mg

Minerals

Calcium	800 mg
Iodine	150 mcg
Iron	14 mg
Magnesium	300 mg
Phosphorus	800 mg
Zinc	15 mg

In addition, some groups need higher quantities of certain nutrients. Children and adolescents have particular needs, and many childhood problems can be traced to either food intolerances or nutrient deficiencies. Smokers, drinkers, dieters and exercisers all have special needs, and as we approach old age we should again reassess our vitamin and mineral intake. In the elderly, alcohol in particular has a more extreme effect in depleting the body of the B vitamins, magnesium and zinc, and vitamin C is often needed in larger doses.

Pregnant women need to watch their vitamin and mineral intake very carefully. While food intake in pregnancy increases by 15–20 per cent, requirements for folic acid, the B vitamins, vitamin C, calcium, zinc and magnesium increase by 30–100 per cent. Pregnant women, above all, should ensure they have a nutrient-rich diet and take supplements if necessary (following the advice of their nutritionist or doctor). Women who suffer stillbirth are often found to be extremely deficient in zinc. Folic acid supplementation can reduce the risk of spina bifida. Early morning sickness can be relieved with vitamin B_6 and magnesium, while recent research indicates that postnatal depression can be due to a lack of the B vitamins and calcium.

Generally, vitamins and minerals are very safe. Research seems to show that, with the exception of vitamins A and D, doses even a hundred times higher than the RNI are safe for long-term use. There are no fatalities on record resulting from vitamin supplementation. However, all minerals show toxicity at very high doses, so take them with care.

If you do think you are suffering from a severe deficiency in any particular vitamin or mineral, you should consult a qualified nutritionist (*see* NUTRITIONAL THERAPY) for further details.

Free radicals and antioxidants

Recently there has been a lot of excitement about the group of vitamins and minerals known as antioxidants. These, we are told, combat the dangers of free radicals in the body. But what exactly are free radicals?

Free radicals occur within the cells of our bodies as a result of a variety of stimuli, including pollution from chemicals, cigarette smoke and the radiation from X-rays. The pollution causes a chemical imbalance: a molecule is one electron short of its normal pair, and so it tries to grab another electron from a nearby molecule. If it succeeds, this leave another molecule short, so it, in turn, grabs an electron from its neighbour, setting in motion a chain reaction which can cause terrible damage. It can cause damage to the DNA, the genetic material in cells, which can, in turn, lead to heart disease and cancer.

Antioxidants are the good guys which appear to race to the rescue. These are substances found naturally in food, particularly in fruit and vegetables. The prime antioxidants are the vitamins A (in the form of beta-carotene which converts to vitamin A), C and E, and the mineral selenium. These inactivate free radicals by giving back electrons to halt the chain reaction of destruction. Having donated their electrons, they simply decay harmlessly into our bodies.

So, the more antioxidants in your diet, the better. Once again, it's back to eating plenty of fresh fruit and vegetables – every day.

Toxins and detoxing

Detoxing is one of the buzzwords of the nineties. We are certainly exposed now to more chemicals and pollutants than at any time in our history. But how alarmed should we really be? If we believe all the magazine and newspaper articles, the only cure seems to be to detox ourselves at every given opportunity. We should be wrapping ourselves in seaweed, eating nothing but garlic and onions, and dousing our innards with 'cleansing' herbal potions. But do toxins really exist in such formidable numbers, or is this just another consumer craze gone mad?

The dictionary definition of a toxin is pretty strict: the poisonous product of the metabolic processes of living organisms. However, its meaning has now been extended to include almost anything nasty that causes what we perceive as an unpleasant effect on the body or the environment. As Dr Stephen Davies, Chair of the British Society for Nutritional Medicine, puts it: 'We live in a very toxic environment.' He cites the insecticides, pesticides and herbicides we spray into the air; the preservatives, taste-enhancers and colourings we add to our food; even the spray polishes, detergents and air fresheners we waft around our homes.

Naturopath Leon Chaitow also firmly believes in the horror of toxins and is convinced we are all crying out for a good detox. 'Do we need to detoxify? Yes, we do need to and we need to badly,' he insists. 'One child in four in this country [UK] now has major allergies which is a 400–500 per cent progression since the war. Breast milk worldwide – whether that of Amazonian Indians or housewives in Hull – is now contaminated with DDT, dioxin and various other contaminants. That is an example of the degree of toxicity that has permeated the planet. There is no-one who is now free of it.'

However, other experts are less convinced. And some feel we are all simply jumping on the detox bandwagon, spending excessive amounts of money and needless anxiety on the issue. 'To be honest, everyone is panicking,' says nutritionist Nicola Griffin, 'a lot of patients and, equally, a lot of practitioners as well.'

One branch of complementary healthcare that has a large question mark over it is colonic hydrotherapy, which purports to cleanse the bowel of an age-old build-up of faecal matter. Some practitioners claim that they can remove pounds of caked-on matter, thus allowing the bowel to function properly. However, critics say that the practice can strip the bowel of helpful bacteria and, if performed incorrectly, can even perforate the gut. Pathologists add fuel to the anti-lobby by stating that, when dissecting bodies, they simply don't see the evidence of caked-on matter. I know many people who swear by colonics: they say it helps them lose weight, makes their skin clearer and gives them bags of energy. I was fondly imagining walking out of the colonic therapist's room with my clothes hanging baggily, but, sadly, it just didn't happen that way.

If you've ever wondered exactly what does happen during a colonic here's the lowdown. After a brief case history, you are asked to take off your clothes and put on a disposable robe which is split up the back. As you lie on your side on a couch, the therapist inserts a small tube into your rectum. It doesn't hurt, but if you're at all squeamish about such things, then this most certainly isn't for you. Next, warm and cold water is alternately passed into your intestines. It isn't painful, but I found it very uncomfortable. The therapist has to keep moving the valve in the tube which gives

38

a dull throbbing ache (a little like the feeling you get from a vaginal internal when they widen the speculum – sorry, male readers but I don't have an analogy for you). But worst of all, is the almost constant feeling that you simply must go to the toilet. It's like having rampant diarrhoea for forty minutes. Of course, the waste is simply taken away through the tube without you having to do a thing, but I found it deeply unpleasant. I lay there feeling utterly miserable. And, sadly, when my time was up, I didn't feel light and clean and full of energy: I felt tired, bloated and as if I had a huge plug stuck up my rear. In fact, I didn't feel right for several days. So colonics isn't something that worked for me – I personally prefer gentler ways of detoxing the body.

So what *does* universally work? Dr Davies suggests that, first and foremost, we should try to steer clear of known sources of toxins, by avoiding unnecessary chemicals and additives. After that, he says, it does not hurt to take a good quality multi-vitamin and mineral supplement to help protect our bodies. 'Substances such as vitamin C, selenium, vitamin E, beta-carotene, zinc and manganese do have a protective effect by enhancing various enzyme activities, as well as increasing, in some instances, the rate of excretion of toxic substances from the body,' he says.

However, as Nicola Griffin warns, while a general supplement and additional vitamin C can be helpful, you should be wary of anyone prescribing very high levels of vitamins and minerals to detoxify the body, since that in itself can be toxic.

She feels that detoxification is becoming almost an obsession with some people and that perhaps the whole craze is so appealing because it appears to offer the opportunity to control a small part of an increasingly uncontrollable and frightening world. But, the very process of physically detoxing can have a detrimental psychological effect if it gets out of control. 'I know people who are squeaky clean inside and out,' she says, 'vegan this, organic that, and yet they are the most "toxic" people I have ever seen. It's not that their *diet* is toxic, but *they* are toxic. People think of toxins just being in food and chemicals, but you have to deal with the emotions as well.'

Leon Chaitow agrees: 'There is mental toxicity as well,' he says. 'We are overloaded with fears and phobias, which is why meditation and relaxation are terribly important as well. It sounds terribly Californian, but doctors are beginning to move away from the prescription pad and look at lifestyle changes.'

His recipe for detoxing, outlined in his book, *Body Tonic – How to Stay Healthy in a Polluted World* (Gaia), includes a variety of home detox programmes, including diet, exercise, massage and hydrotherapy. He insists that all these elements, when practised regularly, can help the body cleanse itself.

I, however, decided to put myself in the hands of the experts and tried the theory out at 'Stop the World' in Somerset where they hold regular week-long detox breaks. It's heavy going: breakfast consists of a juice and garlic shake (not very sociable), while the rest of the food is all alkaline (lots of steamed vegetables and endless salads – no mayonnaise). When you're not feeling hungry you practise yoga and other gentle exercises, have lymphatic drainage massage (*see* MANUAL LYMPH DRAINAGE), and learn how to think non-toxic thoughts. No-one, to my knowledge, has ever measured the amount of toxins you lose by standing under a spreading oak tree performing yoga. And yet I have to confess that the combination of diet, exercise and relaxation *does* seem to have an effect. After two alcohol-free, caffeine-free, meat-free, television- and traffic-free days I was in agony – with a thumping migraine and a complete dose of exhaustion. However, at the end of the week, I left, quite literally, singing. I had a clear head and, so it felt, a clean body. My energy levels were soaring and, quite honestly, I have never felt so good. Was it because I was thoroughly detoxed? Was my overindulged system suddenly squeaky clean? Unlikely. I'm quite sure it would take nearer a year than a week to cleanse *my* dustbin of a body. But whether it was the detox itself or simply the psychological benefit gained from a goodly level of pampering, the effect was pretty miraculous.

And if detoxing does nothing more than persuade us to spend a little time on ourselves, does it really matter whether soaking in a herbal bath actually oozes out the nasties? If the fear of toxins sends us racing off to the gym or slinging out the junk food, is that such a bad thing? Providing you are not spending a fortune on treatments that aren't even enjoyable, or making yourself miserable or unhealthy with draconian diets, why worry? Keep a healthy sense of moderation and a wary eye for improbable claims and then, if it feels good, detox away.

Fasting – the ultimate detox?

You could say that fasting is the ultimate in detox and, come to think of it, the ultimate diet. It requires no fiddly recipes, no special equipment and no complicated rules. You don't need to combine anything, count anything or measure anything, simply because there are no foods to combine, no calories to count and no ingredients to measure.

It's certainly not a new concept. Back in medieval times, fasting was a way of life and, all over the world, religions have espoused the spiritual benefits of purifying and castigating the body by withholding food. Nowadays, however, few people think of fasting as a solely religious experience, and it certainly isn't regarded as punishment: 'fasters' are simply looking for a healthier body, a brighter mind and clearer emotions.

Amidst healthy scepticism, there is evidence to support periodic, sensible fasting. Research has been carried out since 1880 and, since then, medical journals have carried occasional reports on the use of fasting for the treatment of obesity, eczema, irritable bowel syndrome, bronchial asthma, depression and even schizophrenia, to name but a few. Most people nowadays, however, use it as preventative medicine. As medical herbalist Kitty Campion, author of *A Woman's Herbal* (Vermilion) says, 'Not only does it help the body to maintain peak fitness by periodically unburdening itself of accumulated waste, but, if done properly, it nips minor health problems in the bud, decelerates the ageing process, stabilizes body weight and helps the body to utilize nutrition far more effectively.'

She points out that the digestive system uses up to 30 per cent of the total energy produced by the body. So, by putting the system into a state of rest, the body can concentrate on detoxification and healing. On a health level, she says, fasting can improve your immune function and allow your body a decent chance to deal with its problems; on a beauty level, fasting can make your skin look fresher and more toned, your eyes brighter and your hair more lush. And, quite obviously, you also lose weight. Six hours after the last meal, the body starts to use glycogen (the carbohydrate stored in the liver and muscles) as its energy source. But after twenty-four hours the body will adapt to obtaining its energy from stored fat.

However, if you simply want to lose weight, fasting is not your best or safest bet. As the British Medical Association (BMA) point out, after twenty-four hours your body takes its energy, not just from stored fat, but also from the breakdown of muscle. If you continue fasting over several days, your metabolism will slow down to conserve energy and, if you fast for too long, the ability to digest food may be impaired or lost entirely because the stomach gradually stops secreting digestive juices.

Prolonged fasting also halts the production of sex hormones, and your body loses its ability to fight infection. So, fast for too long and fasting will be positively bad for you. However, the BMA says that fasting for twenty-four hours is fine and can even be an effective means of weight control. After that, they advise you to seek medical supervision.

However, Lyndel Costain of the British Diatetic Association is not happy about fasting in any form and is worried about the growing trend. 'People say they're fasting for religious or health reasons, but I still suspect that weight loss is the bottom line,' she comments. 'It's simply not a useful way to lose weight because it very much increases the preoccupation and intensity about food without addressing what your body really needs.' She points out that, after about seven days, fatty acids can be released into the blood. They are converted into ketones which make the whole system acidic and can cause a 'high'. 'People say the extra energy and "high" is their body responding to fasting but, in fact, it's just a switch to a different form of fuel.' She is adamant that fasting can cause more problems than it solves: 'I simply wouldn't recommend fasting,' she says, 'we're all capable of staying healthy on a mixed and healthy diet. Sure, sometimes we might feel a bit sluggish or bloated but our bodies are quite capable of digesting and absorbing all kinds of foods.'

However, naturopaths and other holistic health practitioners insist that, if carried out carefully and under supervision, fasting is quite safe. Many of the people who regularly attend naturopathic clinics like Tyringham Hall in Buckinghamshire undertake a fast as a natural part of their treatment – some for just a couple of days; others for a whole week or so. Patrick Howard of the Purist Foundation, which runs regular fasting weekends, is

42

adamant that, 'No fasting is dangerous as long as you are supervised.' He recommends people start off with a one-day fast and then progress to five- or even seven-day fasts for maximum benefits. The Foundation introduces people to fasting with a weekend explaining how fasting works and incorporating a day-long fast which is carefully supervised. The main difficulty, he insists, is not actually hunger but fear. 'We have been brought up to think that you have to eat to be strong, and so if we think about stopping eating it terrifies us. However, once you get into fasting mode, it's easier than you think.'

As someone who simply loves to eat, the word 'fast' comes close to swearing in my vocabulary. My one attempt, several years ago, had ended in shameful failure in the shape of a vast take-away after less than twenty-four hours. But I decided to give it a second chance and opted for two careful days' abstinence. Clearing the fridge, I felt like a child being sent to detention and spent the whole night dreaming about chocolate gâteaux. The first day was sheer misery: I didn't actually feel that hungry but I was totally abject – cold, shivery and desperately depressed. I kept looking at my watch and thinking, 'great, only another hour to lunch/tea/supper' and then realizing with a hollow sinking feeling that lunch, tea and supper were simply more water.

It was, quite honestly, the longest twenty-four hours of my life. All the literature on fasting advises you to take it easy, to use it as a spiritual experience, shunning the media and anything loud and brash, passing your time thinking, walking in nature and generally purifying your soul. Personally, if it hadn't been for the latest Jilly Cooper and an evening glued to trashy videos, I wouldn't have made it past teatime. As it was, I went to bed at eight o'clock with hiking socks on my feet to keep warm, curled up in a ball and prayed for oblivion.

But by day two I was feeling better. My tongue felt furry, there was a strange taste in my mouth, and however many times a day I showered, I still seemed to smell unpleasant. But the hunger pangs had gone and I felt much clearer and lighter. I found myself looking at my relationship with food and working out why and when I wanted to eat. I discovered I was using food as both comfort and, surprisingly, a cure for boredom, so I started giving myself mini-treats or plunging myself into more involving activities, and the hunger went.

By the third morning I wasn't hungry at all and could easily have kept going. But I broke my fast gently with a glass of orange juice. Lunch was a light salad, and I felt full after a small bowl. Now, although I'm back on a full diet, I am well aware that my attitude to food is better. I'm eating when I feel hungry rather than when I feel sorry for myself, and I'm eating better, healthier food. My energy levels are up and my skin feels remarkably clear and soft. But although my experience was generally good, I certainly accept that fasting is not for everyone. If in doubt, don't do it. And it is distinctly *not* advised if you are pregnant or breast-feeding, if you have any medical condition and particularly if you have any eating disorder.

Always ask the advice of a qualified practitioner and don't fast unsupervised for more than twenty-four hours. Remember, the new form of fasting is supposed to make you feel good – it's not the modern equivalent of a hair shirt.

GOOD EXERCISE

When I was at school I used to dread Wednesdays with every ounce of my eleven-year-old being. Wednesdays meant gym, and gym meant ritual humiliation in front of thirty-odd classmates. Try as I might, I couldn't do a hand-stand; even a forward roll was a trial. And, despite being a tolerable tennis player and quite nifty on a netball court, I dubbed myself a failure at sports. I'm quite convinced that such experiences have a lot to answer for and could well be the major reason why so many adults do no regular exercise at all.

And that is a crying shame because, as we all know, good exercise is simply wonderful – and essential – for good health and vitality. Regular exercise keeps our heart and lungs working at optimum levels and prevents the dangers of heart disease. Stress levels drop when we exercise, and we come out of a workout or sports game feeling a general lift in mood. Regular exercise can perk up our sex life and give us a good night's sleep; it can control our blood pressure and boost our immune system. RAND, the Californian think tank, reckon that every mile you walk or run can potentially add an extra twenty-one minutes to your life. American physiologists even believe that exercise can increase your creativity!

Then, of course, there is the whole question of weight loss. Fitness experts say that if we exercise properly and frequently, we shouldn't have any problems with our weight – the pounds will simply disappear.

There's really no excuse for not exercising. But it can be really tough to get started. I know because I've been there. When I left college I simply stopped doing any form of exercise at all. Several years later I was bullied back into it by my brother – and was it tough. I'm pretty hopeless in the willpower stakes so I joined a gym. I hunted around, checked out a few and dismissed all those where the primary goal seemed to be who could wear the tiniest thong leotard or the most make-up. The last thing you need when you're setting out is to feel a complete failure every time you hit the changing room. My gym was small, honest and down-to-earth. It had well-qualified trainers who knew their stuff. Before I was even allowed to set a foot on a treadmill I was given a full assessment and fitness check. Then my instructor worked out a programme that would stretch but not daunt me and carefully tutored me through the routine.

To begin with I was pathetic: I gasped my way through two min-utes on the lowest level of the exercise bike and I struggled to lift the weight machines – without any weights on them! But it didn't take long before things changed. Within six weeks of going three times a week, I was feeling like a different woman. I could run for the bus without thinking I was going to have a heart attack and, for the first time in my life, I had muscle tone. The flab under my arms simply vanished and my thighs almost rippled when I walked. Watching your body transform in front of your very eyes is simply the most exciting thing you can do.

Realizing I was getting quite fit gave me confidence and so, gin-gerly, I tried an aerobics class. It was a basic class, again taught by someone well-trained and qualified. The moves were simple, the music was fun and I had a brilliant time. Now I do regular step and slide classes and love every minute: not bad for someone who hated school games and thought she had no co-ordination at all!

The point of all this is to try to get you to realize that anyone and everyone can exercise. If I can get back into it, so can you. It doesn't have to be a gym or aerobics – it could equally be swimming, tennis, horse-riding, cycling or hiking. I found working out under supervision a good motivator, but if you hate the idea of revealing yourself in public there are some very good videos available which allow you to exercise in the privacy of your own home. However, you do require a lot of self-discipline and you need to watch very carefully to make sure you get the technique right and don't strain anything.

Variety is the spice of life. The best way, I find, to incorporate plenty of pleasurable exercise into everyday life is to practise a whole variety of different forms of exercise. Hence, the dog gets powerwalked round the fields most mornings – it's a great way to sweep away the cobwebs. When we come back, he crashes out for the morning while I feel raring to go. My aerobics sessions do wonders for my cardiovascular health and are great fun. If I've got time I go out to a class; if not, I pull out the slide, plonk it in front of the video and shoot back and forwards like a demented speed-skater. If I'm feeling really energetic, I drag my husband off for a game of squash.

If you haven't exercised for aeons or have a health problem, do have a word with your doctor before launching on an exercise programme – better safe than sorry.

The mind-body connection

All supertherapists will probably ask you if you exercise and, if not, gently suggest you take up some form of exercise. However, the Indian system of Ayurveda has some quite distinct thoughts about exercise and what forms we should be exploring.

John Douillard is an American fitness expert and author of a book that's well worth reading if you're a recalcitrant exerciser. It's called *Body, Mind and Sport* (Bantam). In it, he backs up my point entirely by saying that time and time again people are put off exercise because of bad childhood experiences. And, he soothes, I wasn't a failure at sport – I was simply doing the wrong sport for my mind-body type.

He has taken the basic tenets of the ancient Indian health system of Ayurveda and applied them specifically to sport. He explains that each one of us has a 'unique psychophysiological constitution or mind-body type.' It sounds pretty daunting, but he promises that if you find your own personal profile you will have a blue-print for better health, greater vitality – and a chance to really enjoy exercise.

There are three main body types – called *vata*, *pitta* and *kapha* – but most people find they are a combination of two. Your individual mind-body type will influence the kind of exercise and sport you should take up.

THE THREE TYPES AND THEIR CHARACTERISTICS

The following are very general pointers – most people tend to be a combination of types. For greater detail, there is a complete questionnaire in Douillard's book – or consult an Ayurvedic practitioner.

VATA TYPES:
- have a light, generally thin build
- perform all activities quickly
- have a tendency towards dry skin
- have an aversion to cold weather
- have irregular hunger and digestion
- are quick to grasp new information but also quick to forget
- have a tendency towards worry
- have a tendency towards constipation
- have a tendency towards light and interrupted sleep

IDEAL SPORTS TO BALANCE VATA: slow, calming activities such as swimming, walking, yoga, horse-riding, bicycle-touring, low-impact aerobics.

PITTA TYPES:
- have a moderate build
- perform activities with medium speed
- don't like hot weather
- prefer cold food and drinks
- have extreme hunger and a quick digestion
- can't skip meals
- take a medium time to grasp new information
- have a medium memory
- have a tendency towards reddish hair and complexion, moles, freckles
- are good public speakers

- tend towards irritability and anger
- are enterprising and sharp in character

IDEAL SPORTS TO BALANCE PITTA: cross-training and general fitness sports, e.g. mountain biking, ice skating, water skiing, sailing, basketball, hockey and other team sports.

KAPHA TYPES:
- have a solid, heavier build
- have greater strength and endurance
- are slow and methodical in activity
- have oily, smooth skin
- have slow digestion and mild hunger
- have a tranquil, steady personality
- are slow to grasp new information but slow to forget
- are slow to become excited or irritated
- sleep heavily and long
- have thick, wavy, plentiful hair

IDEAL SPORTS TO BALANCE KAPHA: stimulating and vigorous sports like aerobics, cross-country running, martial arts, volleyball, fencing, rock climbing, football.

Once you have discovered your type and an exercise programme to suit, Douillard insists the sky is the limit. Exercise, he believes, is far more than a way to keep healthy, slim and toned. It is, he insists, a means of unleashing our full human potential, a pathway to perfection of body, mind and spirit. The good news is that anyone can reach this super-state. And the even better news is that there is absolutely no need to spend half the day on the treadmill to achieve it. This is the antithesis of 'no pain, no gain'. Its key is the Zone, the elusive exercise 'high' in which the body works effortlessly while the mind remains calm and composed – in Douillard's words, 'an inexhaustible reservoir of power and peace'. But why bother? It might feel nice but are there any concrete physical benefits? Certainly. Tests have shown that exercisers using mind-body methods are able to exercise for longer periods of time with their heart and breathing rates lower than those experienced by conventional exercisers. Their nervous systems are more composed and alpha brain waves appear during exercise, showing an inner state of deep calm.

The rules for the mind-body workout are quite simple. First, choose a sport that you enjoy and that balances your type: heavy *kapha* types will never make ballerinas; slight *vata* types will never be brilliant shot-putters. Secondly, choose the right time of day to exercise. Although the timing varies according to each type, broadly speaking, morning is the best time for physical exercise, followed by early evening.

Then start slowly. Ayurvedic lore insists on always breathing through the nose – a tall order for those of us used to gasping in great breaths of air through the mouth during exercise. But, breathe through the nose and, apparently, over time you will build up far greater endurance without sacrificing speed. Learn to listen to your body is the next piece of advice. Find out your average waking heart rate (by taking your pulse for several mornings just after waking) and thereafter, if your heart rate increases or decreases ten or more beats above or below your average, rest during that day and take it easy.

Ayurveda has known for centuries what modern physiologists are only just discovering: that the right amount of exercise can keep you healthy or even help to cure you; but too much simply makes you sick. Experts now realise that over-exercising can even suppress the immune system and the previously recommended training level of 75 per cent of one's maximum heart rate has already been reduced to 60 per cent. High-impact aerobics has been replaced almost wholesale by low-impact for safe effectiveness.

It's good news for the exercise-shy, and next time you pass someone pounding for a solid hour on the treadmill you can smile with the inner knowledge that your quieter, calmer workout will be far safer, healthier – and more effective in the long term.

Ideally, the best way to start the mind-body workout is with yoga. The all-over stretching effect of yoga is the perfect preparation for exercise. Then you move into what is known as the Resting Phase, in which you start your exercise but keep it very slow, breathing deeply through the nose all the time. If you usually run, walk for ten minutes; if you're going to play tennis or hockey, warm up with a walk or light jog. Then comes the Listening Phase in which you gradually build up the pace while maintaining the same breath rate. If you find yourself feeling uncomfortable or your breathing becomes laboured, take the pace down until you can establish your original breathing pattern. Finish with more yoga to stretch and prevent injury.

The whole key is listening to your body, remaining alert to what feels good and what feels painful. Exercise, insist Ayurvedic practitioners, should *not* hurt: it's simply not necessary and is, in fact, defeating the object. But exercise in tune with your body, and your whole life could change. You will, says Douillard joyfully, 'rejuvenate the body and cultivate the mind; remove stress and develop mind-body co-ordination.' And all without the slightest twinge of pain.

The ultimate 'no excuses' workout

I can already hear some great excuses emerging. Yes, exercise sounds great, yes, the mind-body workout sounds wonderful . . . BUT you can't afford to join a gym and you haven't got a video recorder. There's no-one you can coerce into playing badminton and the bike has got a puncture. Sorry, but there's still no excuse. One of the very best workouts around is completely free: you don't need any equipment, you don't need a partner and you don't need any special training or expertise. You can do it in the depths of the country or in the centre of a city: it's called walking.

And, before you dismiss walking as too easy, normal and boring to be healthy, it's worth remembering that Cindy Crawford does it. So does Richard Gere. And Hillary Clinton and Sophia Loren. So you'd be in good company. Do what they do in the USA, call it powerwalking or fitness walking – a simple change of name makes it sound so much more sexy. In fact powerwalking is leaving jogging and aerobics bouncing way behind.

One of its main benefits is that walking is the ultimate low-impact workout. If you have weak joints, then the last thing you need is to run or do high-impact aerobics. And, anyway, why run when you can walk?

Walking is, quite simply, possibly the perfect form of exercise – it provides all the benefits of running (and more) without any of the dangers. The research is crystal clear. Performed correctly, it can raise your heartbeat to around 50 per cent of its maximum, which is seriously good news for your cardiovascular system. It

51

uses all the large muscles in the body in a relaxed repetitive manner which allows more oxygen and nutrients to get into all the cells of your body.

And, perhaps surprisingly, brisk walking is a highly effective calorie-burner. Stride up a 15 per cent incline at around 4.5 miles an hour and you will find yourself sloughing off around 500 calories an hour. Interestingly, a 7 miles per hour jog on flat ground will only notch up around 439 calories an hour. And you won't just lose weight with a regular walking regime, you'll tone up too. Walking uses much the same muscles as running – the quadriceps (front of thighs), hip flexors (front of hips), calf muscles and gluteals (buttocks) – so your legs will firm up quite quickly. If you swing your arms smoothly and rhythmically, you will also provide your upper body with a workout and if you add in a few sharp hills you can certainly expect to tone your thighs and bottom. Put it all together and, if you walk briskly for just forty-five minutes four times a week you would automatically lose ten to fifteen pounds in a year without modifying your diet in any way. Even more importantly, you won't be damaging yourself. Run, and you are jarring your whole skeletal structure. Each time your feet hit the ground when you're running, the impact puts three or four times your weight onto your feet. It's no wonder joggers and runners suffer so many joint injuries. However, when you walk, you are only putting one or at the most one and a half times your weight onto your feet. The action is smooth, so there's no jolting to knees or hips.

Performed correctly, walking is so safe it makes an ideal exercise even for pregnant women, the very overweight and the elderly – quite apart from those who simply want a safe form of training that won't cause or aggravate any injury.

Don't care about losing fifteen pounds? Not worried about a trimmer body? Well, walk for your health, if nothing else. Research from Tufts University in the USA shows that walking has very real benefits for your health and wellbeing. It can help your heart by increasing levels of HDL (the 'good' cholesterol) and it can help prevent osteoporosis – walking strengthens the hip and leg bones while the whole body movement builds a stronger spine. Some studies indicate that walking can reduce your risk of developing colon cancer, and the Aerobics Center in Dallas is convinced that regular walking can even extend your lifespan. It's not just your physical health that will benefit: according to sports psychologists, walking can even improve your mood and reduce stress.

STARTING OUT: WALKING FOR BEGINNERS

The National Register of Personal Trainers in the UK gives the following guidelines for a DIY walking programme that won't terrorize even the most recalcitrant exerciser.

1. Set a manageable target – start off gently. Don't head for the hills or exhaust yourself on your first attempt, or you will be put off for life. Build up slowly.
2. The aim is to build up to a regular three times a week with each session lasting a minimum of half an hour.
3. You need to get to the point where you are perspiring and your heart rate is raised. The easiest way to gauge how you're doing is the 'talk test'. You should be able to pass the odd word between yourself and a friend. If you can't even gasp out his or her name, you're doing too much; if you can indulge in a right old gossip, you're not working hard enough.

Preparing

1. As with all exercise, avoid eating for around an hour before you set off.
2. Drink plenty of water before, during and after your walk – if you're thirsty it means you're becoming dehydrated.
3. Warm up. Walk gently for the first five minutes to get your muscles warm before hotting up the pace.
4. A few gentle stretches after your warm-up can ease your body into the exercise.

The technique

1. Keep centred: imagine a straight line stretching from between your feet ahead of you down the road. Keep your legs parallel to this line and your toes pointing directly ahead.

2. Take the longest stride that is comfortable and let your arms swing naturally at the same speed. Relax your shoulders.

3. The heel of your leading foot should touch the ground just before the ball of the foot and toes. As your heel reaches the ground, lock your ankle and shift your weight forwards with the knee bent. Rock onto your toes and use the movement to push you onto the next step.

4. Breathe from your abdomen, not from your chest. Inhale and exhale rhythmically and easily through your nose.

THE NEXT STAGE

Once you feel happy with such conscious walking and have built up a fair level of fitness, you might want to try the following.

1. You can extend your powerwalk into a whole outdoor work-out. As you go round the park or countryside, incorporate press-ups against the back of a park bench; or do a few triceps dips on the edge of the seat and some pull-ups on a convenient branch of a tree.

2. If you're walking with a friend, you could add in some backwards walking. It uses the muscles in a slightly different way and can be slightly harder in muscular terms. But don't do it for too long or you'll get disorientated.

3. If even this isn't enough, try the following.

Variations

Walking on water In New York, sports clubs have sunk aqua versions of treadmills and stair-climbers into pools to combine the aerobic benefits with the added resistance of water. It's yet to catch on over here, but who needs the machines anyway? You can get the same effect by marching either through shoulder-high water with your feet on the bottom, or through deeper water with a flotation belt to keep you buoyant. Walking (forwards, backwards, side to side) also forms part of most aqua aerobics sessions. For DIY tips, read Glenda Baum's *Aquarobics* (Arrow).

A barefoot boogie An estimated 20,000 Americans now regularly practise barefoot walking, flinging their trainers to the wind and taking a walk on the wild side. They start off with brief skips over deep sand and build up to full-length marches over distinctly foot-unfriendly surfaces such as crushed gravel or hard-packed earth.

It may sound like a recipe for snakebite or splinters but, insists Dr David Winter, Professor of Kinesiology at the University of Waterloo in Canada, it's a wonderful form of exercise. 'With barefoot walking on uneven surfaces, there's definitely a higher level of muscular co-contraction going on,' he says, 'so the body gets a more concentrated workout.' Aficionados claim that one mile of barefoot walking is comparable to walking several miles in shoes. Some even do it at night or blindfolded, to improve co-ordination and increase tactile awareness. And some US podiatrists (specialists in the treatment of foot disorders) believe that barefoot walking can actually help vascular conditions in older people, recommending barefoot walking for pensioners. It may sound too bizarre to be true, just another lunatic American craze, but Oriental medicine backs it up: barefoot walking is often prescribed for strengthening low kidney energy and for stimulating the meridians.

However, UK experts are less convinced. 'I wouldn't advise it on British roads or parks,' says Carol Hampton of the National Register of Personal Trainers, 'you don't know what you might step in.'

Race-walking – walking to win   It's the laughing stock of the Olympics – almost everyone giggles at the sight of race-walkers with their swinging arms and swivelling hips. But the race-walkers might just have the last laugh. Apart from the general fitness and health benefits already outlined, race-walking promotes great hip flexibility and race-walkers have the unusual skill of being able to rotate their hips through ninety degrees at the hip! They also have a brilliant time.

As Peter Cassidy, Honorary Secretary of the Race Walking Association says, 'It's suitable for people of all ages and fitness levels, plus it is an incredibly companionable sport with people of all standards entering the same race. You will have beginners trudging at the back and internationalists whizzing away at the front. But, afterwards, you'll find the experts advising the beginners on their style – they're a tremendously friendly crowd.'

DON'T WALK INTO DANGER

Walking is about as safe a sport as you can ask for. However, there are some warning points.

• Try not to walk in heavily congested areas on days when the air quality is poor. When the ozone levels are high you could find yourself coughing if you exercise on polluted days.

• Don't walk with weights. It may sound like a great way to pump up your workout but it's not a good idea: the shoulder is one of the most unstable joints in the body, and walking with weights makes it very susceptible to injury.

• You might feel like a quick slug of coffee to jump-start your walk, but resist. Caffeine gets the heart pumping, so it feels as though you are warmed up for exercise when you're not. It may dilate arteries in the central part of your body, but it won't reach your arms and legs.

• Be seen and be safe. If you're walking at night on unlit streets, wear fluorescent strips to make yourself noticeable. In an ideal world try to find a friend to share your powerwalks or borrow that old-fashioned walking accessory – a dog. If you do walk on your own, be certain to tell someone where you are going and how long you'll be.

Ancient techniques – tried, trusted and updated

There are fads in exercise just as in everything else in modern life. But some forms of exercise have stayed the same for hundreds or even thousands of years. And surely anything that has *that* kind of track record must be doing something right. At first sight, exercise systems such as yoga or Chi Kung don't look as if they are particularly energetic. But these systems operate on a completely different set of rules than what we think of as 'normal' exercise. Initially, they weren't even considered as pure body exercise at all.

Other forms of ancient exercise that are catching on include the Chinese T'ai-chi, the Japanese Aikido and other exercises that have generally been known as martial arts. While they can be used this way, many people practise them as simply superb ways of keeping mind, body and spirit all fighting fit. I have not yet tried them so I cannot give you my impressions but I do know plenty of people who swear by them. If they appeal, have a go.

Yoga – beyond the lotus

There are many branches of yoga and what we tend to think of as yoga (shoulder stands and lotus positions) is just the tip of the iceberg. Yoga is a spiritual path and, in its purest form, turns into a complete lifestyle. However, nowadays, many people follow it for more basic reasons: it can tone your body like almost no other exercise, giving long, lean muscles; it massages all your internal organs, keeping you fit and healthy; it stretches the whole body, making you supple; it encourages good breathing, helping to oxygenate the body; it fosters calm and is a superb stressbuster. All in all, it's time to rethink yoga.

But, if you still think of yoga as a 'soft' option, then take a look at the fresh forms of yoga that are beginning to catch on.

As with walking, the Americans have renamed yoga, and Hollywood stars like Candice Bergen, Daryl Hannah, Warren Beatty and Jodie Foster wouldn't dream of doing 'yoga'; they practise Crossover Yoga, Power Yoga, Aerobic Yoga, Hard and Soft Yoga or even Fast-Track Yoga. But, at the end of the day, it is all still basically yoga, albeit somewhat more lively than we are used to. The 'new' yoga is a far more athletic breed.

At the Life Centre, in London, they call it 'Dynamis' yoga, and it's reckoned to be one of the toughest workouts around. As a regular exerciser I was slightly affronted when they politely suggested I start off with a Beginners' class. Five minutes into Dynamis, I was lamenting my arrogance. After ten minutes the sweat was forming a pool at my feet, and after twenty minutes my arms were turning into jelly. Forty minutes, and I was lying like a beached whale on the floor, panting and gasping, with every muscle in my body screaming for mercy. As I staggered out, the rest of the class were still fresh as daisies, merrily tying themselves into anatomically deranged positions at the speed of light.

'I would like to challenge any aerobics teacher to go through one of those classes,' says Godfrey Devereux, inventor of the Dynamis workout. 'With weights or aerobics you only work certain

57

muscles. But yoga postures put pressure on different organs very systematically. It tones the whole inner body as well as the outer body: the liver, the lungs, the kidneys, the spleen, the heart.' While 'normal' yoga puts you in poses and leaves you there for several minutes, Dynamis keeps you moving all the time. One moment you're standing up, the next you're on the floor; one moment you have one leg stretched back, the next they're both back and you're in a form of push-up position, all the time moving seamlessly (or, in my case, inelegantly) from one pose to another.

Devereux promises, however, that it does not take years to get to a fit state for the Dynamis challenge. One man in my class had only been doing yoga for a few months but he looked as though he had been born in the lotus position. The key apparently is all in the breath.

To begin with, I thought my fellow students all had bad colds. But their explosive, noisy breathing is actually a precise technique calculated to help you get into and out of each pose. 'This particular breath generates heat in the body which helps to dissolve fatty tissue,' explains Devereux, 'it mobilizes liquid and fat out of the tissue which gives you greater freedom of movement. If you get the breathing right, you will be able to keep going. If you don't, you won't stay the course.'

And if you do stay the course, and keep going regularly, the benefits are legion. Devereux claims his yoga can cleanse the internal organs, bring muscles and bones back into correct alignment, soften the ligaments and tissues and give greater freedom of movement. All that *and* it will hit your mind as well. 'You're not just working on the anatomical body but on the nervous system as well,' he says. 'You might feel a little tired when you come out of a class, but within a few minutes you'll have a lot of energy. Yoga poses are designed to refresh your body while calming the mind. It's not like athletics because you're not pumping the muscles, you're stretching them. By doing that, you take the blood deeper into the cells of the tissues to oxygenate them and to remove toxins.'

But is it really as good as a tough aerobic workout? Can you seriously class this yoga, however energetic it may be, alongside the cardiovascular forms of exercise which doctors say we need for healthy bodies and healthy hearts? Devereux shrugs, 'Who says that a cardiovascular workout is the only way to get those benefits? This class will give you stamina, improved oxygenation of your blood, improved circulation and improved discharge of toxins – without having to sustain a high heart rate for the thirty-minute optimum time.'

One thing nobody argues about is that yoga has a tendency to give you a brilliantly toned body. While weights can bulk up muscles and aerobics can give you a 'chunky' look, yoga habitués generally possess long, lean muscles – without an ounce of fat. Godfrey Devereux says that you can always tell when someone is doing a dynamic form of yoga because their body shape changes. 'Someone said to me, "Look at Kris Kristofferson – I bet he's doing yoga" and, sure enough, he is. And Sting is another example – he's practising yoga and his body is definitely changing.'

A lot of people automatically lose weight when they get into a yoga routine but, even if you have a large frame, Devereux swears yoga will change your relationship with your body. 'Yoga can help you, not to resent your body, but to really like, enjoy and appreciate it. You lose weight in your mind even if you don't lose it in the body.'

And those who start yoga purely to trim up and stretch out often find some surprising side benefits. 'If you want a good body then do yoga but, in the process, you will also find that you'll get fit and you'll get a calm, clear mind and brilliant concentration. It's as much a workout for the mind as it is for the body.'

The latter sounds suspiciously like the old image of yoga as a spiritual path; a kind of active meditation which might just link you into some essential truth. Devereux shakes his head vigorously: 'In the past, people who went to yoga were often the guru type, looking for guidance in life. We're completely against that: all we want is to teach people something that will make them feel good.' He points out that the new yoga is appealing to a younger audience, with everyone from businessmen to ladies who lunch doing the new form of 'working in'.

Rock star Chynna Phillips, who goes to yoga classes in Hollywood explains the appeal: 'I get so stirred up every day that it takes me forty-five minutes of the class just to relax. But it works. I feel like I'm another person when I leave.' Devereux thinks she might be talking quite literally: 'It's so powerful that you can actually shift your personality,' he says. 'If you just did Dynamis or something similar you would become far more outgoing, you'd become a real live wire. Equally, if you did more meditative, breathing work you'd become more inward-looking. Ideally, we advise people to get a balance or they become unbearable to live with.'

A few hours later I could understand what he means. Every muscle in my body was aching and my arms felt as if they belonged to someone else entirely, but I was buzzing with energy. I hurt, but it was a good kind of hurt; my head felt clear and my concentration seemed sharper.

All the signs are that the UK will go the way of the USA, and already yoga classes are springing up like mushrooms in sports clubs and village halls all over the country. You might have to hunt around to find anything like Dynamis, but even if you can't get a dynamic yoga class, don't dismiss the quieter version. It's deceptively tough and will still give your body a complete tone-up.

Chi Kung – the Chinese stressbuster

The Chinese have been using the Chi Kung system as a stressbuster and total exercise and meditation system for thousands of years. Unlike other Eastern systems such as T'ai-chi and Kung Fu, Chi Kung (sometimes also known as Qi Gong) is not a martial art. It is a holistic system that combines breathing techniques with precise movements and mental concentration: its aim is total health and wellbeing – and an incredible energy boost.

It's been a well-kept secret. Although archaeological records indicate that even Neolithic cavemen in China were using elements of the system, Chi Kung has only been practised openly in the West for the last ten to fifteen years and there are still only a few practitioners of the art.

Hopefully this will change: if Chi Kung can deliver all its promises, it could make us all far healthier, happier, brighter and even sexier. 'There is no doubt at all that everyone could benefit – from a child to an eighty year old,' insists Dr Malcolm Kirsh who has been practising and teaching Chi Kung for the past five years. He found the system worked for him – after a series of sports injuries and fourteen operations, his knee looked (and felt) like a war zone. He is convinced Chi Kung helped him recover, and his doctors are amazed that he can even walk. A psychotherapist by profession and a specialist in stress management, he began to incorporate Chi Kung into his sessions with clients and soon became convinced that it could provide a missing element in the healing of both mind and body. 'Chi Kung makes you learn about yourself,' he says. 'You understand yourself better and you learn how to tackle problems physically as well as mentally.'

Reading through a list of its supposed benefits is like scanning through the menu of a paradise therapy. Practise Chi Kung regularly and you could increase your energy levels, manage your stress and prevent or cure any number of chronic or acute diseases. You would improve your concentration and academic performance, and gain increased creativity and inspiration. Your sex life would naturally perk up. Your weight would automatically adjust itself to the optimum for your body, and your skin would become clear and healthy. And, for the icing on the cake, you could find yourself adding years to your life.

It sounds too good to be true, so how does it work? 'By cleansing the meridians to achieve harmonious energy flow and by restoring the yin-yang balance,' says Dr Kirsh, bluntly. Chinese philosophy teaches that we can achieve almost anything if our vital energy, or *chi*, is flowing freely and easily. Chi Kung breathing and exercises work, much like acupuncture without the needles, to unblock any stagnant *chi* and allow it to flow freely through its pathways, the meridians.

The theory sounds straightforward, but when it came to the practice I almost fell at the first post. As with yoga and mind-body exercising, correct breathing is essential to Chi Kung, and Malcolm Kirsh first asked me simply to breathe from my abdomen, letting my stomach extend like a balloon as I breathed in. It sounded simple enough but when you've spent all your life consciously trying to keep your stomach held *in*, this really goes against the grain. And everything else was wrong too. 'Relax your shoulders,' he urged, 'relax your buttocks, and relax your abdomen. Your breath should be coming from what the Chinese call Dantien, about four centimetres [one and a half inches] below the navel, where all our energy comes from.' In

China students can spend anywhere up to a year simply learning how to breathe: fortunately we moved on once my breathing moved from near-hyperventilation to something approaching calm. (*See also* Abdominal breathing – the Chi Kung way in GOOD BREATHING.)

The next series of exercises were aimed at general health and wellbeing with an emphasis on stress reduction. Standing with my feet just over shoulder-width apart, I was instructed to bend my knees and, with my back straight, imagine I was holding a huge balloon in front of me. At the same time I had to imagine myself sitting on a second balloon while yet another balloon was balanced between my legs. 'Now imagine you are being held up by a string from the top of your head,' Kirsh urged, 'and *breathe.*' I could barely keep myself in the correct position, let alone breathe at the same time. 'But you're not *doing* anything,' he laughed. 'Now relax those elbows, and those shoulders, keep your back straight and relax those knees.'

Chi Kung may *look* effortless when performed by a master but in practice it is a precise discipline, demanding meticulous concentration and patience. It is also surprisingly tough on the muscles. Within a few minutes my muscles were aching to a degree I normally achieve only after a good forty minutes in the gym. Other exercises followed: movements with wonderful names such as Pushing Open the Window to Look at the Moon; Rock Spreading its Wings; and Shouldering the Sun and the Moon. Fluid, almost balletic in feel, the movements are utterly graceful and, once again, deceptively difficult.

Ideally, says Kirsh, you should practise Chi Kung every day, even if it is for only five or ten minutes. Obviously, though, the more effort you put in, the more results you will see. 'It's not a quick fix,' he insists, 'but there's no doubt that the more you practise it, the more it creates energy.' This is perhaps the strangest aspect of Chi Kung – while other forms of exercise take away your energy, Chi Kung puts it back. And, while you won't burn calories, he insists that you will find your body shape changing as you practise the exercises as a result of the combined effects of the breathing, the movement and the liberation of *chi*.

The real beauty of the system, however, is that absolutely anyone can practise it. Kirsh has seen clients with severe heart problems perform the exercises with ease. One woman hobbled into his clinic on crutches and departed after an hour of exercise, walking in a much freer manner.

And, although Kirsh is nervous about claiming too much for the system, books on Chi Kung extol its healing virtues too. By unblocking energy, they say, you can cure almost anything – from asthma and arthritis to cancer and failing eyesight. 'Some of the claims are hard to believe,' Kirsh cedes, 'but I do know of innumerable examples of what we might call miracles. I haven't had a client who has been cured of cancer but I have had one who has come off cocaine after fourteen years of addiction and I have seen people relieved of asthma. I've found it wonderful for all kinds of unlikely problems, such as giving up smoking and even marital problems.'

After around an hour of Chi Kung I was certainly feeling more energized – at certain points I felt a distinct shimmer of energy tingle through my body. And, at the same time, I felt calmer too. The session ended with an exercise designed to still the mind and quiet the body. Standing with my hands over my stomach, knees bent and eyes closed, I was instructed simply to be aware of my breathing and be silent. It seemed like an eternity before Kirsh told me I could open my eyes but he assured me that only two minutes had passed. Given time and practice, apparently I could stand like that for twenty minutes and it would pass like a few seconds. And then, I suppose, I would no longer have any problems with my tension: I would have conquered the ogre of stress – Time itself.

Putting it all together: Qi-netics

If you want ancient exercise moulded into a modern package, seek out Lydia Wong. Wong takes a bevy of ancient exercise practices, whirls them together and has created her own unique exercise and healing system. A host of stars sing her praises – from Melanie Griffith to Michael Keaton, from James Taylor to Roger Daltrey. 'She has made all the difference to my working days,' gushes Angelica Houston, while Jack Nicholson simply sent her a card saying: 'Thanks for walking all over me.'

Wong does frequently walk up and down her clients' spines, but she's just as likely to have you swooping round the room pretending you're an eagle or stamping around uttering grunts like a gorilla. Her unique brand of healing combines shiatsu, yoga, T'ai-chi, Chi Kung and dance with visualization, deep breathing and profound relaxation. She calls if Qi-netics and it's a potent brew.

'I had tried everything out there and was really cheesed off with what was available,' says Wong. 'People simply don't have the time to do three hours of yoga or T'ai-chi every day, and lots of people find aerobics or pushing weights doesn't work for them. So I thought if there isn't something out there, I'll create it.'

The result is a one-hour holistic workout that stretches and soothes mind, body and spirit. It can easily be learned and adapted for home use and, if you can't fit in the full hour, never mind – simply do what you can. 'Even if you do just one minute, one full stretch, but with total intent, I believe it can rejuvenate you,' says Wong. 'People think I'm crazy but I really believe we can control how we age. If we loosen up, everything gets easier.' Rejuvenation in just one minute? It's no wonder the stars love Lydia.

Born in Singapore, Wong has spent her life travelling all over the world learning Kung Fu with Vietnamese masters, T'ai-chi in China and Native American ceremonies in the Black Hills of South Dakota, to name but a few. She found it quite natural to fuse elements from both Eastern and Western cultures into Qi-netics. But the fundamental principle behind the system is the Chinese concept of Tao – the eternal flow of the universe. Get into the Tao and, the Chinese believe, everything will happen easily and effortlessly. It doesn't involve straining or struggling – in fact, try too hard and the flow will pass you by – it requires the ability to sink into the moment and simply be.

Wong uses movement and music because, as she says, 'Movement takes you out of your head. You simply can't do these movements and think about cooking dinner or anything – it's like a centipede trying to think before it moves its legs.'

She's right. Although her sequences of movement are fun to do, they are disciplined and precise. Everything focuses on the breath and her aim is to shift you into a state in which your movements are both natural and relaxed. Instead of concentrating on logically moving your body, you try to allow your body to almost move itself, gently guided by the breath.

My Qi-netics experience started with something called

Meridian dance massage – or Qi-rubs – a full-body self-massage which is practised in a rhythmic circular motion. The aim is to reactivate the body's vital energy, to improve blood circulation and stimulate the lymphatic system. It releases tension and the rocking motion calms the nervous system by encouraging the release of natural opiates.

Then Lydia moved me on to Qi-centring, exercises based on ancient Chinese movements mingled with the rhythms of Native American ceremonies. They have wonderful names like 'Embracing the Tiger', 'Hovering in the Air' and 'Heaven and Earth are Limitless' and, alongside fluid expansive movements, Lydia uses plenty of sound. 'Aaaah,' we sighed as we sank down as if we were sitting on a huge balloon; 'Huh! huh! huh!' we panted as we marched round the room, feet stamping and arms flapping. 'Baaaaah,' we vibrated as we shook our whole bodies. At first you feel like a complete idiot but, after a while, the sounds just emerge automatically. The Tao starts to move.

When Wong teaches classes, she is never sure quite what will happen. Sometimes the mood will be quiet and meditative, with soft soothing classical music; at others the beat will pick up and the class will end up flying round the room to the sounds of solid boogie. But when Wong works one to one, she focuses more on individual problems and needs. My session included exercises to strengthen weak knees and to get more 'earthed'. She taught me the best way to walk, to lie down and how to get up in a beautiful sinuous circling movement. And, although she didn't walk up and down my spine, she came close: kneeling on my lower back and twisting and manipulating my legs and back to free tension and realign the body. At the end of the hour I felt quietly relaxed and my posture certainly seemed improved.

Practise Qi-netics regularly, says Wong, and your life will change. 'When people leave the class they look about five to ten years younger,' she says. 'People get more confidence and far more self-esteem. By freeing up your body you can discover your true self and, once you do that, things start to come to you. You can have anything you want as long as you have the intent, as long as you can be totally in the moment, in the Tao.' Many clients report weight loss and a speedier metabolism, better muscle tone and improved circulation, clearer thought patterns and a sharper memory. The body becomes more flexible, energy levels rise, and stress levels plummet.

'A lot of my work is about expansion,' says Wong. 'If you expand the body, you expand the mind. It helps you to explore, to take risks. If you are joyous, everything works. I'm not saying this is a miracle cure but, if you can tap into it, the sky's the limit.'

Psychocalisthenics[1] – the new superexercise for the terminally lazy

Some people just aren't into exercise, and even more of you might loathe the idea of taking on a whole ancient philosophy with your daily exercise. So, if by now you're still shaking your head and groaning, then don't give up, try Psychocalisthenics.

If you can get your tongue round the name, you've conquered the hardest part. This little-known exercise system was developed way back in 1958 by an American called Oscar Ichazo. Well aware of the importance of regular physical exercise for health, Ichazo felt convinced that spending endless hours pounding round circuits or pushing weights was a terrible waste of precious time. Surely, he thought, there had to be a better way. So he started the quest for a system that could totally revitalize the entire body in the shortest possible time. Taking inspiration both from the esoteric traditions of the East and the scientific mechanics of anatomy and biochemistry, he devised a series of twenty-three movement and breathing exercises which would affect every muscle group in the body. The entire sequence would take just fifteen minutes a day, but its effects would be far-reaching. It's the perfect exercise system for anyone who hates exercise but wants to reap the benefits.

Practise Psychocalisthenics each morning before breakfast and, its practitioners promise, the world really *will* look a brighter place. You will feel bright and alert yet also calm and centred; your

[1] 1971, 1996 Arica Institute, Inc. Psychocalisthenics is a registered service mark of Arica Institute, Inc., a non-profit making educational organization admitting students of any race, colour, national or ethnic origin. Further information may be obtained from **Arica Institute**, Inc., 134 Elk Avenue, New Rochelle, New York 10804.

body will become relaxed and flexible and you will notice your mood automatically lifting. Psychocalisthenics, it seems, reaches the parts other exercise systems leave far behind.

Sarah Birrell, who has taught the system for the last seven years, is totally convinced. 'I used to have a very stressful job and I was driving long distances all the time,' she recalls. 'Psychocalisthenics was one of the things that actually kept me sane. If you do the exercises on a continual basis, you amass this amazing vital energy in the body; it's like building up a protective mechanism. You feel so good, so in control, and so strong. When you stop, you really notice the difference.' Sarah was hooked on exercise and had tried every variation in the book but, while other fads came and went, she kept with Psychocalisthenics.

She's in good company. Shirley Maclaine is a fan and Lindsey Wagner loved the system so much she has made her own video of the exercises. But why, if Psychocalisthenics is so wonderful, have so few people heard of it? Sarah Birrell puts it down to the name: 'People see the psycho bit and think it's counselling, or they get confused with Callanetics. Most people come to it by word of mouth.'

It's a great shame because Psychocalisthenics deserves to be better-known and appreciated. The exercises are easy to learn and, once you've mastered the moves, you can practise them at home, swiftly incorporating them into your daily routine. However Ichazo and his organization, Arica Institute, monitor teaching of the system very carefully and at present there are only eleven registered teachers in the UK.

Consequently I made the trek cross-country to Bury St Edmunds where Sarah Birrell teaches, to have my initiation into the feel-good exercise. Before I even started, I liked the idea of Psychocalisthenics. Firstly, it's cheap to learn: a course of either five one-hour lessons or two longer sessions costs around £40–50, depending on the teacher. And once you've learned it, there's no need to keep paying for classes: you're fully equipped to practise your own DIY sessions at home. There is no expensive equipment to buy and no fancy clothes to wear – all you need is a small clear space in the living room, comfortable clothes and bare feet. Pretty well anyone can do the exercises although, as with all forms of exercise, it is advisable to check with your doctor, particularly if you have a heart or back problem. In addition, some of the exercises should not be practised during pregnancy.

The first step to conquer is the breath. Breathing is an integral part of the system and in between each exercise you perform what is known as the Integration Breath. 'Just teaching people to breathe helps,' says Birrell. 'This is the most powerful breathing exercise and a great stressbuster: do it and you calm down immediately.' Basically, you inhale to six beats through your nose as your arms sweep up over your head and then exhale to a further six beats through your mouth, as if you were blowing out the candles on a birthday cake. Knees are bent, toes bent slightly inwards. You feel like a pigeon-toed chimpanzee, but the breathing *does* feel good. 'You're completely expanding the lungs and opening three sets of muscles in the chest and neck,' explains Birrell. 'It allows you to take in the maximum oxygen.'

From there we move through the rest of the exercises. Some, like the aptly-named Picking Grapes, are quite dynamic, involving swinging the arms and intense stretching. Others, such as the neck exercise Side-to-side involve only minimal movement. Throughout the session Birrell keeps a beady eye on your performance, making tiny adjustments to posture, correcting almost imperceptible inaccuracies of movement. This is exercise pared to perfection and no element is there just for the sake of it.

Oscar Ichazo divided the body into five 'cavities': the cranial cavity (the head); the thoracic (the lungs, kidneys, heart); the abdominal (the guts); the pelvic (the reproductive area); and the dorsal (the spine and all its nerves). The exercises move systematically through each cavity of the body, flexing not only the external muscles but working the internal muscles, massaging the organs and strengthening the spine. 'People forget that the lungs are a huge muscle, so is the heart and the colon,' says Birrell. 'With Psychocalisthenics you are effectively moving the Chinese acupuncture meridians which stimulate the internal organs. Meanwhile the deep breathing helps to clear the blood and get it flowing.' This, in turn, can apparently even help problems such as depression and ease cravings for food and cigarettes.

Although Psychocalisthenics is not specifically a weight-loss plan, Birrell says that many people do find they lose weight or change shape quite radically. One woman lost two inches from her waist after learning the technique. 'Often people who hold fat aren't necessarily eating too much or not exercising enough,' she adds, 'it can be a problem in their internal organs. Many people start losing weight when their digestion starts working properly.'

But, perhaps most alluring of all, is Psychocalisthenics' reputation as an age-buster. 'Oscar Ichazo says that, if you perform the exercises properly and regularly you shouldn't have to age,' says Birrell. 'Your body should be the same at twenty, forty, sixty and eighty. That's a very large carrot and it does seem to work. You really can feel the difference when you do the exercises over a long period.'

After my first lesson I wasn't sweating buckets as I would after a good aerobics class, but I could certainly feel I had exercised far more muscles. I was feeling clear-headed, bright and delightfully bushy-tailed rather than wiped out like a limp flannel. The real beauty of Psychocalisthenics is that it neatly fulfils all your exercise needs. If you hate exercise and only traipse down the gym through feelings of guilt, its fifteen-minute brevity is perfection on a plate. If however you actually *enjoy* hurling yourself round a squash court or grunting and groaning in the gym, that's fine too. As Birrell says, 'With Psychocalisthenics you are creating a maintenance and rejuvenation strategy for your body. After fifteen minutes you have done your exercise; you have wakened the body and worked through everything. If, after that, you want to go swimming or play tennis or pump iron, fine. Anything else you do should be purely for fun.'

GOOD BREATHING

It's curious that we so rarely stop to think about our breathing. There are hoards of books telling you about good eating: too many, in fact, as there's so much conflicting advice you hardly know which way to turn. Equally, there are masses of exercise and fitness gurus who will insist that their form of exercise is best. But you don't see shelf-loads of books on how to breathe, or witness different breathing masters slogging it out in 'best-breathing marathons'. Yet, good breathing is fundamental to health.

I suppose we simply take breathing for granted. We all know how to do it and, because we are doing it all the time, we tend to forget about it. After all, no-one got fat by over-breathing, did they? And it's not as though you can simply not bother to breathe out of laziness. However, if you're truly serious about good health you have to take on board the need for good breathing. And, even if you're a complete health slob and picked up this book by mistake or out of sheer boredom, it's worth bearing in mind that, if you do nothing else for your health, simply taking the trouble to breathe in a slightly different way from time to time can have a quite amazing series of benefits for your body.

So many of us only use a small part of our lungs. We breathe shallowly and cautiously and, in so doing, we are depriving ourselves. If you've read this far you're probably already catching on to the importance of good breathing. It's the cornerstone of good exercise and the first thing you'll learn if you take up yoga, Chi Kung or any other form of ancient exercise. If you follow the mind-body guidelines, you'll also be concentrating on correct breathing to boost your exercise targets and sports performance.

What is breathing? Quite simply, it's the way we pull in oxygen and circulate it around the body to 'feed' each and every cell. You can't overdose on deep breathing – the more oxygen you can get around your body, the better. Practitioners of yoga and Chi Kung reckon that breathing fully can do everything from improving your moods, increasing your resistance to colds and illness, fostering better sleep and even helping you resist ageing. It feeds the brain, calms the nerves and assists the process of waste elimination.

So what are we doing wrong? Well, few of us breathe right through our lungs. If, like me, you spend hours a day sitting behind a desk, you may well find you breathe up high in the upper area of the chest. You're getting by, but a vast proportion of your lungs (probably around two-thirds) simply isn't being used. Less oxygen is getting around the body and you run the risk of losing vital elasticity in the lower part of your lungs. Some people breathe slightly further down towards the navel which is better. But best of all is to use the whole of the lungs.

Abdominal breathing – the Chi Kung way

Correct breathing is essential in Chi Kung. Practitioners say that deep breathing can gradually cleanse the body of pollutants and improve lung capacity. Greater lung capacity, they say, gives better energy. It's not just mythical claptrap either: in China, hospitals have cured patients of tuberculosis using solely Chi Kung. Experiments have shown that the exercises increased their lung capacity from an average of 428.5 cc to 561.8 cc. While they were performing Chi Kung itself, their lung capacity expanded right up to 1,167.8 cc. Breathing rate calmed and dropped and their brainwaves dropped into the theta level, allowing the patients to stay alert yet deeply calm.

The average person breathes around sixteen times a minute while a Chi Kung practitioner, through practice, breathes slowly and deeply just five or six times a minute.

There are hoards of breathing exercises within Chi Kung but the basic technique for better breathing is the Abdominal Breath. This will probably seem very strange at first but persevere, even if just for a few minutes every day.

1.   Stand with your feet about shoulder-width apart, your knees slightly bent. Make sure you are totally relaxed. Place your hands gently over your stomach, just below your navel.
2.   Take in a slow steady breath through your nose, allowing your abdomen to swell out like a balloon as you breathe. Hold the breath gently.
3.   Then exhale, allowing the breath to come out slowly through your mouth as your stomach subsides.

This form of breathing directs *chi* – vital energy – right around the body. As you become more proficient, you can boost the power of this breathing by visualizing 'good' health-giving energy flooding into your lungs and thence to your whole body as you inhale, and stale, spent energy pouring out as you exhale. The Chinese Taoists say that breathing like this will enliven the metabolism and invigorate all the cells of the body, resulting in increased health and, supposedly, an extra shot of beauty as well!

Pranayama – the yogic breath of life

In the Indian tradition, breathing is just as important as it is to the Chinese. The first thing you will learn in a yoga class is correct breathing. While the Abdominal Breath will tend to waken you up and give you increased energy, the following exercise is aimed at calming and relaxing the entire body and mind. Many yogis use it before going into meditation. Breathing from one nostril to the other (which is all it basically involves) is said to make your respiration more regular and balanced which, in turn, should calm the whole nervous system. Ayurvedic practitioners and yoga experts say that this form of breathing does more than just calm the system: it brings the two hemispheres of the brain into balance and communication.

So here goes . . .

1. Sit comfortably in a chair, with both feet on the floor. Don't slouch. Then gently allow your eyes to close, your body to relax and your mind to still.

2. Place your hand (whichever one you use most naturally) around your nose. If you are right-handed the most natural way to do this will be to rest your right thumb against your right nostril with the rest of the fingers of your right hand lying gently towards your left nostril. The aim is to be able to easily and comfortably close off one nostril at a time without constantly moving your hand.

3. Close the right nostril gently and slowly exhale through your left nostril (notice you start the breath on an exhale rather than an inhale). Then inhale through the same nostril.

4. Swap nostrils by exhaling through the right and inhaling again. Always keep the breath smooth and relaxed. Don't try to breathe very deeply – just let your breath be natural. To begin with, you will probably find, as I did, that you need to keep blowing your nose. Don't worry, it's perfectly normal.

5. Alternate between the two nostrils for around five minutes if you can. If you feel uncomfortable at any time, breathe through your mouth for a while until you can go back to the nose.

6. When you've finished, allow yourself to simply sit and relax with your eyes closed for a while.

Thinking about breathing

The two previous exercises are just the tip of the iceberg and, if you want to take it further, I would recommend you find yourself a good teacher of either yoga or Chi Kung. But, simply incorporating these exercises into daily use will help your body and mind no end.

Some people say that how you breathe is a good indication of how you look at life altogether. Symbolically, breathing is all about taking in the new and eliminating the old. The Buddhists look on every new breath as giving new life and every exhalation as a little death. So, taking in deep joyful breaths is a way of affirming life and vitality and your desire to be here enjoying the moment. Breathing minimally and shallowly is, in a way, turning your back on life or accepting it only grudgingly.

If the idea of this appeals to you and you want to take the art of good breathing still further I suggest you invest in a small book full of a rather delightful wisdom. Called *Breathing into Life* (Hazeldon) and written by yoga therapist Bija Bennett, it's a collection of breathing 'poems' full of insights into what good breathing is all about, cleverly interwoven with exercises. It makes you realize just how your breathing represents your emotions and psyche.

I'm sure Bija Bennett would agree with the yoga proverb which says: 'Life is in the breath. Therefore he who only half breathes, half lives.' Breathe for the sheer joy of it.

Cautions

Sadly, however good your breathing, there's not much you can do about good air. It's outrageous that we can't even trust the air we breathe but, at present, it's a fact of life. If you live in the heart of the country, far away from motorways and flight paths and chemical works, you're lucky. If you live in the thick pollution of our inner cities, get away for a literal breath of fresh air whenever you can. When you're stuck in the city (and particularly if you run or cycle in heavy traffic) and the pollution levels are really high, wear a mask. It looks daft but so what? And those breathing techniques are even more vital for city dwellers – they will help your body get rid of all the toxins and pollution it is forced to take in, day in, day out.

STRESSBUSTING

Sometimes it seems as though the whole world is against you. The alarm clock doesn't go off and you're running late. The cat has chosen that morning to be sick over your shoes and the dog has chewed your cheque book. By the time you've left the house for work, it feels as if you've been up for hours, and yet the day has hardly begun. We live in a world that seems to be brimming over with stress. Our days are run against the clock: we talk in terms of deadlines, of 'getting through' the day, the week, the month, the year. We get stressed about our jobs, about money, about our relationships, about our kids. We even get stressed about enjoying ourselves. How many people go away on holiday and find themselves worked up into even more of a state? They lie on the beach worrying, 'Am I getting enough out of this?' 'How are they coping without me at work?' 'Should I have tipped that waiter last night?'

Stop it! Just stop getting in a state, stop worrying, stop panicking, stop being so darn stressed. It's easier said than done, isn't it? I can almost hear people replying with great irritation, 'Yes, but it's all right for you, *you* haven't got four kids screaming,' or 'You're not flat broke with a husband who won't get off his backside . . .' Sure, life is stressful and for some people the stresses are greater than others. Yet, conquer the demon stress and life will truly be a more pleasant place, whatever your problems. In fact, the very act of learning techniques to overcome stress will probably even help your situation. Children react to their parents' stress: calm mothers generally have quiet babies; stressed mothers frequently have highly-strung, difficult kids. And once you stop panicking about the financial situation or whatever, it can often become much easier to see alternatives, ways to improve the situation.

But, first and foremost, conquer stress for your health's sake. It's common knowledge that stress lies at the root of health problems such as ulcers. Doctors recognize it also as a factor in a host of other problems, from gastrointestinal disorders to strokes, from indigestion, migraines, insomnia and constipation to colds, eczema, impotence and phobias. Many natural health practitioners would go even further and say that stress is a factor in virtually all disease. And, quite apart from what stress does to your physical health, just think about what it does to your mind and emotions. Look at the number of marriages that have collapsed because one or both partners were so stressed they couldn't even enjoy their relationship. Look at all the workaholics who can't even relax long enough to think.

Most telling of all is the fact that experts in child development now realize that even our children are suffering from chronic stress. There's a lovely little book called *Relax* by Catherine O'Neill (Child's Play) which fills me with utter sorrow. It's aimed at quite young children and tells them how to recognize stress and how to deal with it. I'm glad it's there because kids nowadays need books like this. But in a better world, such books wouldn't have to exist.

I'm not saying that all stress is bad. Far from it. In fact, what does the harm is often not the actual stress itself, but the way we react to it.

If you take up the supertherapy challenge, you will doubtless find that your stress levels should begin to drop. Almost all the supertherapies attack stress in one way or another. Some will teach you breathing techniques; others will change the way you react to stressful stimuli. Some techniques, especially the massage and other bodywork therapies, are automatically stress-reducing in themselves. Some, such as herbalism, aromatherapy and nutritional therapy can give you natural products to soothe your nerves if you constantly over-react to stress.

So, you will find ways of reducing stress all the way through this book. This section however focuses on a few techniques which are simply superlative stressbusters. If stress is a particular problem, try some of them for starters.

Meditation

Learn to meditate and you have at your fingertips the key to instant stress relief. There is absolutely no doubt that meditating is a supreme way to beat stress: once you have learned how to do it, you have the secret for life. You don't need to take anything to calm you down and you don't have to race off to your masseur every time your shoulders rise.

So why don't more of us practise it? Probably because when we think about meditation, up pop images of plump lotus-positioned yogis gazing into thin air with beatific smiles on their faces for days on end. The idea fills busy (and lazy) Westerners with horror: surely meditating must mean you have to spend hours with your legs tied in knots; that you have to be a bit of a hippie on a spiritual quest and, worst of all, that you have to be prepared to be singularly bored. Myths, all of them. The modern meditator is as likely to be a board director as a drop-out; most fit meditation into the daily slog with the greatest of ease, and not one would ever say that meditation is boring. On the contrary, most insist it has totally changed their lives.

The benefits of meditation are myriad and they are certainly not all in the mind. Meditation, said the ancient yogis, is a powerful tonic which produces an acceleration of energy in the body. Positive thoughts, they believed, could rejuvenate cells and put the brakes on decay. For thousands of years, disciples had to take their word for it but now science is proving that meditation really is powerful medicine.

Over 450 scientific studies into transcendental meditation alone have produced impressive evidence. Researchers have found that meditation reduces hypertension, serum cholesterol and blood cortisol, which is related to stress in the body. It has been found effective in reducing the effects of angina, allergies, chronic headaches, diabetes and bronchial asthma, and can help relieve dependence on alcohol and cigarettes. Meditators, they found, see their doctors less and spend 70 per cent fewer days in hospital. Anxiety, depression and irritability all decrease while memory improves and reaction times become faster. Meditators, it appears, have more stamina, a happier disposition and even enjoy better relationships than the rest of us. It's not a bad payback for a simple input of around forty minutes a day.

And if, despite all the evidence, you still find the idea of sitting doing nothing a complete turn-off, there are forms of meditation to suit every style and every taste. There's simply no excuse not to get your mind in gear.

TM: TRIED AND TESTED

Nearly four million people practise transcendental meditation (TM) around the world, and few would give up their twice daily sessions. Now even GPs are beginning to advocate the benefits of TM: a growing number are prescribing TM for patients, with the cost being picked up by the NHS.

There's a wonderful element of mystery to TM. The best bit has to be that you are given your very own secret mantra (a word in Sanskrit to repeat). Simple relaxation exercises follow and then you simply sit quietly and repeat your word to yourself. After a minute you open your eyes and then close them and carry on with your mantra. You build up that pattern and focus on your breathing. Students have daily supervised sessions every night for five days and go back for 'check-ups' after one month, three months and six months.

TM isn't cheap to learn but once mastered, it's yours for ever. The effects, almost all students agree, are incredible. Some find it gives a greater perspective on life, most feel more in control, more happy and much less stressed. Ideally, you give yourself two sessions of TM a day – one in the morning and one in the evening.

MANTRA MEDITATION: CHANTING FOR INNER PEACE

Through the ages, religions have used sound as a means to meditation and now a bevy of teachers are bringing the technique up to date. Jill Purce is a leading figure in the field and she teaches workshops in a variety of techniques, including Mongolian overtone chanting which she promises is a powerful meditation technique. 'Sound,' she says, mystically, 'is one of the most effective ways of going beyond separation.'

Purce and other workshop leaders generally teach chanting techniques over weekend workshops. You should leave, knowing all it takes to chant happily on your own, although many people choose to join a regular group – chanting sounds spine-chillingly wonderful when practised in groups.

Fans say that chanting is simply the quickest way to still the mind. In addition, it vibrates and gives you energy right through your body. Overtone chanting (which finds a chord in every note) is the real crème de la crème of the chant world: it sounds very complicated but, well taught, is surprisingly easy to pick up and, once learnt, totally addictive.

The Native Americans say that meditating is like experiencing 'the bliss in the crack of the universe'. Listening to the almost unearthly sounds of chanting can give you a taste of something beyond this life. Some say it helps you to face your fears. But it's certainly not all floating on a cloud – meditation makes you look in the mirror and face yourself. Things you have suppressed for years can resurface, and learning to meditate – in any form – can make you reassess your entire life.

YOGA: MEDITATION ON THE MOVE

If even the *thought* of sitting still makes your stress levels rise and you hate the sound of your own voice, then yoga might be the answer. Swami Saradananda of the Sivananda Yoga Vedanta Centre stresses that yoga is not just about a healthy body. 'That is really a side effect,' she says. 'The *asanas* (postures) were originally designed as meditation techniques. They are points of focus for meditation and, as you become more experienced you can hold the *asanas* for longer and longer – both the mind and body benefit.'

Don't expect to jump straight in. It can take some time before you are proficient enough in the postures and breathing of yoga to be able to stop concentrating on your body and liberate your mind. But once you get there, it's worth the wait. And your body is benefiting as much as your mind: remember that yoga postures can help your whole being: your circulation, your respiratory system and your digestion. Yoga makes you very fit, and you'll find you often become almost immune to colds and flu. Yoga experts say that the ideal time to meditate is between four and six in the morning but, frankly, I would find getting up quite so early would defeat the stressbusting objective. You have to fit it into your lifestyle and many people find yoga meditation is a great way to unwind in the evening.

ZEN: THE PURE APPROACH

The classic form of meditation – simply sitting – can seem almost boring compared to more exotic practices. But Zen devotees need no external trappings or incentives to bring them their peace. Possibly the hardest form of meditation for us frantic Westerners to grasp, Zen is all about being open to the moment and recognizing that you can't grasp on to anything, you can't cling on.

Practitioners say Zen meditation makes it easier to let go of things and have much less fear about daily life. Some Zen teachers use *koans* to break through the rational mind, paradoxical questions which don't mean anything to the mind such as 'What is *mu*?' Others just ask you to sit, breathe and simply be open to what comes up.

Most Zen meditators sit for around half an hour a day, generally in the morning. They think of it as a small quiet space in their lives, a little sanctuary. Many light candles or burn a little incense and then just sit, maybe focusing on the breath or the posture.

The process, although simple, can be far from boring. It is often more like therapy, as the unconscious allows issues to come to the surface when you stop and sit. When you're sitting on a cushion for half an hour you're stuck with yourself.

Most Zen meditators practise both on their own and also with a group. There are also regular Zen retreats during which you can sit for between eight to eleven hours a day. It sounds excessive, but apparently the benefits make it all worthwhile.

DIY MEDITATION

Although it's often easier to get started with meditation with a tutor, there's nothing to stop you learning on your own. All it takes is a quiet room, twenty minutes and a touch of self-discipline.

Basic meditation exercise

1.   Sit with an alert and relaxed body posture so that you feel comfortable (either in a straight-backed chair with your feet flat on the floor or on a thick firm cushion, three to six inches off the floor).
2.   Keep your back straight, aligned with your head and neck and relax your body.
3.   Start to breathe steadily and deeply. Notice your breathing and observe the breath as it flows in and out, feeling your stomach falling and rising. Give it your full attention.
4.   If you find your attention starts to wander, simply note the fact and gently bring your thoughts back to your breath, to the rising and falling of your stomach.
5.   Try to sit for around twenty minutes.
6.   Don't jump up immediately afterwards. Bring yourself slowly back to normal consciousness. Become aware of the room around you, gently stretch and 'come back' fully before standing up.

Autogenic training

If meditation still seems too lengthy and laborious – or simply too 'Eastern' or even boring – try autogenic training. Some people call it the Western version of meditation and you can see why: it's short, sharp and speedy; there's no need to get involved in anything remotely approaching a spiritual discipline and, more importantly, it works – fast.

Autogenic training (AT) is simplicity itself, consisting of a simple series of mental exercises designed to switch off the stress 'fight or flight' system of the body and allow you to deal with the stresses of the day coolly, calmly and in total control.

It may be simple to learn and simple to practise, but the effects of AT are far-reaching and profound. Extensive research over the last twenty-five years has shown a multitude of benefits. First, and foremost, people report feeling calmer, more able to cope – they are in control of their lives rather than life controlling them. But there are measurable health benefits too: AT has been proven to significantly relieve tension and insomnia and lessen anxiety. It lowers both blood pressure and blood cholesterol (key factors in preventing heart attacks). In fact, its effects can be so dramatic that people with medical conditions have to be carefully monitored while they train. Some diabetics have been able to halve the amount of insulin they take, and other forms of medication can also be lessened in many cases.

In some areas AT is available on the NHS. In Manchester there is a group using the training for psychosomatic disorders, and it is also part of the programme at the Bristol Cancer Centre. In Dublin it is even being used to treat infertility: it was found that a fair number of women had high levels of a stress hormone, prolactin, that acts as a natural contraceptive and stopped conception. After a course of AT, the stress hormone levels in these women dropped, and a good proportion of them conceived. In fact, AT is a godsend to all pregnant women, as it reduces the stress of childbirth.

Meanwhile, AT is equally effective and popular in industry. Many airlines use the technique to combat jet lag and insomnia in their staff and it is used quite widely in other industries to reduce stress and improve performance at all levels. AT has even been taught to astronauts and cosmonauts as part of their space training programmes.

Dr Malcolm Carruthers is the doyen of AT in the UK, having brought the technique here almost twenty years ago. He had been researching the effects of stress all his working life and, at first, he thought that the answer to dealing with stress would come from chemistry. 'I thought originally that there would be a magic pill you could take, a stressbusting drug,' he says, 'but that's a bit like turning off the fire alarm because you don't like the sound of bells.' Dissatisfied with the side effects of beta-blockers, he looked elsewhere. He researched the effects of meditation on stress and was impressed – it certainly appeared to lower blood pressure and reduce blood cholesterol. But he found that people were resistant to what they considered a 'far-out foreign Eastern technique'. And then he discovered autogenic training.

AT came into being in Germany in the 1920s, originated by a

Berlin doctor, Dr Johannes Schultz. Another German, Dr Wolfgang Luthe took AT and developed it into the form it takes today. Carruthers himself learned of the technique from Professor Hans Selye, a pioneer in stress research and founder of the International Institute of Stress in Montreal, Canada. Fascinated, Carruthers then went on to study with Luthe. As a doctor and research scientist he was impressed, not only by the results of AT, but also by the meticulous research on the method. Over three thousand scientific publications have run reports on the beneficial effects, making AT probably the best-documented and most consistently researched method of stress relief.

'It's a bridge between alternative and conventional medicine,' says Carruthers. 'It's a bit like a Westernized form of meditation, but it doesn't demand any belief systems at all. I like to call it mental circuit training.'

So, what does this mind-workout comprise? It's simply a case of learning how to focus your attention inwards by a series of mental exercises. There are three basic components: firstly the art of passive concentration (quietly allowing your mind to focus on your body); secondly the repetition of certain phrases or words which allow you to target certain parts of the body and induce feelings such as heaviness or warmth. And thirdly, putting your body into certain standard postures to cut out the effects of the outside world. The three positions are: lying flat on the floor in a totally relaxed position (akin to a yoga *asana*); sitting in a chair with your hands resting on the arms of the chair or on your thighs; and perching on the edge of a hard chair in a kind of slump, with the back and head hanging forward and loose. 'It's very flexible,' says Carruthers. 'Once you've learned it, you can practise it sitting in your office, on the train, in a parked car, lying in bed.'

Next, you are taught how to focus on sensations in the body, imagining warmth in the arms and legs. Breathing is calm and easy; you learn how just to watch your breathing rather than trying to control it. Simply thinking about the exercises makes you feel calm. 'Abdominal warmth like a soothing, hot water bottle on the stomach,' suggests Carruthers, and you instantly feel like a kid curling up in bed. 'Cooling of the forehead like the cool hand on the fevered brow,' he continues, and a delicious chilly tingle runs through the body. The system is taught in weekly one-hour sessions over a period of eight weeks. Then, says Carruthers, 'you can have tranquillity without tranquillizers, sleep without sleeping pills and help with a whole range of psychosomatic problems.'

The effects go even further still. Sportspeople have found that their performance improves with autogenic training; creativity seems to shoot up and many businesspeople discover that, not only do their stress levels drop, but their communication skills and ability to make clear effective decisions improve dramatically. The reason, apparently, is that AT brings the two sides of the brain into better balance, allowing you the advantage of the intuitive, imaginative right side of the brain which is normally switched firmly off during waking life. In addition, when you practise AT you tend to need on average an hour less sleep at night.

There are books on autogenic training, but Carruthers firmly advises that you learn the technique properly with a qualified teacher. Not only should everyone have a medical consultation before starting the course but, as he insists, 'It has to be emphasized that this is not a superficial cosmetic relaxation technique; it actually works at quite a deep level. It's good medicine, but it's powerful medicine if it's properly applied.' This sounds suspiciously like a sales ploy but apparently not. Aside from the sheer physical effects that AT can have, the training can also work quite deeply on the mind. Sometimes quite deeply hidden anxieties, feelings of anger or frustration can surface when you start the training. Occasionally, people report headaches or chest pains. It is clearly important to have qualified advice on hand. That, however, is not a problem: there are around a hundred trained teachers around the UK, most of them doctors or nurses.

Inevitably, you only get out what you put in. Some people have found AT less than satisfactory but then, they admit, they do not practise it regularly. Given the fact that it takes no more than ten minutes a day to take your mind from a state of war to a cessation of hostilities, there's no excuse. Autogenic training is a peace process from which most of us could benefit.

Floating

Lying in pitch darkness and utter silence in eighteen inches of highly salted water sounds a strange way of beating stress. And yet, thousands upon thousands of people regularly spend good money for the privilege of crawling into a small cubicle and simply floating on their backs for an hour or so. Personally, I never quite understood the attraction of floating – until I tried it. I slumped in, feeling as if the weight of the world was on my shoulders, and I sprang out feeling reborn. Now I grab the chance to float whenever I possibly can.

The principle behind floating is simple. It was developed in the 1950s by Dr John C. Lilly, a medical doctor who was also trained as a psychoanalyst and a specialist in neurophysiology. He was intrigued at what happened to the brain and body when all external stimuli were removed, and conducted experiments in the soundproof chambers in which the Navy used to train their divers. Although the Navy were actively trying to put their divers under stress, Lilly found that, by floating people in a few inches of water, the results were exactly the opposite: the stress levels plummeted. From this initial work, he developed his own tank and continued his research. The results were far-reaching and, many said, far-fetched. People who floated claimed they thought and worked better, that they could learn more easily and concentrate better. Some said their creativity improved; others went so far as to say they felt younger and healthier. Some even claimed their sex lives rocketed. Almost without exception, they insisted they felt much calmer and more relaxed.

Although little research has been undertaken in the UK, several centres in America have spent the last twenty years analysing what actually happens when we float. Their results have shown that floating can indeed do all those things – and more. The almost complete sensory deprivation caused by floating seems to agree with both our bodies and minds. Blood pressure and heart rate become lower and calmer, while oxygen consumption improves. People suffering chronic pain find that they can obtain relief, often not just for the hour or so they float but for up to three days afterwards. Research suggests this could be attributed to the way floating seems to stimulate the body to produce endorphins, natural pain killers.

Meanwhile, on the mind front, musicians, actors and writers frequently float, because floating allows the right hemisphere of the brain to operate freely, stimulating much more creativity, imagination and the ability to solve problems. In America, students revising for exams drop into their local float centre with tapes of their revision material and simply lie back and listen – the 'superlearning' effect of floating helps them take in far more than a normal hour's study. And many psychotherapists find that therapy is much more effective with the client in the tank rather than on the couch: not only do clients relax quickly, but they also find it much easier to recall past experiences and are much more responsive to positive suggestions and visualizations. One of its most successful applications is in the treatment of addictive behaviour: overeating, smoking, drug-taking and alcoholism all respond remarkably well. Phobias often clear up quickly and anxiety states frequently disappear altogether.

It all sounds wonderful, but my interest was most sparked by the idea that an hour's float is the equivalent of around four hours' sleep. Quite a few people spend a night in the tank to overcome chronic tiredness, while others snatch four hours in lieu of a whole night.

My first float was at the South London Natural Health Centre. Before I took the plunge, there were two burning questions: is it really very hygienic to lie in the equivalent of everyone else's bath and would I come out looking like a wrinkled prune? Ian MacFarlane who runs the float centre reassured me on both counts: Epsom salts are an effective cleansing agent, plus the tank is filtered after every float and, no I wouldn't wrinkle – again an effect of the salts. Then he introduced me to the tank, which at 8 ft x 4 in x 7 ft 6 in is one of the larger models, explained what to do and left me to my own devices.

I undressed and showered in a pleasant, private room and then approached the tank. Stepping through a small door I lowered myself into eighteen inches of water laden with 300 kilos of Epsom salts. Propping my head on an inflatable pillow I lay back – and floated. I had imagined it would feel horribly claustrophobic, but I surprised myself by quite happily shutting the door behind me and switching off the light. Many claustrophobes, in fact, find floating a wonderful way to overcome their fears.

At first, whale music echoes mournfully through the chamber, but after ten minutes or so it faded away and I was left in silence

– and total darkness. It sounds terrifying but, truly, it felt quite safe. The chamber is neither hot nor cold and after a few minutes you become almost hyper-aware of your body and where you hold tension. It must have taken ten minutes for me to totally relax my jaw. Then the sensation disappears and it becomes hard to remember you've got a body at all. Time swiftly twisted and, as I drifted in and out of sleep, it became harder and harder to work out whether I had been in for twenty minutes or an hour. Some people find they spontaneously recall childhood incidents; others that they suddenly find solutions to tricky problems; still more report almost 'out of the body' experiences. I underwent none of these, but I did have very vivid dreams. After an hour and a half the whale music returned as a signal that my time was up, and I showered and washed the salt out of my hair (I don't recommend floating as a hair-conditioning exercise).

Many complementary health centres are now combining other therapies with floating. Aromatherapists and other masseurs find that a float before a massage relaxes the client and allows him or her to benefit even more from the massage. Reiki healers also find people are more receptive to healing energy when they emerge from a tank.

And plenty of centres are combining floating with another super-relaxation technique – mind machines. These curious space-age machines work by flashing lights on to your closed eyes at specific speeds and in specific combinations. They can swiftly take your brain into a different frequency and many people use them to train themselves to relax at will. The theory is that once you become accustomed to switching your brain swiftly from one frequency to another via the machine, you will soon be able to do it at will.

Floating and mind machines go well together. Of course, the major benefit is to amplify the stressbusting effect. A quick burst on a mind machine before you float will allow you to relax even quicker and gain more benefits from floating. However, not everyone wants to just relax. Certain brain frequencies have been linked with accelerated learning; others with enhanced creativity: by using the mind machine to get the brain into the right pattern before entering the tank, the effects of floating can be considerably boosted. In addition, says Ian MacFarlane, research is showing that certain frequencies encourage the brain to instigate healing. 'It is very recent research,' he says, 'but one specific frequency seems to encourage the release of serotonin [a substance in the body which reduces bleeding, stimulates the intestine and controls consciousness and mood in the brain], while another promotes the release of endorphins [natural substances which control pain, relieve stress and improve mood].'

Floating, he insists, is set to stay, and he firmly believes that in the not too distant future we will all have float tanks in our own homes, as common as CD players and microwaves.

GOOD SLEEP

Good sleep is certainly part of the supertherapy healthcare package – not for nothing do we talk about beauty sleep. Funnily enough, it is probably the one area of our lives many of us worry most about. Every time I have written a feature about sleep, it seems to strike a massive chiming chord with people. Most of them are worried that they don't sleep enough, that they sleep too much, that they don't sleep well enough, that they sleep at the wrong time and in the wrong places; some worry that they hardly sleep at all.

Quality over quantity

It seems as though the search for good sleep is becoming big business. Americans are rushing to swap the shrink's couch for the somnologist's bed, firmly believing that by sorting out their night-time neuroses, they can solve everything from relationship problems to finding a new job to getting a better orgasm. There are over three thousand sleep centres nationwide and 'sleep hygienists' are almost as common as their dental counterparts.

And, if pursuing a good night's sleep is a serious goal for Statesiders, they take the effects of bad sleep equally seriously. Lack of sleep is blamed for up to 40,000 road crashes a year, bad decision-making in business and even for such disasters as the

Challenger space shuttle, the Three Mile Island nuclear power accident and the Chernobyl disaster.

Britain has only around twenty sleep centres and few of us would know what a sleep hygienist does. But as life becomes tougher and more stressful, we too are becoming more and more obsessed with sleep. How much sleep do we really need? What is the *best* kind of sleep and how can we get it? Do we get enough sleep or are we sleeping too much?

Ask the experts and you end up confused. 'People benefit from getting as much sleep as they can. Ideally you should sleep until you are slept out,' states Dr Timothy Roehrs from the Henry Ford Hospital in Detroit. He, along with other experts, claim we are all sleep deficient, sleeping, on average, between an hour and ninety minutes less than we should. But Dr John-Yves Chauve of the French Biomedial Institute for the Study of Life and Sports is equally insistent that five to six hours' slumber is plenty. Professor Jim Horne, Director of the Sleep Research laboratory at Loughborough University backs him up, considering we are all as prone to oversleeping as we are to overeating: 'Adults can successfully adapt to around six hours' sleep without increased daytime sleepiness or difficulty in getting up in the morning, provided it is a gradual process,' he avers.

So who should we believe? The answer seems to be our own bodies, which undoubtedly know how much sleep we need and when. The majority of us will kip for around eight hours a night, but some people quite happily manage on five or six, while others feel lousy without nine. Curiously enough our very personalities can determine how much sleep we need. American expert Ernest Hartmann discovered that short sleepers tend to be efficient, energetic, ambitious people who were relatively sure of themselves, socially adept and decisive. They were satisfied with their lives, while their social and political views were conformist. Long sleepers, by contrast, were nonconformist with mild neurotic problems and tended to be less sure of themselves. Nevertheless, they appeared to be more artistic or creative.

However, it's not really the *amount* of sleep we get that is important for our health and wellbeing, it is the *kind* of sleep we get – quality over quantity. Sleep is divided into three types: light, deep and REM (dreaming) sleep. Cut down on sleep, and our bodies will compensate by automatically cutting down, first, light sleep and then, if necessary, REM sleep too.

When Randy Gardner took the record for lack of sleep back in 1965, he stayed awake for a staggering 264 hours and 12 minutes. When he finally slept he crashed out for a mere 14 hours and 40 minutes and woke up practically totally recovered.

But did he dream? The importance of REM or dreaming sleep is another thorny topic of debate amongst the scientists. Some insist our dreams are merely the detritus of the day, spewed out like so much garbage. Others are convinced that, by using our dreams creatively, we can solve many of our waking problems. Many researchers are fascinated by the idea of 'lucid dreaming', of learning how consciously to direct your dreams. Dr Rosalind Cartwright of St Luke's Medical Center in Chicago found that people who cope best with divorce tend to have helpful dream patterns. She recommends reshaping dreams with a happy ending. 'Once the dreaming changes, the morning mood changes,' she says. 'If people stop having unpleasant, guilt-ridden anxious dreams, they wake in the morning more refreshed and better able to face the world.'

But if you still feel grouchy and tired when you wake, regardless of wonderful healing dreams, there could be another answer. Many scientists believe the Spaniards, far from being lazy, have had the right idea all along with their afternoon siesta. The body's circadian rhythms show that we are ready for sleep around three or four in the afternoon and that many problems of overtiredness could be solved by a half-hour nap in the afternoon. Researchers discovered that careful use of naps could help long-distance lorry drivers, overworked junior hospital doctors and those on night shifts; that an afternoon cat nap significantly sharpens mental alertness and improves mood.

We all feel better after a good night's sleep – relaxed, bright and ready to face whatever the day might throw our way. But what actually happens to our bodies and brains when we turn out the light? Remarkably little is known about the actual physiological effects of sleep, but the facts, as they emerge, are intriguing. In the first three hours of sleep, large amounts of growth hormone are released into the body. Although the reasons for this in humans are not quite clear, growth hormone in animals is known to give immune systems a boost. As deep sleep ensues, more immune activities get under way. Other hormone levels rise rapidly too: such as prolactin, which is believed to regulate glucose and fatty acids in the blood, reduce water loss in the kidneys and generally balance our bodies; and melatonin, understood to influence regeneration and regulate water. So, while we slumber, our bodies appear to be fine-tuning, balancing, protecting.

Is this the basis of the beauty sleep myth? 'People who lose a lot of sleep do look different,' says Dr Jacob Empson of the University of Hull. 'Skin loses its bounce, dark circles appear under the eyes, and skin loses its tone with sleep loss or disruption. It's something most shift workers notice.' He is convinced that, although we are not sure of the exact mechanisms, sleep is vital for repair. 'In experiments depriving rats of sleep they found that the rats became bedraggled, their fur lost its tone and they developed sores on their tails. Eventually they died. Sleep is absolutely essential.'

Even more so if we are under particular stress. Soldiers preparing to go into combat have been known to increase their sleep up to twelve to sixteen hours a night; if we are depressed or angry we find it easy to sleep ten to twelve hours, and studies of people moving from hard manual labour to intellectual study show that the brain-work makes them want one to two hours' more sleep. Disrupt your normal way of doing things, and you need more sleep.

Deprive yourself, on the other hand, and you could find yourself becoming more angry, irritable and anti-social. Your memory will not be so good and your co-ordination might suffer. And, believe it or not, you won't be so sexy! Research has discovered that our sex hormones are suppressed when we deprive ourselves of sleep. As Ernest Hartmann says, 'Sleep lets us stay optimistic, energetic and self-confident.'

This is why so many of us panic when our sleep becomes disturbed. Up to ten million people in the UK suffer from sleep disorders, first and foremost from the dreaded insomnia. The problems often start way back in infancy. Sometimes there are simple causes, such as bad habits or the effects of moving house. But sometimes there is the deeper fear of separation. Parents who suffered childhood separation themselves often associate sleep with loss. Losing consciousness becomes frightening for them and they pass their own anxieties on to the child.

As we grow up, our sleeplessness generally falls into three categories: transient insomnia, brought on by a change in routine such as jet lag or switching shifts; short-term insomnia, caused by illness or emotional problems; and chronic insomnia which has myriad causes ranging from depression or anxiety to abuse of drugs or alcohol.

The standard doctor's response to 'I can't sleep' has for years been simply 'Well, take this', with prescriptions of sleeping pills running to over ten million a year in the UK. But medical research is now showing that, far from being a valuable lifeline, these drugs can cause more problems than they solve. Benzodiazepine drugs (such as temazepam, nitrazepam and triazolam) are the most commonly prescribed pills, but research has shown them to be highly addictive. Withdrawal after long-term use can cause quite severe side effects such as cramps, vertigo, palpitations, panic attacks and seizures – not to mention rebound insomnia.

Fortunately, doctors are now viewing sleeping pills with more caution and are starting to use them only as a short-term rescue package for crisis management. It's small comfort for insomniacs, but scientists are finally discovering the very hormones that *cause* sleep. A substance called prostaglandin D_2 appears to be the major factor in inducing sleep: disrupt the levels of this hormone, and you can induce narcolepsy. Researchers are now hoping that, when the whole picture becomes clear, they will be able to manufacture natural sleeping pills from the body's very own sleep regulator.

Until then, we will have to rely on less scientific remedies. But, before we go the way of the Americans with their somnologists and sleep hygiene (simply teaching what is good for sleep and what's not), let's try to get back to real basics and remember that untampered sleep is the most natural thing in the world. Listen to your body, sleep when you feel tired and you won't go far wrong. Don't feel guilty if you need to be in bed by ten o'clock while your friends want to party and, on the other hand, don't think you are alone if you feel fresh as a daisy after four or five hours' kip. If you feel your eyelids drooping at teatime, resist a body-jolting shot of caffeine, and realize it's a perfectly natural and normal response. Above all, remember that, unless you have a medical problem, everyone gets the amount of sleep they need. Just relax, and sleep on it.

Solving insomnia without sleeping pills

You will probably find that, if you have a sleep problem, it will gradually lessen and disappear altogether once you start a supertherapy. As I have explained already – and will keep reminding you – a good therapist will be treating you as a whole, not just your obvious symptoms. Most of them will ask you about your sleep patterns as a matter of course. The fact that you wake up at three o'clock every morning will be an important pointer for a homeopath, as will the kind of dreams you have. An Ayurvedic practitioner will want to know what times of day you feel sleepy; an acupuncturist will be fascinated to know that you have recurring nightmares. However, if lack of sleep is causing you sleepless nights in itself, try these quick self-help hints culled from a variety of supertherapies.

THE COMMONSENSE APPROACH

Look for any underlying psychological causes behind your insomnia and, if necessary, seek appropriate help (e.g. counselling, stress management etc.). If you find that you can't sleep, or that you wake up because you are worried about things you need to do or remember during the day, a handy hint is to keep a pad and paper by your bed. Every time you think of a worry, write it down and tell yourself that's all you can do about it until morning. Who knows – you might even find a brilliant answer to your problems in your dreams?

Keep your room cool and airy – a stuffy room is bound to affect your sleep. Avoid caffeine, alcohol and heavy meals late in the evening as they will all interrupt your sleep. Make sure your bed is comfortable and right for you – many people find they get a good night's sleep once they change their bed. Ensure you get enough aerobic exercise – plenty of desk-bound workers can't sleep because, although their minds are exhausted, their bodies are still frisky. Some sports psychologists say that the problem lies in the fact that we have absorbed stress all day but our bodies haven't had the chance to get rid of any excess adrenalin surging round the body from all that stressful arousal. Exercise allows a safe release for it, but don't exercise *too* late at night or it will tend to wake you up.

Sometimes the oldest cures are the best: have a warm bath and a milky drink before you go to bed – it's comforting and just might do the trick.

TAKE A BATH – HYDROTHERAPY

A simple bath isn't just an old wives' tale. Naturopaths recommend hydrotherapy for a host of ills, especially for insomnia. The key, it seems, is in the temperature of the water. Very hot and very cold water are both very stimulating to the body, and so it's no use plunging into a boiling bath or taking a brisk shower just before bedtime: it will simply tell your body to wake up. As naturopath Leon Chaitow explains, your bedtime bath needs to be at body temperature. 'You can create your own home floatation tank if you use a bath at body temperature with Epsom salts,' he says. 'You need to spend a good half hour in there. It's quite magical and quite cheap.'

The Austrian Moor-Life bath has been prescribed for thousands of people suffering insomnia in Austria, Switzerland and Germany, and naturopathic clinics in the UK also swear by the potent herbal bath. For peaceful sleep, naturopaths suggest putting two-thirds of a cupful of the solution in a warm (again, not hot) bath. Soak for twenty to thirty minutes. Don't rinse off but wrap yourself in a large towel and go to bed.

Health expert Leslie Kenton has an even more curious water cure. 'Take a pair of cotton socks and dip them in icy water,' she advises, 'then wring them out as much as possible. Put them on and cover with a pair of thick wool socks and then go to bed. People always laugh but it works superbly well.'

FOOD FOR SLEEP: NUTRITION

Eating a heavy meal late at night can cause indigestion and insomnia, but often food affects our sleep in more subtle ways. Linda Lazarides, Director of the Society for the Promotion of Nutritional Therapy, says that she used to have terrible insomnia before she applied nutritional therapy to herself. She found her sleep problem had been caused by a combination of vitamin and mineral deficiencies and food allergies. Only a qualified nutritionist will be able to tell you if you have any serious deficiencies and it is not advisable to take a cocktail of supplements unsupervised. However, everyone can benefit from taking a good quality multi-vitamin and multi-mineral supplement daily. In addition, says Lazarides, you should stop taking caffeine completely if you can't sleep and make sure your diet is healthy and balanced: 'Sort out your basics,' she advises. 'Your diet should be based on whole foods with lots of fruit and vegetables, brown rice and a bit of fish and chicken. Plus nuts and seeds which are high in calcium and magnesium, which are essential for good sleep.' After that, if you're still not sleeping, she suggests you look for allergies. Try cutting out wheat, dairy produce and additives for a month and see how you feel. You can then try reintroducing them one at a time and see which, if any, is the culprit.

In addition, Leon Chaitow suggests trying a protein snack (like yoghurt) about an hour or so before you go to bed. He also points out that, although alcohol has a reputation for sending people to sleep, a tipple before bedtime could be your worst enemy: 'No alcohol,' he insists.

SWEET-SMELLING DREAMS – AROMATHERAPY

The essential oils used in aromatherapy can have very powerful effects on the body, mind *and* emotions – often all connected to sleeplessness. Robert Tisserand, Principal of the Tisserand Institute, says that, even when people consult an aromatherapist for other reasons than insomnia, they almost all comment on how their sleep has improved.

Nothing beats a professional massage, but you can achieve wonderful results at home with aromatherapy. However, because the oils are very powerful, do exercise caution. Use good-quality oils, and always dilute them in a base oil. Lavender is probably the best-known sleep aid, although orange blossom, sandalwood and geranium are also very effective. Use around five drops in approximately 10 ml of a base oil such as almond oil.

Robert Tisserand says the ideal insomnia cure is to have

someone give you a massage late in the evening or last thing at night: 'It doesn't have to be expert – you don't have to know a lot for a back rub with oils,' he says. Alternatively, soak in an aromatherapy bath. 'The important thing is not to see it as a cleaning exercise but as a relaxing exercise,' he points out. 'Make it into a sensory event: burn some candles instead of putting on a bright light; play some music – whatever relaxes you.'

Last but not least, make your own herb pillows. Fill a sachet with lavender flowers and any other sweet-smelling dried herbs and flowers and then keep it topped up with a few drops of lavender oil each week.

ADJUST YOUR SLEEP TIMES – AYURVEDIC MEDICINE

Ayurvedic practitioners have very definite views on why we don't sleep. The main problem, according to the famous endocrinologist and Ayurvedic expert Deepak Chopra, is that we are all sleeping at the wrong time. He's even written a whole book about it called *Restful Sleep* (Rider). It may sound controversial (and for many people downright impractical), but he swears that we should ideally be asleep by ten o'clock at night and up well before seven in the morning. These, he insists, are the natural times for our bodies to go to sleep and wake up.

Even more difficult for many people would be Chopra's insistence that anyone who has trouble sleeping should avoid watching television in the evening – apparently it overstimulates the senses. If you *must* watch, says Chopra, switch off by nine o'clock. More pleasant and practical is the recommendation for a massage with sesame oil before going to sleep. And, if you don't have time for a full-body massage, simply massage your feet with oil. Massaging the feet is said to balance the acupressure points that affect the nervous system, promoting sound sleep. In addition, you should massage vital points called *marmas* – one in the centre of the forehead and the other just below the navel – using light, circular, clockwise motions for about one minute.

THE GENTLE POWER OF HERBAL REMEDIES

Before the advent of valium, pharmacists prescribed extract of valerian for insomnia and nervous conditions. Its results were more gentle but still highly effective. Even better, it was non-addictive and lacking in side effects. Valerian was bypassed in the race for drugs which have instant effects, but now it is being rediscovered, along with other herbs, as a highly effective way of conquering insomnia. If you have heard vague rumours about valerian being toxic, rest assured that the herb has been very thoroughly vetted by authorities all over Europe and America and has been shown to be entirely safe. Supplements in tablet form such as Valerina and Natrasleep contain valerian and are widely available from chemists and healthfood stores. Alternatively, try herbal teas as a bedtime alternative. Chamomile is an old favourite, but less well-known herbs such as skullcap, catnip, vervain, passiflora and hops are equally effective in soothing the body and mind into slumber.

Barbara Griggs, author of *The Green Witch – A Modern Woman's Herbal* (Vermilion), uses two teabags of limeflower herbal tea with a bit of honey to ensure a good night's sleep. And if she finds sleep totally impossible, she uses a herbal and homeopathic preparation from Weleda called Avena Sativa Compound: 'It's very, very good,' she says, 'and has even been used to help people come off tranquillizers.'

RELAX AND MEDITATE – CHINESE MEDICINE

Doja Purkit, a consultant in alternative medicine at London's Hale Clinic says that, according to traditional Chinese medicine, most disorders, including insomnia, stem from an imbalance of energy in the meridians, the unseen lines of energy that run through the body. Practitioners would usually use acupuncture to correct any imbalance – and possibly a herbal preparation as well. However, Purkit also recommends meditation and gives this simple exercise:

Lie in bed with your arms beside you, palms facing up. Close your eyes. Take a deep breath in and slowly count 'one, two' as you inhale, then slowly exhale to the count of three. Repeat this as you concentrate on the rhythm of the breath. Do this initially for five minutes and increase up to 30 minutes a day.

Oriental texts also suggest some curious guidelines for good sleep. Sleep only on your left side. Sleeping on your back will stimulate the pituitary gland and, hence, your conscious brain; while sleeping on your right side stimulates the left side of the brain, the analytical part. Drink hot water one hour before you intend to go to bed in order to improve your circulation and soothe the brain. Put a bucket of cold water or an ionizer next to the bed to allow a good supply of oxygen while you sleep – this will stop you feeling groggy in the morning. And never sleep with your feet pointing south, at night, says Purkit. Gravity will pull the water in your body like a tide and, as the strongest pull is from the south, you could end up with bad sleep and puffy legs.

Finally, he says, if you wake up in the night feeling gaseous, try a cup of ginger tea to help you back to sleep. And if you wake up hot and sweaty, try cinnamon tea.

GOOD POSTURE

The very word 'posture' is enough to make most of us instantly slump. Memories flood back of childhood lessons in correct 'deportment'; of cold rulers rammed down shivering backs and of books balanced precariously on protesting heads. The new idea of posture however is far removed from such draconian ways and we could all feel much better in body, mind and spirit by paying a little more attention to our poise.

As young children, we possess unselfconscious poise and perfect posture; we are ideally balanced and fluid. But as time and the twentieth century take their toll, we all learn to adapt ourselves to a harsh environment and therein begin our problems. We lose perfect poise because we're not really evolved to deal with the effects of modern life. We begin to lose our easy freedom of movement when we start adapting ourselves to our environment, to furniture which is not well-designed, and to difficult emotional situations such as going to school. Also, as children, we often copy adults and pick up their pattern of movement. Unconsciously, we acquire patterns of movement which work against our bodies' design and, in doing so, create tension.

We all know the short-term effects of tension but, if bad posture becomes habitual, we risk not only the possibility of back pain but of effects reaching far further than the spine. The ribs are attached to the thoracic (upper) spine and they work through expansion.

When we stoop or round our shoulders the lungs are not able to expand properly and, with long-term misuse, respiratory problems can occur. Equally, slinging ourselves into our favourite armchair might not be the best idea for a healthy body. It might *feel* comfortable, but you are putting pressure on all your internal organs. Your heart, your digestion, your lungs are all compressed and cannot work as effectively. Eventually that will cause problems.

Basic good posture is having everything in balance, making sure that your back and abdominal (stomach) muscles are equally strong and your spine is in a good position. And, not only does good posture make your body operate more effectively, but it can also even put you in a good mood. As any supertherapist will tell you, the mind and the body are inextricably linked. All the nerve pathways that leave the brain eventually go through muscles, so that there is a definite connection between what we think and what we experience. People with an upright posture tend to be confident and extrovert, while those who slump and slouch veer towards depression and uncertainty. Turning that fact around has interesting effects. If you are feeling down and depressed, try sitting up straight with your eyes looking ahead, and you'll find it immediately lifts your mood. So, if good posture is worth having, how do we gain balance and poise?

Good posture: the basic rules

STANDING

Stand straight Think about standing on both feet. That might sound strange and feel odd – we're all so used to slouching on one side. Most people always stand with their weight on one leg, tending to favour one particular side, which puts them out of balance.

The pelvic tilt Tuck your bottom in and pull your stomach in so that you are using your muscles almost like a girdle to hold yourself. That provides good support for the lower back.

Chin in Apparently, most of us poke our chins out too far. The head should be balanced with the chin tucked in.

WALKING

Take even strides   Some people pull themselves along, overusing their hamstrings (back of thighs); others lean forwards and over-stride. The most sensible walk is one that uses even strides.

Keep your balance   Remember, when walking, we are designed to balance on one leg after the other. Don't throw your weight around.

Walk low   High heels can throw the pelvis forward which, in turn, will throw the whole body out of alignment. Eventually, it can cause shortening in some muscles, which could lead to back pain. Low, well-cushioned shoes are best for everyday wear, but obviously there will be times when you can't resist high heels. That's fine, but just make sure you don't wear them all day, every day. Keep them for special occasions.

SITTING – IN THE OFFICE

Chair comfort   Ideally, you should be seated with your knees lower than your pelvis. The seat should be high enough for you to relax your shoulders, leaving your arms at a ninety-degree angle to your desk. If the chair has arms, they should be low enough to fit under your desk.

Screen daze   If you use a screen at work, your computer should be on a stand rather than on the desk, so that you can look directly *at* it, rather than down towards it. Equally, make sure it is directly in front of you rather than situated to one side.

SITTING – AT HOME

Don't slump   You race through the front door and hurl yourself at the sofa like a bag of potatoes. We all do it but, say the experts, it's not a good idea to permanently slouch in front of the television. It may be the most comfortable position, but it's the worst position for your back. You should have a reasonably firm support behind you – a firm cushion can help.

Watch your eyes   Your eyes lead your head which, in turn, leads the whole body. If you're watching TV, you should be directly facing it with your head balanced. If you're reading a book, lift the book up towards you rather than bending over your lap.

SLEEPING

Get the right support A good mattress is very important to a relaxing night's sleep. Too soft, and the curves of your back sink in and reinforce bad posture, but not everyone can take a super-hard mattress.

Choose your pillow carefully Pillows are also important. Ideally, you should have a malleable pillow that will mould to the curves of your neck. There are specialist pillows on the market, but you can equally well roll up a hand towel and place it inside your pillow case to provide support for the neck.

Check your position It's fine to sleep on either your side or your back, but watch out if you sleep on your front with your head turned to one side. It twists the upper neck and can create imbalance.

What not to do – the posture no-nos

1. The heavy shoulder bag You may think the weight of the bag is pulling your shoulder down, but in fact you are pulling your shoulder up to compensate. As a consequence, your body over-balances and twists to compensate. Try a rucksack, or, at the very least, make sure you constantly shift arms when carrying heavy bags.

2. The phone shrug Clutching the telephone between your ear and your shoulder frees your hands but can cause serious problems. If the action becomes habitual, you could end up with 'telephone neck syndrome', a form of repetitive strain syndrome which can eventually cause searing pain between the shoulder blades, running down your arms and making your fingers tingle. If you spend most of the day on the phone, you should have a headset with a boom microphone.

3. The reversing rick Many people suffer injuries when reversing their cars. The tendency is to pull the head back sharply and jerk the neck around. Instead, try dropping the tip of the nose to your shoulder and then turning it while imagining your spine lengthening.

4. Post-exercise trauma Many people come unstuck after vigorous exercise. Good posture after vigorous sport is very important, because all your muscles are warm and pliable. A lot of people tend to slump in the changing room, and things start to stiffen up. Either stand straight or walk about – don't scrunch your body.

5.   The hip bend   Never pick up anything by twisting and bending; always squat down before lifting.

Home help

Here are a few simple exercises to help your posture.

1.   The Alexander Technique (which is wonderful for good posture) recommends the following exercise to be practised each day for between fifteen and twenty minutes. This exercise can replace the fluid between the discs of your spine and add an inch or more to your height during the day.

•   Lie on the floor with your head balanced on a small pile of paperback books (about the same height as your hand span). Hands should be gently resting on either side of your navel. Gently roll on to the books and bring your feet in towards your buttocks so that your knees point towards the ceiling.

Try to become aware of any tension in your body and, as you feel it, *don't* try to correct your position, just *think* about your spine lengthening and the tension disappearing.

2.   Before you settle down to work, you should aim to run through the following. You can practise these exercises whenever you have a few spare minutes – they are equally effective in a sitting position.

•   Stand straight with your weight distributed evenly, your stomach and bottom held in and your shoulders back. Turn your head gently to the left and then to the right (five times each side).

•   Move your left ear down to your left shoulder then repeat on the other side (five times each side).

•   Raise both shoulders up towards your ears and down again, breathing in on the way up and out on the way down (five times).

•   With your left hand on your left shoulder and your right hand on your right shoulder, bring your elbows together in front, then circle them outwards and backwards (five times).

104

• Place your knuckles in your back and gently stretch backwards.

Further care

Just becoming aware of your posture and remembering to correct it from time to time can have enormous benefits. But, if you want to take your poise really seriously there are several self-help techniques which can have invigorating effects on your balance, health and mood.

• The Alexander Technique is recognized as the best system for promoting good posture. It is often recommended by physiotherapists, and some NHS doctors employ teachers of the Alexander Technique in local health promotion clinics. The technique is *not* a therapy, it is a process of re-education, insist its teachers, and most recommend about thirty lessons in order to be able to apply the technique to everyday life. Lessons usually last between thirty and forty minutes and are very gentle, as the teacher helps you to 'unlearn' the patterns of tension which create stress and strain and to relearn your body's ideal way of moving.
• Pilates is a good form of exercise, sometimes described as 'Alexander Technique in motion'. I haven't tried it personally, but many people swear by it and it seems to be very popular amongst dancers.
• The Feldenkrais Method is similar to the Alexander Technique but slightly more dynamic, taught in either individual sessions, evening classes or workshops, which makes it cheaper.
• Bodywork techniques like Rolfing and Hellerwork also teach good posture, as do many osteopaths and chiropractors. For more information on these see the individual sections later on in the book.

The Complete Systems for Total Health

If you really want to rethink your life and commit yourself to a healthier way of living, start with the supertherapies in this section. Although many of the therapies throughout this book have very ancient lineages, Ayurveda and traditional Chinese medicine (TCM) are unique in that they have been handed down to us virtually intact. Both are complex medical systems, quite able to deal with virtually all the ills of society. However, these doctors won't just give you a pill and tell you to come back next week; they will demand that you take full responsibility for your own health. To help you, there are precise rules and advice for all segments of your life: you will probably have to alter your diet, take up exercise, learn correct breathing and even practise meditation. But do all this, and there is little or no doubt you will transform your life and boost your energy levels sky high.

Strangely enough, the most ancient of them with the purest pedigree is also the least-known. Ayurveda is really the root of so many systems: Chinese medicine developed from it, although this has now become quite individual in its philosophy. We can trace many forms of massage and bodywork from it; also concepts of nutrition, diet, breathing and meditation. Had it not been for the

British rampaging through India, Ayurveda might be *the* leading healthcare system of the world.

Traditional Chinese medicine fared better and has maintained its stature in its homeland and has been transported all round the world by emigrant Chinese. It is well known here for its seemingly miraculous cures for skin conditions such as eczema. However, this is just the tip of the iceberg – TCM is a complete medical system which has very powerful results.

Our home-grown Western system of complete natural medicine is naturopathy which encompasses so many other disciplines: like Ayurveda and TCM, it is a complete system, looking to improve health by a complete re-evaluation of lifestyle – from diet and exercise to meditation, with the use of herbs, homeopathy and osteopathic manipulation.

AYURVEDA

WHAT IS IT?   The traditional medicine system from India. A complete philosophy that covers every aspect of health from nutrition and lifestyle to psychology and surgery.

USED FOR   Everything – although few Ayurvedic practitioners now perform surgery.

SUITABLE FOR   Anyone who has a condition that has not responded to orthodox or other alternative medicines. Ideal if you are looking for a complete philosophy and way of healthy living.

NOT SUITABLE FOR   Anyone who doesn't want to make changes to their lifestyle, or who is squeamish about bodily functions.

PERFORMED   Varies. Naked for massage; fully clothed for other treatments.

ANYTHING TO TAKE ORALLY?   Very likely you will be given herbal preparations. Diet will often be modified or changed.

STRESSBUSTER   Some of the massage techniques are deeply relaxing. Ayurveda, as a whole, aims to reduce stress which it sees as a cause of ageing.

COST   Varies. Medium to high.

NUMBER OF SESSIONS REQUIRED   Varies again. Normally fortnightly to begin with, then monthly. Eventually, you should only need a check-up and balance every season.

DIY   Anyone can introduce Ayurvedic principles into their lives: correct living, exercise, meditation and diet. Other treatments must be carried out by a qualified practitioner.

IF YOU LIKE THIS, TRY   If you find Ayurveda too earthy, try TRADITIONAL CHINESE MEDICINE. If it is simply too 'Eastern' and weird, look to NATUROPATHY. See also YOGA – BEYOND THE LOTUS (*see* GOOD EXERCISE); CHAVUTTI THIRUMAL; MEDITATION (*see* STRESS-BUSTING); THE MIND-BODY CONNECTION (*see* GOOD EXERCISE).

Ayurveda is the most ancient form of medicine, but it is perhaps one of the least well known of the supertherapies. Despite its antiquity, there are relatively few practitioners, particularly in the UK, due in part to the very lengthy training and the huge complexity of its philosophy and teaching. Classical Ayurvedic training is conducted in Sanskrit. Most Ayurvedic practitioners tend to be orthodox doctors as well.

However, unlike Western medicine, the whole aim of Ayurveda is preventative. The ancient texts say that the human lifespan should be around 100 years, and that all those years should be lived in total health, both physical and mental. So the Ayurvedic practitioner is looking to balance the body and mind, to ferret out health problems before they occur, or to nip them in the bud before they do any real harm. Unfortunately, the texts say, the causes of illness (and the shortening of life) are caused by virtually every ill of modern life: constant stress; irregular meals; eating the wrong kind of food; taking the wrong medication; living an unhealthy lifestyle; having bad body posture; breathing in polluted air; allowing micro-organisms to enter the body; becoming injured; not digesting food properly; and even indulging in too much sexual activity!

So an Ayurvedic practitioner's job is pretty complex, to put it mildly. However, Ayurveda does have remarkable results: even changing your diet to fit your body type or readjusting your work schedule can have surprising effects on your health. Even if you decide that the whole Ayurvedic package is too much to take en masse, it would be well worth investigating some of its principles.

The history

Ayurveda is quite simply the oldest form of medicine on earth. Its principles were said to have been passed down to humankind from a chain of gods leading back to Brahma, the father of all gods. It has been called 'the mother of medicine' and is generally accepted to be the forerunner of all the other great world healing systems: the Chinese and Tibetan, the Greek and the Arabic. Written texts show that the Ayurvedic medicine practised from about 1500 BC to AD 500 was incredibly advanced.

Students studied six philosophical systems: the study of logic, of evolution and causality, of the discipline of body and spirit (yoga), or moral behaviour, of pure esoteric knowledge and even the theory of the atom. As far as medicine itself was concerned, there were eight disciplines: general medicine, pediatrics, psychiatry, ear, nose and throat and opthalmology, surgery, toxicology, geriatrics and sexology. No modern medical student would have had so thorough a grounding in such a broad spectrum of disciplines.

Historians of the ancient world wrote of the great universities which taught Ayurveda, but when India started to suffer invasions in the Middle Ages, the system began to fall apart and the universities were broken up. The British were the final nail in the coffin of Ayurveda: they brought their own brand of modern Western medicine with them and established their own universities. Ayurveda was in danger of dying out altogether. Fortunately, the Indians realized what they were losing and the Indian Congress affirmed support for Ayurveda; in 1921 Mahatma Gandhi opened the first new college for Ayurvedic medicine. Now Ayurveda is being practised alongside Western medicine in India. And it is gaining in popularity in the West largely due to the work of Deepak Chopra, whose bestselling books have intrigued people with his claims that Ayurvedic principles offer a real chance of great longevity – even immortality.

The lowdown

Ayurvedic philosophy is incredibly complex and takes years of study to begin to comprehend. Remember, these people understood the concepts of atomic physics thousands of years ago. They even knew that the atom was divisible. Ayurveda taught that each atom consists of five elements: its weight comes from earth, its cohesion from water, its energy from fire, its motion from air and the spaces between its particles are made of ether. So, the whole human body is made up of the five elements, and Indian philosophy says that an excess of one or more elements can be the cause of imbalance and so lead to illness.

Over the centuries, Ayurveda came up with a simpler method of working out imbalances – the *tridoshas* or bio-energies. The three *doshas* or bio-energies are combinations of the five elements. So the bio-energy *vata* comes from a combination of ether and air; *pitta* from fire with a little water; and *kapha* from water and earth. In an ideal state, we would have all three *doshas* in perfect balance but this is rare. Most of us have one or perhaps two which overbalance the others. The whole of Ayurvedic medicine aims to balance the *doshas* in order to restore health.

A little more about the *doshas*: *vata* produces movement in the body; *pitta* produces heat and so is responsible for the metabolism, while *kapha* produces growth and structure. All three are essential for life: without *vata* we couldn't breathe, our blood wouldn't pump round the body, food wouldn't move through our guts and nor would any chemical impulses fly to and from the brain. Without *pitta* we would not be able to process the air, water and food that runs through our system. And without *kapha* we simply wouldn't hold together: it keeps our cells bonded together and fuses bone, muscle, fat and connective tissue.

The *dosha* that is in excess within our body gives rise to our *prakriti*, or body type – the basic predominating psychophysiological force which affects everything about us – from our shape and our weight to our predisposition to different illnesses, to the forms of exercise that suit us, to how we think, how we react to situations, to how we perceive the whole world. It sums us up body, mind and soul.

The session

There is no typical Ayurvedic session. Even the methods of diagnosis may vary from practitioner to practitioner. The basic Ayurvedic diagnosis is known as the three-point diagnosis and involves detailed observation of your appearance, examination by touch (evaluating body temperature, pulse, reflexes) and questioning (a detailed questionnaire about your life and health).

However, many practitioners go further with an eight-point diagnosis, which includes pulse diagnosis (as in Chinese medicine, the taking of pulses is an exact science – pulses are read in twelve positions and can be slow and steady, thready like a snake or jumpy like a frog); examination of urine (expect to be asked about quantity, frequency, colour, smell and temperature of urine); examination of stool (similar questions to urine); tongue diagnosis (a normal tongue is reddish, supple and clear without a coating); examination of body sounds (your voice, any coughs, plus intestinal sounds); eye diagnosis plus examination by touch and appearance as for the three-point diagnosis.

After diagnosis comes treatment. And the range of treatments is vast. But, without doubt, you will be given guidelines for healthy living and instructed in the diet which will soothe and correct imbalances in your body type. Ayurveda teaches that what is food for one person could be poison for another: your diet will be tailored precisely for your body type. However, there are some general points which are usually made. Food has three basic qualities:

LIGHT: said to bring the psyche into a state of harmony. Foods with light qualities include vegetables and fruits, nuts, milk and dairy produce, wheat, rice and rye, honey. Choose most of your diet from foods with a light quality.

PASSIONATE: said to stimulate the sensuality of the person, increasing motivation, ambition, jealousy, egotism. Foods with passionate qualities include all highly spiced, sour, salty, hot and dry foods, plus wine and beer, tea and coffee. You need a certain amount of these foods to sustain you in a tough world, but don't overdo them.

SLUGGISH: foods with a sluggish quality increase pessimism, ignorance, greed, laziness, stinginess and feelings of inferiority.

Some texts even go as far as to say they will seduce people into crime. Foods with a sluggish quality include all highly processed foods (canned, dried, frozen and fast foods), peanuts, leftovers and overcooked food, strong alcoholic drinks and all meat and meat products. Naturally, it is advisable to avoid these as much as possible.

All food should be as fresh as possible and, if cooked, only cooked lightly to preserve the life force inherent in food. In addition to a new diet, you may well be advised to take up exercise (or plunge wholeheartedly into yoga), learn to breathe properly and possibly to meditate as well. Aside from these basic guidelines, Ayurveda has a host of other treatments. There are herbal preparations to swallow, oils and unguents with which to anoint yourself.

Whole books are written about the different forms of therapeutic massage. Some forms involve oil dripping onto the forehead; others are more like our normal idea of a therapeutic massage. Full body massage is usually performed with you lying naked on a couch. Sesame oil is most commonly used, although coconut and olive oil are also popular. I clearly remember one such massage I had in India. I was expecting a straightforward, 'normal', nice soothing massage and at first felt very exposed lying without a stitch on. Then I proceeded to feel very greasy – the head is often massaged very thoroughly. When Ayurveda talks about full body massage it really *means* full body. Fingers and toes are pulled and stretched. And I was rather surprised to find my breasts getting a good rub as well. Sometimes the touch was very painful: my back felt as if it were being used as a wash-board. But the net effect was pretty wonderful, and days later my skin was still baby-soft.

I have not experienced all the strange and curious Ayurvedic practices and some of them, to be honest, sound quite revolting. Oil is generally seen as a wonderful healer. Eye conditions can be treated by warm oil being poured onto closed eyes, kept in with a dam. You then open your eyes and allow the oil to freely flow over your eyes. Other treatments involve having you gargle with oil or having oil poured into your ears.

Ayurvedic rules for a healthy lifestyle – the daily routine

• Get up between 4 a.m. and 6 a.m.! Ideally, you should have between six to eight hours sleep (but no more). Ayurveda teaches that our habit of going to bed late and sleeping in late can lead to all sorts of health problems, from digestive disorders to headaches and eye problems. At the very least, get up as soon as you wake up – by going back to sleep you will make yourself sluggish.

• Have a pee first thing after rising. If it's difficult, drink a glass of water or herbal tea (not coffee). Then attend to mouth hygiene: brush your teeth, clean your tongue and gargle with cold water. Rinse your eyes with cool water and trim finger and toenails every fifth day.

• Take some exercise. A long fast walk, swimming or yoga are ideal.

• Massage after exercise reduces fat and removes dead skin. Rub oil into your whole body and then take a warm (body temperature) bath to revitalize your body and stimulate your energy levels.

• As you leave the bath, dry and put on a little natural perfume. Dress in loose comfortable clean clothing.

• Take a few minutes for meditation, prayer or simply thinking about beautiful things.

• Then (at last) have breakfast. Breakfast should be eaten before 9 a.m. (no wonder you need an early start, to fit it all in!).

• Lunch should be at least three hours later than breakfast – around one o'clock is fine. Lunch should be the largest meal of the day as this is the time when your body can most easily digest food.

• Dinner should be eaten no later than 9 p.m. Six o'clock is ideal, and dinner should be quite light.

• You should aim to be in bed by 10 p.m., asleep no later than 11 p.m. If you are awake later, your body will move into a different *dosha* and you will find it harder to get to sleep. Keep a window open in your bedroom – air should circulate freely. Do not share your room with animals.

• Sex is a strong part of Ayurveda and is recommended in unrestricted amounts in winter. In spring and autumn it is recommended no more than three times a week, while in summer the texts say you should only have sex two or three times a month.

114

If you can follow all this, I'd be very surprised. There's no way on earth I could do it all. I did try it for a while but found I was utterly shattered – I think my problem was that while I was getting up early, I simply couldn't seem to get to bed before eleven or twelve. Also, my cat stuck her claws in when I suggested she sleep anywhere other than the bed. However, the basic concepts are sound: eat at regular times (and don't eat the last meal of the day too late); perform regular exercise and keep your body clean and your mind healthy.

Some Western practitioners are incorporating Ayurvedic principles into their work, for example Angela Hope-Murray who practises at the Hale Clinic is a Western-trained nutritionist who then learnt Ayurveda. Now she follows broadly Ayurvedic principles of nutrition but blends it with Western wisdom as well. The combination seems to work very well.

TRADITIONAL CHINESE MEDICINE (TCM)

WHAT IS IT? A complete system of medicine with a very ancient lineage. It includes acupuncture, herbalism, massage, diet therapy and exercise.

USED FOR Most people think of TCM as a salve for eczema and skin conditions, but it will treat absolutely anything and everything.

SUITABLE FOR Anyone willing to look at all aspects of their health.

NOT SUITABLE FOR Anyone with a phobia about needles or anyone who finds it impossible to take unpleasant-tasting concoctions. If consulting a Chinese practitioner, Westerners might find the approach quite clinical and detached.

PERFORMED Depends on the treatment. You might have to take off some clothes for acupuncture and possibly all of them for massage.

ANYTHING TO TAKE ORALLY? Again, it depends on your

practitioner. Be warned, Chinese herbs can be very pungent and quite unpleasant.

STRESSBUSTER　Acupuncture can directly ease stress as can the massage, but TCM will aim to persuade you to deal with the root cause of your stress.

COST　Medium to high.

NUMBER OF SESSIONS REQUIRED　Varies enormously. Generally, once a fortnight to begin with, then once a month. Once your body is in balance you should see your practitioner once a quarter, as the seasons change, for a balance and tune-up.

DIY　No, this is a complex system of medicine which should only be performed by a professional.

IF YOU LIKE THIS, TRY　TCM encompasses so much you shouldn't need to look elsewhere. However, if you fancy a change of continent, look at AYURVEDA which has the same all-encompassing spread of treatments. NATUROPATHY provides a more Westernized approach.

NOTE: Choose your practitioner with care. TCM is a powerful system of medicine and needs to be treated with great respect. There have been cases of fraudulent practitioners and also of Western doctors prescribing Chinese herbs without the relevant knowledge. For safety, find a practitioner only through the organizations listed at the back of this book. One other factor to think about is how much feedback you want on an emotional level. Chinese practitioners will generally simply prescribe and treat, without delving into your psyche. Western practitioners, however, often spend time counselling as well.

In old China, you paid your doctor while you were well and stopped paying him when you got sick. Can you imagine any modern GP daring to adopt such a system? TCM had no such fears: patients were taught a combination of right food, right exercise and right breathing and, as preventative medicine, it worked very well. If, however, a patient *did* happen to fall sick, there were powerful ways to bring her or him back to health: acupuncture, herbalism and massage. Sickness was simply not a way of life.

117

Nowadays and in the West, we generally use only a small part of TCM. Many people practise solely acupuncture; others purely herbalism. Both can have powerful effects alone but, if you really want to use this supertherapy in its most potent form, seek out a practitioner who can counsel you on all aspects of the Chinese way to health. It may take some time, effort and extra cash to begin with but, rest assured, you will reap the rewards for the rest of your life. Once you are eating, exercising and breathing properly you shouldn't need more than a quarterly check-up and maybe the odd tweak of a needle or the stray tonic to keep you in perfect health.

The history

From the earliest times, people have stumbled across the healing power of certain foods and herbs. But whoever discovered that sticking a needle in a certain part of the body could have an effect on other parts – even curing disease? No-one knows for sure, but one story is that the ancient Chinese noticed, after battles, some curious side effects of arrow wounds. If the victim survived his wound, sometimes he would discover that an old, chronic disease had mysteriously improved or even vanished. What is clear is that, however it started, acupuncture became a sophisticated and precise system of medicine several thousands of years ago. By the sixth century, it had spread to Japan, and it was here that the French Jesuit missionaries discovered it many centuries later, and brought it to the West in the seventeenth century.

However, it was generally overlooked, practised only by Chinese emigrants, until well after the Second World War. And it has only been in the last thirty odd years that TCM has become popular in the West. To begin with, it became famous for short, sharp cures – such as the needle in the ear to stop smoking. Or for the shock of the bizarre: needles being used in place of anaesthetics on the operating table. Recently, TCM has hit the news again with pages of publicity testifying to its use in the control and cure of skin diseases. Queues form every morning around a clinic in London's Soho, as sufferers from eczema and psoriasis wait patiently to see a doctor who will prescribe a disgusting herbal mix. They wait patiently because it generally works exceedingly well. So well, in fact, that now many Western doctors have been

118

convinced and are working alongside Chinese doctors to bring their ancient secrets out into the modern Western air.

One open-minded doctor, David Atherton, a consultant pediatrician at Great Ormond Street Hospital, decided to test the herbal approach and, convinced of its efficacy, has brought ancient herbal preparations into the NHS. Now further research is being carried out to determine how useful Chinese herbalism can be for other conditions. 'There are several areas of research which will hopefully be undertaken,' says Richard Blackwell, President of the Register of Chinese Herbal Medicine, 'including irritable bowel syndrome, arthritis and possibly ME.'

A recent report in *The Lancet* expressed promising results of the treatment of malaria with Chinese herbs; the effect of herbs on asthma is being studied, and some practitioners are following the lead of doctors in China who use a combination of Chinese herbs and acupuncture to alleviate the side effects of chemotherapy and radiotherapy for cancer patients. In Hong Kong, scientists are even looking at the possibilities of herbal birth control.

Meanwhile, in the USA, Chinese herbal medicine is being used in the fight against HIV and AIDS. Research published in China has indicated that the use of Chinese herbs can have a positive effect, increasing survival times and reducing symptoms of the virus.

However, despite the general feeling of optimism that surrounds the field, some critics are worried about the possible dangers connected with such treatment. Dr Robin Graham-Browns of the Leicester Royal Infirmary has expressed concern about toxicity and warns of the possibility of liver damage from herbs with unknown active properties. And a recent case in Belgium in which a number of women developed kidney damage following treatment with Chinese herbs also sounded warning bells. But closer examination revealed that the Belgian episode resulted from the wrong herbs being prescribed in the incorrect dosage – not by a Chinese herbalist but by a Western doctor apparently untrained in the complex discipline of Chinese herbalism who combined a cocktail of Western drugs with two Chinese herbs.

Generally, however, there seem to be no ill-effects from the herbs when prescribed by a qualified practitioner. However, tests *are* being carried out to monitor the precise effects of herbs on the body, and Dr Atherton's team is conducting a study taking blood samples before, during and after treatment.

'It is absolutely essential that people consult a qualified practitioner,' warns Richard Blackwell. 'I have heard recently of a case of Chinese doctors in this country [UK] giving out skin creams for eczema which turned out to contain steroids. We were appalled by this – it is not only illegal but also highly unethical to give patients such creams which they think are herbal.'

The lowdown

The underlying philosophy behind TCM is that good health revolves around the correct flow of *chi*, the subtle energy of the body. *Chi* flows around the body in channels called meridians, and along the meridians lie hundreds of points which link the various organs and functions of the body. While Western doctors often scorn the idea, new medical instruments such as the PIP scanner (*see* ELECTRO-CRYSTAL THERAPY) have actually shown what the Chinese have known for years: the position of the meridians and the acupuncture points.

If we look after ourselves, eat the right kinds of food, do the right kinds of exercise, we can increase the amount of *chi* in our bodies. If we fall into bad ways, our levels of *chi* drop or are blocked, and the consequence is lack of vital energy or even disease. The whole Chinese life-view is immensely complex and, some might say, almost obsessive. *Chi* can be depleted or lost through too much, too little or the wrong kind of food, drink, exercise, work and even sex. Even your emotions can become out of balance and affect your health.

According to TCM, the world is also divided into two forces – *yin* and *yang*. *Yin* is considered to be dark, cold, negative, passive and feminine, while *yang* is light, active, warm, positive and male. Disturb the balance of *yin* and *yang*, and the result is disharmony, possibly ill-health. In addition, there are the five elements to consider: each of us contains within us the elements of fire, earth, air (or metal), water and wood. When a TCM practitioner diagnoses, he or she does not just check for the flow of *chi*, but also looks to see how much of each element is within the body and what kind of energy is being transmitted. Then it is possible to stimulate or quieten unbalanced organs or body systems by food, exercise, massage, herbs or the needles of acupuncture.

The session

As with most supertherapies, a TCM session starts with questions, although not as many as some other systems. The Chinese have remarkably sophisticated diagnostic tools at their fingertips and, were you not to say a word, they could easily tell you what your problems were by looking at your face, your eyes and your tongue and by taking your pulses. Unlike Western medicine, the Chinese take a whole variety of pulses, testing energy levels and detecting the faintest imbalances. Then they can decide on the best course of treatment.

Although acupuncture can be given in pretty well any position, whenever I have had it I have been lying down on a couch, fully clothed. If the acupuncturist needs to get to a certain area, you can simply fold back or take off the relevant bit of clothing.

I can clearly remember my first experience. My acupuncturist found the point she wanted to treat and first used moxibustion on it. This involves placing a tiny piece of a burning herbal mixture (known as *moxa*) on the point. It smelt very pungent, but not unpleasant, and suddenly became very warm. I had been warned to tell my practitioner when this happened and she swiftly removed the moxa – it was just beginning to burn my skin. Then came the needle. 'Breathe in,' she demanded and then, with a twist, she pushed the needle in. Did it hurt? Well, yes, it did to be truthful. As the point was 'hit', there was a strange twisting feeling, as if she'd hit a muscle. My first practitioner didn't leave the needles in; she pressed in deep and then twisted them out. However, I have to say, since then, I have seen many other acupuncturists who do not use this technique, but, instead, merely pop the needles in and leave them there. Somehow, this second approach seems to be quite painless.

The first effect I noticed from regular acupuncture sessions was a marked increase in energy. Perhaps the strangest effect I noticed was how my dreams changed. Since childhood I had suffered from terrible nightmares and, during one session, I mentioned this.

'Why on earth didn't you tell me before?' asked my therapist. She gave me a precise configuration of needles and, like clockwork, my nightmares stopped. It felt almost uncomfortable, rather like a computer being programmed.

The herbal approach can be no less dramatic. I have never been treated over a long period by a Chinese herbalist, but I have direct experience of how swiftly it can act on an acute problem. I was suffering from a ghastly bout of flu and, although I should by rights have been tucked up in bed, I was forced to keep on working. By chance, I happened to be near Covent Garden and the East West Herb Centre. I flew in and begged them for something to get me through. The doctor swiftly looked at my tongue and felt my pulse. Within minutes I was out the door with a powder to mix with hot water. It tasted so revolting that it was virtually past belief, but within twenty minutes I was totally stunned to find that my sinuses had cleared and I could breathe through my nose. My headache vanished and I felt so much better that I could hardly believe it.

Good healthkeeping – the Chinese way

There are simple changes we can all make to our daily lives which might help us live healthier, and maybe even longer, lives.

DIET AND NUTRITION

The first rule is to eat sparingly. The Chinese say you should eat, not until you can barely move as is the Western custom, but until you are 70–80 per cent full. All food should be chewed thoroughly to allow the enzymes in the saliva to start digestion, and liquids should also be drunk slowly.

Avoid extremes of temperature – the Chinese do not tend to eat or drink things which are very hot or very cold. Ideally, food should be steamed, poached or stir-fried.

The traditional Chinese diet follows the World Health Organisation guidelines almost exactly, being high in complex carbohydrates, vegetables and fruits, while low in saturated fat. Fish is rated highly and meat *is* eaten, but in small quantities. Chinese physicians have always recommended 'earth chickens', or free-range chickens as we know them.

The Chinese diet avoids dairy produce, as it is believed to cause allergies and infections, and eggs are eaten only rarely. They also traditionally avoid most of the nightshade family of vegetables, which includes potatoes, tomatoes and peppers. Caffeine and tobacco should also be shunned.

EXERCISE

As far back as the first century, Chinese physicians were recommending exercise for conditions as varied as arthritis and rheumatism to nervous afflictions and circulatory problems. They believed that exercise helped the free flow of *chi*. However, strenuous activity of the aerobic kind is not the Chinese way – their exercise for health regime is more akin to moving meditation.

Chi Kung is halfway between meditation and a martial art. Its aim is to balance and harmonize the body and the brain, establishing a healthy relationship between the nervous and endocrine systems (*see* Chi Kung – the Chinese Stressbuster in GOOD EXERCISE). Practitioners believe this form of exercise plugs the body right into the earth's energy field (a frequency of 2–10 Hz), which apparently has a soothing, rejuvenating effect on the human system.

The Thymus Tap is a good introductory exercise to try at home. It is used to strengthen the immune system and also energizes the lungs, heart, bronchial tubes and throat.

Stand in the Horse stance (feet shoulder-width apart, weight evenly distributed, knees relaxed, elbows slightly bent with arms hanging loosely down the sides and palms facing the rear). Make a fist with one hand and raise it to the middle of your chest. Tap the spot between the nipples with a rhythm of one hard beat followed by two softer taps (*one*, two, three; *one*, two, three). Tap hard enough to create a deep drumming sound in the chest and continue for three to five minutes, breathing naturally and focusing your mind on your chest.

SKIN-BRUSHING

One of the best ways to cleanse the entire lymphatic system is by brushing the skin with a soft dry brush. The traditional Chinese method used the dried fibres of a gourd – the loofah – but a good-quality body brush is equally good.

Dry skin-brushing stimulates the lymph canals to drain toxic mucoid matter into the colon. It should be practised once a day, preferably first thing in the morning before your bath or shower.

Use a natural-bristle brush and sweep the brush in long, smooth strokes, always working towards the heart. Brush up the arms from the hands to the shoulders; up the legs from feet to hips; down the back and torso; up the buttocks; down the neck and across the shoulders.

Perform skin-brushing daily for the first three months, and then twice a week should be enough to keep your lymph clean. If you feel ill, resume daily brushing.

(*Note*: if you suffer any problems relating to your lymphatic system, check with your physician before starting such a course.)

BREATHING

Most ancient healthy systems regarded good breathing as essential for optimum health and the Chinese are no exception. Shallow, erratic breathing is thought to impair vitality and impede the assimilation of energy from the atmosphere. Deep breathing however allows the diaphragm to move up and down, which not only fills the lungs fully, but also massages and stimulates all the other internal organs.

The Chinese use many different forms of breathing for different purposes. Deep breathing is one of the most beneficial. It is, in effect, abdominal breathing – drawing the breath deep down into the bottom of the lungs via a flexing of the diaphragm, which causes the abdomen to expand on inhalation and contract on exhalation. Keeping the breath long and slow increases the amount of oxygen absorbed and the amount of carbon dioxide expelled. (*See* GOOD BREATHING.)

MEDITATION

The Chinese take meditation as a part of life – they simply call it 'sitting still, doing nothing'. The ancient sages, however, called it 'mental fasting' because they believed that, by withdrawing all distracting thoughts and disturbing emotions from the mind, they could purify the mind and restore the body's original power.

Very similar to the Hindu and Buddhist systems, the two rules of Chinese meditation are *jing* (quiet, stillness, calm) and *ding* (concentration, focus). At first, banishing all thoughts can seem almost impossible, but persist and the benefits are enormous with stress levels plummeting.

Choose a time when you won't be disturbed. Sit quietly in a comfortable position, and start to slow your breathing down and become calm. Shift attention to the inflow and outflow of air coming through your nostrils. Then focus attention on the expansion and contraction of your abdomen as you breathe. Now, imagine energy streaming in and out of the spot between your brows. With your eyes half-closed, focus your vision on a candle flame, focusing on the centre of the flame but also taking in the edges with your peripheral vision. Start with ten minutes and try to build up to half an hour a day.

FASTING

From ancient times, Chinese practitioners have recommended fasting – from twenty-four hour mini-fasts to ten-day purges. They say that when the intestine is cleared of the old impacted faeces and accumulated dried mucus, it will digest food more efficiently and absorb nutrients more completely than before.

Long fasts should only be undertaken under medical supervision, but everyone can benefit from the occasional mini-fast. In fact, a once-a-week mini-fast of between twenty-four and thirty-six hours is an ancient Oriental practice which allows your body the chance to 'catch up' with all the various foods you have put in your alimentary canal during the week. Fasting not only involves eliminating food but also drinks such as tea and coffee (which are toxifying because of the caffeine they contain) and alcohol. Instead, drink plenty of pure still spring water. Alternatively, select one variety of raw vegetable or fruit juice and drink just that. Dark grapes are good for people with gastrointestinal and liver ailments; carrots regulate the whole endocrine system; beetroot balances the metabolism and detoxifies the liver.

PSYCHONEURIMMUNOLOGY

The latest buzzword in health circles, psychoneurimmunology (PNI) concerns the mind's ability to effect change in the body. Only grudgingly accepted by a few Western doctors, it is widely practised by Oriental cultures. Over the past 5,000 years the Chinese have accumulated a vast reservoir of evidence linking the powers of body and mind, neurology and immunology, and have developed specific techniques for activating that link.

Visualization combined with meditation is a powerful healing technique in which the patient focuses the mind to visualize healing energy flowing into ailing organs, dissolving tumours, repairing tissues and so forth. PNI works best when the image you choose has some meaning for you: one young boy with cancer imagined jet fighters zooming into his body to bomb the tumours. His strategy worked – the tumours shrank and disappeared without recourse to chemotherapy, radiation or surgery.

Equally important to the Chinese are the twin virtues of enthusiasm and love. If you are bored by your job or marriage, the Chinese say your mind will lack enthusiasm for life which will sap your will to live. Find a way to enjoy life to the full and spend your time with people you like and love – and your body will show its gratitude.

NATUROPATHY

WHAT IS IT? A complete system of natural healthcare that believes the body has the knowledge to heal itself. Treatment includes diet, exercise, hydrotherapy and osteopathy and may also use homeopathy, herbalism and acupuncture.

USED FOR Virtually all chronic diseases respond and it has particular success with rheumatic and arthritic conditions, hypertension, allergic conditions and fatigue conditions.

SUITABLE FOR Almost everyone – particularly those who feel the need for clear education about health.

NOT SUITABLE FOR Anyone who is unwilling to change their lifestyle: naturopathy will ask for quite sweeping changes in diet, lifestyle and attitude. Certain treatments are not suitable for pregnant women, and some are to be avoided if you have high blood pressure or a heart condition.

PERFORMED Varies. Naked for much hydrotherapy, fully clothed for other treatments.

ANYTHING TO TAKE ORALLY? Very likely you will be given herbal or homeopathic preparations. Diet will often be modified or changed.

STRESSBUSTER Many of the baths are deeply relaxing. Naturopathy as a whole regards stress as a major enemy and, if necessary, you will be advised in stress management.

COST Low to medium.

NUMBER OF SESSIONS REQUIRED Normally fortnightly or monthly to start. Eventually, you should only need a check-up and balance every season.

DIY Anyone can introduce the principles of naturopathy into their lives. Many of the baths, for example, can easily be carried out at home. Other treatments must be carried out by a qualified practitioner.

IF YOU LIKE THIS, TRY You shouldn't need to look elsewhere, but if you would prefer the same all-over emphasis with a more Eastern slant, look to TRADITIONAL CHINESE MEDICINE or AYURVEDA.

Naturopathy is to the West what Ayurveda and traditional Chinese medicine are to the East – a gentle, nature-based, holistic health system that aims to put the whole body in balance. And many of the naturopathic 'cures' involve simple DIY routines that can be incorporated into every regime. It's part of the reason why naturopaths see themselves as much teachers as physicians. If you want to benefit from naturopathy, you have to be prepared to take a long hard look at your life and decide whether you really want to make the changes that will help your body heal itself.

The history

Historically speaking, the roots of naturopathy lie in darkest antiquity. Hippocrates spoke of *ponos*, the body's incessant labour to restore itself to normal balance, while Aristotle spoke of the life-force having a purpose beyond simply existing. Both these viewpoints echo the British Naturopathic and Osteopathic Association's description of naturopathy as 'a system of treatment which recognizes the vital curative force within the body.'

In its current standardized form, naturopathy has been around for over 100 years. One of the early pioneers of naturopathy, Dr Henry Lindlahr, defined disease as 'abnormal or inharmonious vibration of the elements and forces composing the human entity on one or more planes of being'. These disturbances are, he believed, due to lowered vitality; an abnormal composition of blood and lymph; an accumulation of morbid materials and poisons within the body. What brings on such disturbances? Partly hereditary factors and partly early environment (both before and after birth) but, most importantly, in the lifestyle we lead. Most toxic of all is mesotrophy, the slow decline of the cell, which is caused by poor diet.

Naturopathy is the great detoxing therapy. Many of our problems are blamed on incomplete elimination of the waste products of our metabolism and the accumulation of toxins. The body tries to live with a growing accumulation of waste and the result is low-level disease – not a particular illness but a sense of feeling below par. So the aim of all naturopathic processes is to help the elimination of waste, bolstering every one of the body's excretory functions.

The lowdown

The whole aim of naturopathy is to allow the body to return to its natural equilibrium, and its philosophy dictates that our bodies really do contain the wisdom and power to heal themselves – provided we don't interfere. Interference, unfortunately, is almost unavoidable in modern life: toxins build up because of bad lifestyle habits, and the body almost inevitably succumbs to disease. Readjusting one's whole lifestyle can be unpleasant, if not downright painful, and naturopathy is certainly no easy option. Naturopaths see health as a dynamic state of equilibrium, not just within the body itself but between the body and its surroundings. They see health as a precarious balance between our physical structure, our biochemical functions and our emotional nature.

What this boils down to is that our health can fall down at virtually any point. Muscle tension, joint misalignments or other postural problems brought on by stress or injury can interfere with healthy nerve function: naturopaths will use osteopathy to correct such problems. The biochemistry of our bodies can be affected by incorrect nutrition: diet forms a large part of the naturopathic cure. And, like most holistic systems, naturopaths recognize the fundamental importance of mental and emotional health. Not only does the naturopath look for balanced health in all these areas, a fourth aspect is considered as vital: the patient's energy or basic vitality.

Balance is achieved by using the most natural cures available: fresh air and sunlight, fasting and a fresh clean diet, relaxation and psychological counselling and, very importantly, the healing power of water.

Some naturopaths are purists and work only with these most basic tools. They believe that our health is our own responsibility and that we should take strict measures to keep it under control. They consider the use of herbal or homeopathic medicines as taking away the element of personal responsibility. However, many others have incorporated other disciplines, and most naturopaths are masters of many arts: using herbalism, homeopathy and acupuncture in addition. They see these systems as important catalysts, pushing the body towards health and helping its self-healing mechanism.

The session

I plumped for jumping in at the naturopathic deep end, booking myself in for a few days at the Tyringham Naturopathic Clinic in Buckinghamshire. The clinic has been educating people in the naturopathic creed since 1967 and, in its own way, could be labelled one of the very first 'health farms'. But, despite its setting (a stunning Sir John Soane mansion), there's no posing or pampering on display – the emphasis is strictly on health and healing. A week is the minimum stay – just long enough to re-educate the body and persuade the mind that there really is life beyond TV suppers. For the true 'cure', diehards stay for three weeks. I met one of the clinic's consultants and discussed what I wanted to achieve during my stay – it's much like a standard medical consultation (if you have serious problems, then blood tests, ECGs or X-rays are taken) but there are some extras. I was tested for allergies using the Vega machine (*see* NUTRITIONAL THERAPY) and was told a programme would be devised for me.

Diet is the first shock to the system. The naturopathic diet is wholefood, vegetarian, low-fat and low-sodium with a high preponderance of raw vegetables and fruit. Some people are put on fasts or fruit diets; others are allowed a light or full diet. Alcohol is out, herbal teas are encouraged and smokers are urged to quit. I must confess the diet did absolutely nothing for my taste buds, but then gastronomy wasn't exactly the aim of the exercise. I would be hard pushed to incorporate such a stringent diet into everyday life.

Next stop exercise. Regular exercise is as intrinsic to naturopathy as diet. Aqua aerobics in either the indoor pool or the huge outdoor pool are held every day. Sessions in the small but well-equipped gym are taught clearly and carefully to small groups with the idea that you can continue the programme on your return to the 'real world'. On alternate days, yoga sessions encourage flexibility and relaxation and, in addition, patients are encouraged to make the most of Tyringham's acres of farm and woodland for bracing walks. If you visited a naturopath outside such a clinic, the advice would be the same – find a gentle, natural form of exercise (walking, swimming, yoga, cycling) and practise it religiously.

After this, the specific treatments depend on your problem. The consultant could decide that you would benefit from a herbal or homeopathic consultation or a session of acupuncture or osteopathy. One thing you won't miss is hydrotherapy. Naturopathy believes strongly in the healing power of water and there are myriad treatments for every problem. My introduction to hydrotherapy was brutal to put it mildly. Standing naked in a shower a nurse directed a hot jet of water up and down my spine, followed by a freezing cold stream. She alternated hot and cold for several minutes before rubbing down my back with salt and allowing me to shower off. Known as the Scottish douche, it certainly sweeps away the cobwebs as effectively as a dose of Highland air and, apparently, stimulates circulation and improves immune functioning.

Next stop the steam bath. Sitting in a sealed 'pod' with just my head sticking out I felt like a caterpillar in a cocoon. Twenty minutes later I emerged sweating and virtually swooning with the heat. Light relief comes in the form of wax baths in which hot wax is applied to hands, feet or knees and left to soothe joints and muscles. Naturopaths use it most commonly for stiff or tender joints and rheumatic conditions, but a welcome side effect is blissfully smooth skin.

I soaked in seaweed, was caked in mud and plunged myself in alternating hot and cold pools. But perhaps the strangest treatment of all was constitutional hydrotherapy. As I lay on a treatment couch, the nurse applied towels soaked in hot water to my chest. Then, with a flick of the wrist, she whisked away the hot and replaced it with a freezing cold towel. I was swathed in blankets and instructed to imagine myself generating heat – as if I were lying in the sun or by a hot fire. Easier said than done when the shivers start to run through your body. It's hardly the most comfortable of treatments, but the benefits, say the nurses, are almost too numerous to mention. The immune system and circulation are stimulated; circulation of white cells increase, gastrointestinal function is normalized and it helps the body to detoxify. Somewhat optimistically, it is also supposed to help you relax. Tyringham prescribes the procedure for anything from infertility to PMS and from hypertension to haemorrhoids.

If you seriously want to change your life for the healthier, a week at somewhere like Tyringham is a wonderful introduction to naturopathy and gives you a good chance of incorporating its tenets into normal daily life. I certainly felt as if I had undergone a thorough internal spring-clean when the time came to leave. However, it's easy to lapse back into bad habits so, if you embark on the naturopathic way, I would suggest you keep up regular appointments with a practitioner back home in order to keep you on the straight and healthy.

DIY naturopathy: take a bath

Water therapy is intrinsic to naturopathy. It's cheap, it's easy to administer and it's literally on tap. There's no excuse not to borrow a few tips from the naturopaths and extend your use of water beyond the odd glass to drink and the odd bath or shower to clean. Naturopaths use water in the treatment of injuries, to relieve pain, to reduce fever, as a stimulant *and* a relaxant, even as an anaesthetic.

Here are just a few suggestions to get you started.

Water   Drink water – lots of it – throughout the day. But make sure it's clean, either pure spa water or tap water that has been filtered. Two glasses of cold water before breakfast is said to help overcome constipation. If you feel you're going down with a cold, drink water at room temperature interspersed with hot herbal teas.

The salt massage bath   If you're feeling low or lacking in energy, this is an essential. It helps the circulation, is helpful in easing rheumatic pain and will also get rid of all your dead skin. It's also simplicity itself: simply make a slushy paste from salt and warm water and apply it in circular movements all over your body. It should only take a few minutes and then you can slide into the bath (filled with quite warm to hot water), and soak. It is possible to stop a cold in its tracks this way, but do not use if your skin is broken – it will sting unbearably.

(*Warning*: Do not use if you have high blood pressure or a heart condition.)

The apple cider vinegar bath   A wonderful tonic if you're feeling tired, this is also a prime detoxifier. Pour a little apple cider vinegar onto your hands and splash it all over your body. Then add a cupful of the vinegar to a warm to hot bath, and soak. This vinegar is also very useful in the summer if you suffer from sunburn or have itchy skin.

(*Warning:* Do not use if you have high blood pressure or a heart condition.)

The Moors bath   Lauded by naturopaths for years, the Moors herbal preparations are now becoming very popular again and are generally easy to find in health shops. The bath itself looks like pure mud sludge. You simply pour it into a warm, not hot, bath and then soak for around twenty minutes. It is absolutely wonderful for relaxation and promotes very sound sleep. In addition, it has been used medicinally for rheumatic conditions with very good results.

The Nutritional and Herbal Approach

As we've already discussed, good nutrition is one of the absolute essentials for good health. If you decide to see a practitioner from one of the complete systems (AYURVEDA, TCM, NATUROPATHY), you will undoubtedly be given sensible eating guidelines. If not, then your first stop to good balanced health should be a nutritionist.

Herbs are used in many other systems – especially in the ones mentioned above. However, there are a great many medical herbalists who concentrate solely on the herbal side of things.

NUTRITIONAL THERAPY

WHAT IS IT?   The diagnosis and treatment of illness through diet and supplements which can help to stimulate the body's self-healing powers.

USED FOR   Absolutely everyone can benefit from correct eating. In addition, many illnesses and long-term conditions will clear up, given the correct diet or correct supplementation.

SUITABLE FOR   Everyone. However, some people might simply not be willing to cut out foods or adapt their eating habits.

NOT SUITABLE FOR   No contraindications. A well-qualified nutritional therapist can help everyone. However you often need discipline to stick to regimes.

PERFORMED   Fully clothed.

ANYTHING TO TAKE ORALLY?   Yes, often you will be given supplements – vitamins, minerals, or maybe herbal preparations, amino acids or other nutritional aids.

STRESSBUSTER   Stress can be irritated by deficiencies of vital micronutrients or from the additives in food. However, if stress is a major factor, a nutritionist will usually recommend another or an additional therapy to deal with it more directly.

COST   Medium to high.

NUMBER OF SESSIONS REQUIRED   Generally, fortnightly for around ten to twelve sessions. As your body gets into balance you should gradually need fewer sessions.

DIY   It doesn't hurt to give yourself a good quality multi-vitamin and mineral supplement on a daily basis but, if you think you have a serious problem or are deficient or allergic, then see a qualified practitioner. It's not a good idea to try to treat yourself – nutrition is a highly complex subject.

IF YOU LIKE THIS, TRY   Any of the forms of massage (*see* THE MASSAGE THERAPIES) – you're feeding your body the right foods, now pamper it even more. If you want something similar but slightly more exotic, then TRADITIONAL CHINESE MEDICINE and AYURVEDA have definite ideas on how we should eat. They also treat with herbs, as does HERBALISM.

We are what we eat – so runs the old adage and, more and more, it's being proven to be true. The food we eat affects us on every level: our looks, our health, our energy, even our moods and, according to some experts, our intelligence and memory. It's a sad fact that we often don't get all the nutrients we need from our diet. Deficiencies can lie behind a surprisingly large number of diseases, and nutritional therapists can detect where we are deficient and correct the problem. Equally, allergies and food intolerances have a large part to play in many health problems – particularly digestive problems, asthma, eczema and PMS. Again, nutritionists can test for allergies and will try carefully to correct the problem.

The history

It seems as though the idea of nutritional therapy is something quite new. We never used to trot off for personal diet plans or fill our cupboards with piles of pills, did we? Well no. However in fact, the use of foods therapeutically is nothing new. In ancient Egypt and Greece, garlic was touted as a cure for respiratory infections, wounds, insect bites and gastrointestinal disorders. In China and India, the tradition of treating medical conditions with food has continued unabated for thousands of years as it has in numerous other cultures worldwide. One of the ancient Ayurvedic sages once sent his pupils out and told them to return with only those plants that had no medicinal use. One returned with an empty basket and the master praised him saying that, in truth, every growing plant had some therapeutic value.

In the UK also, we held to the tradition, until relatively recently. The old herbalists well knew the importance of correct diet and the healing powers of a vast variety of foods, not just herbs. It was the advent of modern 'scientific' medicine that drove the herbalists underground, with many of them being murdered as witches. However, researchers in the twentieth century began once again to realize that food could cure disease, not merely keep hunger at bay. Christian Eijkman, a Dutch doctor, found that prisoners in the East Indies who ate polished rice got the disease beriberi; those who ate unrefined rice, did not. But it was left to a Polish biochemist, Casimir Funk, working in London, to discover the element in rice husks that prevented beriberi. He believed it to belong to a group of chemicals known as amines and so coined the phrase 'vitamine', literally meaning 'an amine for, or essential for, life'.

By the 1940s, researchers had discovered that we need a complex web of nutrients to live healthily. They had isolated around a dozen vitamins and also began to recognize the importance of the minerals in the regulation and smooth-running of the body. Since then, the study of nutrition has become increasingly scientific. And, as more knowledge accrues, the picture becomes more and more complex.

The lowdown

The basic nutritional guidelines given in the first part of this book are just that – basic. The corner-stone of all natural health is that we are all individuals with individual needs. When it comes to diet there is no difference. The food I thrive on might give you terrible indigestion; the diet that gives me masses of energy might simply make you put on weight. Equally, the diet that cures one person's arthritis might have no effect on someone else with the condition. There are simply too many factors to take into consideration.

Nutritionists look at your whole lifestyle – not just what you eat, but how you work, how you sleep, what exercise you take, how you feel. The goal is to build up an entire picture of you and then find a diet and supplement programme to bring you back into health. It's also a process of education – finding out why you have become ill and how you can correct it. Nutritional therapy is not a quick fix and it can be tough going. To gain the best results, as with any therapy, you have to be committed and to make sacrifices for your health. You might well be told that you need to give up quite a large number of foods for at least a month; you might equally be told some home truths about your lifestyle and urged to cut down on harmful practices. If you eat heart-attack fry-ups, drink like a fish and smoke like a chimney, there's a high probability that a nutritionist will strongly advise you cut down – if not cut out – all three.

However, the rewards can be enormous. Many people find that their diet is the root of quite serious ailments. Arthritis and rheumatism respond well to this therapy as does eczema and other skin conditions, asthma, migraine, PMS, chronic fatigue and nervous disorders. Experts now acknowledge that diet can form an important part of the treatment of cancer, heart disease and multiple sclerosis. Even so-called diseases of the mind, such as depression and schizophrenia, can often be helped by nutritional therapy. Correcting your diet and any deficiencies can have a profound effect on infertility, while nothing can be so important as having the optimum diet both before and during pregnancy.

And it goes without saying that if you are concerned about your weight, then a nutritionist should be your first port of call.

The session

I have visited several nutritionists over the years but my most recent visit was to Nicola Griffin of the Ultimate Health Clinic in south-west London. The first stage of the consultation was a detailed questionnaire, asking about all aspects of health – both my history and current symptoms. Nutritionists are pretty pragmatic people on the whole – rather than let you forget anything, they often give you a prompting sheet full of symptoms and ask you to check off those you have. Some of the questions seem irrelevant, if not downright nosy: what, you might ask, does your sex drive have to do with nutrition? Or mood swings? Or if there are certain times in the day when you lack energy? Quite a lot, as it happens.

The questionnaire is a good starting block which allows the nutritionist to get a pretty fair idea of what your main problems are and what might be causing them. But, of course, you get the chance to talk about what you are concerned about and which symptoms are causing you the worry.

Next stop was a thorough testing on the Vega machine. Developed as a swift easy way to detect allergies and imbalances, it appears a curious means of diagnosis. I was asked to take off any jewellery and also my socks. Nicola then took my left foot onto her knee and tested an acupuncture point on my big toe with a probe. Meanwhile I held another probe in my right hand. Popping a phial containing wheat into the machine, she pressed the point on my toe, and the machine emitted a high-pitched squeak. The counter on the machine flew over to one side. Nicola nodded as if her suspicions had been confirmed: I was intolerant to wheat. It wasn't just wheat: apparently I couldn't take cows' milk or cheese, coffee or tea, citrus fruits or (horror of horrors) red wine.

Next she tested me for deficiencies and found I was pretty well OK (not that surprising seeing as I take a regular multi-vitamin and mineral supplement). However, she felt my digestion needed some support, and she went back to the machine to find out what would help the best: in my case, I didn't particularly need probiotics (the 'friendly' bacteria of the gut); instead she prescribed a supplement of hydrochloric acid and pepsin.

That was the easy part. To really sort myself out, she explained, I would need to exclude all my 'problem' foods, at least for a month. To help, she suggested alternatives: goats' milk and cheese; herbal teas and coffee substitutes like Wake-Up or Barley Cup.

It sounds easy but, in effect, my whole eating pattern changed overnight. You'd be surprised just how much food contains either wheat or cows' produce in one form or another. The only cereal I could eat was pure oats with goats' milk; the only bread I could eat was the heavy Russian 100 per cent rye. Eating out was a nightmare: sauces were hopeless (they almost all use flour); even my beloved pasta was *verboten*. But I soon got used to it and within a couple of weeks felt much much better. My energy levels rose and my skin and hair seemed fresher, clearer and brighter. My bowel movements (which had beforehand been erratic to say the least) became delightfully regular and firm. I slept better and felt less stressed. And, not surprisingly, I lost a lot of weight as well. It wasn't all easy: giving up coffee and tea was torture for the first few days (many of us are addicted to the caffeine), and I looked with pathetic longing as friends gulped glasses of wine while I sat with a mineral water. I was allowed spirits, but it wasn't the same.

After a month, Nicola tested my levels again and found they had improved. I could introduce a little dairy produce back into the diet if I wanted, but wheat was still a bugbear.

HERBALISM

WHAT IS IT?   The use of herbs to treat illness and to restore the body back into a state of balance.

USED FOR   A wide variety of illnesses – both chronic and acute.

SUITABLE FOR   People who like 'taking things'. Herbalism is ideal if you are a little suspicious of anything too 'weird' and want a straightforward introduction to alternative health.

NOT SUITABLE FOR   Muscular, bone or joint problems that require manipulation. A herbalist would probably refer you to an osteopath or chiropractor.

PERFORMED   As for an orthodox doctor's examination – depending on the condition, you may or may not have to take off your clothes.

ANYTHING TO TAKE ORALLY?   Herbal tinctures or pills, or fresh herbs.

STRESSBUSTER   Some herbal preparations have a distinct sedative effect. However, herbalists would search for the underlying cause and probably suggest lifestyle changes to deal with chronic stress.

COST   Medium.

NUMBER OF SESSIONS REQUIRED   Acute conditions may only need a couple of visits; long-standing chronic complaints can take some months to clear.

DIY   Herbs are potent medicines and you should be wary of treating yourself for serious conditions. However, there are plenty of simple DIY techniques – from herbal tisanes or teas to herbal pillows or baths that are totally safe.

IF YOU LIKE THIS, TRY   AROMATHERAPY uses the healing power of herbs in massage and baths – a nice adjunct to herbalism. If you would like something less conventional but still using the healing power of herbs, look at AYURVEDA or TRADITIONAL CHINESE MEDICINE. If you are interested in the energetic qualities of herbs and other substances try HOMEOPATHY or the FLOWER AND GEM REMEDIES.

We chuck a bit of rosemary in with the roast lamb and pour mint sauce on it once it's on our plates. Dill goes with fish and tarragon makes a meal out of chicken. Garlic, we know, adds a bit of zing to virtually anything. We merrily add herbs to our cooking without a second thought because they bring out flavours and generally taste nice: we certainly don't stop to think about their healing virtues or choose our flavourings to fit our symptoms. And yet herbs have been used for centuries as a potent form of medicine. Discovering the healing power of herbs can be a fascinating journey – and can have deep, long-lasting effects.

If you're new to the field of natural health and slightly wary of the more esoteric side of the field, then I would recommend you start here. Herbalism is very similar in many ways to conventional medicine – certain herbs are used for certain conditions. So far, so straightforward. However, be assured that this is not just a pseudo-medicinal cure. Herbalists look long and hard at all areas of your life, and your remedy will be picked just for you. Two people with the same condition would be unlikely to receive the same herbs unless they also had identical patterns of stress, eating, sleeping and exercise, and unless they had precisely the same saga of hereditary illness and medical history.

The history

It's safe to say that herbalism is probably the very oldest of all forms of medicine and the great-great-grandparent of all the supertherapies. It doesn't take much imagination to think that early hunter-gatherer societies would have discovered, by trial and error, that not only were certain plants good to eat, but also that some had powers over and above those of satisfying hunger pangs. Herbal remedies most probably held pride of place on the shelf in the cave.

Take a culture, any ancient culture you choose, and you are bound to find a tradition of herbalism: Native American shamans, Hawaiian Kahunas, Aboriginal peoples of Australia, the shamans of Mongolia, the healers of Tibet, to name but a few.

In more modern times, the second century Greek physician, Galen, spoke of plant remedies. The herbal tradition stayed firmly centre-stage until the advent of modern chemical medicines. Then the doctors and surgeons began the steady campaign to discredit herbalism that exists up to the modern day. Even now, the large pharmaceutical companies and orthodox doctors fear the popularity of herbal remedies. Because they are purely natural plants rather than complex chemical commodities, they cannot be patented and so there is little chance of making huge profits from their sale. If the public turn from expensive patent medicines to cheap herbal preparations, profits will be (and indeed are) likely to plunge. Consequently, there have been several attempts to restrict or ban the sale of herbal medicines. These have met with unprecedented opposition from the general public and, for the time being at least, herbal medicine is safe.

The lowdown

Herbal medicines work on a simple biochemical level – they trigger neurochemical reactions in the body and so directly affect the organs and systems of the body. Basically, they are still fulfilling the same function they did in all the ancient traditions: to cleanse, to heal and to nourish. Before a body can start to bring itself to health, it needs to be rid of toxins and dead and decaying matter which litters the body. Herbs can be used as diuretics, laxatives and blood purifiers to help the processes of elimination and detoxification. The next step is to bring the body back to optimum health – herbs are used to stimulate the body's own self-healing powers and to attack the causes of illness. Thirdly, herbs are used to tone the organs and to nourish all the systems of the body, helping the body to keep on an even, healthy keel.

The aim is that, by taking the herbs over a period of time in moderate doses, the biochemical responses of the body will become automatic and it will start fending for itself again, even when the herbs are stopped.

Herbs have powerful effects, and modern orthodox medicine has often taken the active ingredients of them and synthesized them to turn them into modern drugs. Perhaps the best known is aspirin. Native Americans have long chewed the inner bark of the willow tree as a cure for headaches. The chemists analysed it and found willow to be high in salicylic acid, the active ingredient of aspirin.

The session

Like all supertherapists, herbalists are looking at your whole life, so don't expect a simple quick fix in a bottle or a wonder-pill that will sort you out in an instant. Medical herbalists have been trained in the same examination techniques as GPs, so you can expect a physical check-up and also to answer questions about your symptoms. However, this is where your herbalist and GP will diverge: your initial consultation will take around an hour and you can expect to answer questions in considerable depth. What was your childhood like? What illnesses and accidents have you had throughout your life? What is your appetite like? And your sleep? And how is the health of your family? Then again, more questions on the emotional/mental side of your life: how do you get on with your family; with work colleagues? How is work and do you have much stress? A whole picture is being built up of you as a person, rather than you as a disease. How does your body function at the moment: what are your bowels like; your circulation, your menstruation and so on? Then, and only then, will the herbalist want to know about your specific problem – how it started, what makes it better and what makes it worse.

The examination is quite standard: a blood pressure check;

listening to heart and chest with a stethoscope; possibly examining your ears, nose and throat and eyes; perhaps feeling your abdomen to gauge bowel tone. If necessary, your herbalist will take blood tests as well.

All this information enables the herbalist to make a precise diagnosis of your problem and find the best way to treat it. It's highly unlikely you will just be packed off with herbs. Most probably, the herbalist will advise you on beneficial changes to your diet, will try to persuade you to take up some form of regular exercise and will also counsel you on the best ways to avoid or diminish the bad effects of stress. Like naturopaths, herbalists take the problem of toxicity very seriously – don't be surprised if you're put on a detox diet or regime.

Then come the herbs. Most are prescribed in the form of tinctures, solutions of the herbs which are often mixed together to make an individual remedy for you. Usually you will take them much like a conventional medicine, by mouth, two or three times a day. Unfortunately, they often don't taste too good. Sometimes you will be given pills instead of fresh or dried herbs to use in infusions (steeped in boiling water) or decoctions (where the herbs are boiled down into a concentrate, strained and drunk). Compresses, lotions and creams can be applied directly on the skin. Herbs can also be put in the bath or breathed in through inhalations. Occasionally, a herbalist will suggest herbal douches, enemas, or suppositories (rectal or vaginal) to further draw out toxins.

Healing herbs: safe DIY techniques

HERBAL TEAS

Herbal teas make a pleasant (and highly healthful) change to tea and coffee. Try the following:

Chamomile If you're stressed or suffer from insomnia, chamomile is your best friend. Drink a cup at night to ease you to sleep. Chamomile will also ease indigestion, stimulate a poor appetite and soothe an irritable bowel.

Fennel This forms the perfect after-dinner digestive: drink fennel for all kinds of digestive problems from flatulence to indigestion.

Hops These are another great insomnia aid – many herbal teas will combine hops with valerian, vervain, chamomile or meadowsweet for a good night drink.

Lemon balm If you're feeling worn-out and depressed, try a cup of lemon balm. It will also help if you feel the beginnings of cold or flu.

Mint Another great stomach soother, mint is wonderful for nausea, travel sickness, indigestion and flatulence. It is also helpful in easing headaches and makes a wonderful pick-me-up.

Nettle The great cleanser, nettle stimulates the circulation and makes a great tonic. It can be very helpful in cleansing the system in conditions such as arthritis, rheumatism and eczema.

Rosemary Not the nicest of teas, but as a healing infusion add 25g/1oz fresh rosemary to a litre of water and leave to steep for fifteen minutes. This is wonderful for treating headaches, colds, flu, rheumatic pains and indigestion.

HERBAL BATHS

Why pay a fortune for bath unguents when you can make your own? Herbal baths are wonderfully soothing. I'll never forget being put in a bath at a Maltese spa – the room was softly lit with candles and quiet music was playing. I lay down and felt like Ophelia, surrounded by flowers floating on the water and a giant bag of soothing herbs. The scent was delicious and, as I relaxed (for half an hour at least) the herbs gradually seeped out of the bag. I ended up massaging myself with the bag and came out feeling fantastic. It's easy to do something similar at home – it just takes a little forward planning and a committed imagination. (Forget the traffic outside, ignore the kids banging on the door – relax.)

The following is a lovely soothing bath that works well with this set-up (this quantity will make enough for quite a few baths and will keep well in a tightly closed container).

Mix six handfuls of dried or fresh lavender, five of rosemary, four of rose petals, three of lovage, two of verbena leaves and half a handful each of thyme, mint, marjoram and (if you want it to keep) orris powder. Put a good handful or two in a large piece of muslin and tie into a bag (make sure it's secure). Pop the bag under the hot tap as you run the bath. Then relax and use it at the end of your bath as a scrub.

For a refreshing bath, try mixing equal parts of lavender and pine needles. Boil and steep them together for a quarter of an hour, then strain and add to the bath. You can add a drop each of rosemary, lemon and thyme essential oils to give you a real wake-up boost.

HOUSEHOLD HERBS

Herbs can be used around the house to great effect. Use lavender bags to freshen clothes and give bed-linen a delicious scent (but be warned, lavender has a reputation as the herb of chastity!). Bunches of sage hung in wardrobes are said to keep away moths and, although I've never tried it, an old wives' tale says that if you hang bunches of dried tomato leaves they will keep away insects.

Bodyworking

It doesn't take an expert to tell you how therapeutic touch can be. A cool hand soothing a feverish brow, a gentle ruffle of the hair, that wonderful feeling when someone gives those tense muscles a quick neck rub – we all know how healing hands can be. Sometimes the process is purely mechanical: a joint needs to be nudged back into its ideal position; a muscle needs to be relaxed. But the effects of bodywork are rarely just physical. We actively need to be touched. It is a physiological urge that, if unsatisfied, can have quite profound psychological effects.

In the USA, at the Touch Research Institute at the University of Miami Medical School they have found that massage can actually reduce depression. A thirty-minute neck and back massage had a pronounced effect on a wide range of patients, from anorexic and bulimic girls, abused children and adolescent mothers to psychiatric patients and those suffering from severe trauma. The effects were measurable: levels of stress-related hormones, cortisol and norepinephrine went down and the patients were more alert, less restless and more likely to sleep.

Virtually anyone can practise the healing touch and, to my mind, we could all benefit from learning basic massage techniques to use on family and friends. Many massage schools offer short courses for those who just want to use techniques at home or you can pick up the essentials from a video. However a fully trained expert will know exactly where to locate tension and precisely how to relieve it. In an ideal world I would have a massage every week – no, let's be honest, make that every *day*.

While anyone can give a soothing neck rub and can learn the rudiments of straightforward massage, I would most certainly not recommend you take any of the therapies in this section lightly. Most of them should only ever be practised by a fully qualified and experienced practitioner. I know there are shelf-loads of books showing you how to teach yourself reflexology, shiatsu, aromatherapy and so forth, but I truly cannot recommend you learn anything like this from a book. These are precise disciplines and should only be carried out by people who know exactly what they are doing. I'll never forget, in my foolish younger days, trying to emulate a masseur I had seen on television, treading carefully up his client's spine. I merrily bounced all over my boss's back and put him out of work and in agony for a month. I also came close to putting myself out of work, permanently.

But, in expert hands, bodywork can be miraculous. Aside from curing aches and pains, even aside from easing depression, its effects go deeper still. Bodywork, in general, is *the* supreme stress-buster. If you need a short, sharp release from tension, go see a bodyworker – the stress will melt away. It will also make you feel better about yourself: if you are feeling under par in either body or mind, bodywork can do wonders. For example, I would recommend regular bodywork to anyone who is trying to lose weight. In my experience, the last thing dieters do is love and care for their bodies, they are too busy ignoring or punishing them. In reality, it is the one thing they should focus on. Putting yourself back in touch, literally, with your body will subtly change your relationship with it – it's harder to abuse something you care about.

It's not just for dieters. If you're recovering from an illness or injury, see a bodyworker. Equally, if you have a chronic complaint of pretty well any kind, bodywork could help too. You may have to shop around to find the right therapy or therapist: some forms of bodywork aren't suitable for particular forms of cancer; others will not suit people with epilepsy or those with ME. Always tell a potential therapist about any medical problems or any medication you may be taking – it's vital information.

Many psychotherapists and counsellors also like their clients to have some form of bodywork alongside therapy. It's not just to make them calmer and more relaxed. There is a growing band of evidence that memory is held, not just in the brain, but in the body as well – in the muscles, the fascia (connective tissue) and even in the bone itself. Bodywork practitioners have found for years that their clients would spontaneously 'remember' incidents long past or forgotten when certain parts of their bodies were touched or manipulated. So, in this way, bodywork can have a strong psychological effect, releasing old traumas and helping to resolve unfinished business. It doesn't always happen – don't go to your next massage expecting to relive your birth trauma – but it often does.

For ease, I have broken the therapies in this section into groups, depending on the level at which they work.

The Manipulation Therapies: Working on the Skeletal Structure

OSTEOPATHY

WHAT IS IT?   A system of manipulation aimed at bringing the structure of the body back into balance.

USED FOR   Works well with all muscular and joint pain; sports injuries, arthritic and rheumatic conditions; headaches; digestive problems; PMS.

SUITABLE FOR   Most people. Those who feel uneasy with straightforward osteopathy should find an osteopath who performs the very gentle cranial techniques.

NOT SUITABLE FOR   Anyone who is scared of the cracks and crunches. Replacement joints need to be handled with great care.

PERFORMED   Usually in underwear.

ANYTHING TO TAKE ORALLY?   No.

STRESSBUSTER   Can ease tense muscles.

DIY   None.

COST   Low to medium.

NUMBER OF SESSIONS REQUIRED   Three to five normally sees an improvement, but it does depend on the problem.

IF YOU LIKE THIS, TRY   ZERO BALANCING works on the bone level but is very gentle and non-invasive. Osteopathy works very well in tandem with NATUROPATHY. If you would prefer a more gentle approach, investigate CRANIAL OSTEOPATHY or MCTIMONEY CHIROPRACTIC.

Most people think of osteopaths as simple bone-crunchers, but that is a long way from the full story. Osteopathy has become highly diluted over the years and now, certainly, most people will go to see an osteopath because of a problem with their back or neck. However, in the USA it's a different story – osteopaths are medical doctors who treat everything and anything. In the UK too, osteopaths can do much more than simply fix your back. They deal with developmental problems, with the elderly, with chronic conditions such as bronchitis and asthma, with postural problems, with pregnancy and post-pregnancy. Few women would think of osteopathy as a useful adjunct to pregnancy but in fact it's a wonderful pre- and postnatal treatment. During pregnancy the body goes through major postural changes and osteopaths can make those nine months much more comfortable. It is also superb at dealing with the, often considerable, post-pregnancy problems: stress incontinence, breathing difficulties and postural problems. Sort out your body structure, and everything else will follow suit.

The history

Osteopathy originated in the mid-west of America in the nineteenth century. Its founding father was Dr Andrew Taylor Still, who was not just a medical doctor but also a mesmeric healer and a Methodist minister. He became sorely disillusioned with 'modern' medicine when he watched three of his children die of viral meningitis and found his healing unable to help them. Like so many other originators of alternative systems, he became fascinated by the theories of Hippocrates – particularly his idea that the cure of disease lies within the body. In addition, Still had studied engineering and was intrigued with the idea that the body was a sophisticated machine with moving parts that needed to move smoothly in order to function properly. He observed people and began to feel convinced that much of the illness and injury in the world was caused by strain – particularly that brought about by tension in muscles and badly aligned bones. The causes for such strain were myriad: physical injuries, bad posture continued over a period of time, even psychological causes such as grief, anger, depression or fear.

Still believed that by adjusting the structure, the framework, of the body, its internal systems would be relieved and could once again function properly. Then, and only then, would the body be given the chance to restore itself to health. He therefore developed the system that became known as osteopathy, and began to train others in his methods. Gradually, osteopathy became accepted in the USA – mainly because it had been instigated by a doctor. Initially, the American osteopaths gained local but not state recognition. However, they wanted more, and the only way to receive formal recognition was to become more medically orientated. Now in the USA, osteopaths are MDs (Doctors of Medicine) and incorporate full medical training in their courses.

Osteopathy came to Britain around the turn of the century, and the British School of Osteopathy was founded in 1917. In the UK, common law allowed osteopaths to practise without recognition. However, they still had to work alongside the medical profession who were, quite naturally, generally antagonistic towards what they saw as a real threat to their livelihood. The osteopaths soon realized that the path of least resistance lay in dealing with conditions that the medical profession didn't like handling so much. So, while in America osteopaths became doctors who practised osteopathy, in Britain osteopaths moved to the periphery and became known as joint specialists.

The lowdown

The whole philosophy behind osteopathy is that if the anatomy and physiology are working well, then the person is well. Osteopaths stress that they themselves don't cure anything; they simply attempt to help the body into a state where it can get itself better. As osteopath Corina Petter says, 'The body is always going towards health – the only time it fails is when you die. Up until the last moment it is struggling and struggling. Its aim is to keep you well. It is only when tissues are overcome by tremendous odds that the body says "I give up." We just enhance that healing potential.'

Sadly, we have a design problem working against us. In terms of human evolution, we have only recently made the transition onto two feet. Standing upright causes stresses and strains that our bodies were never intended to carry: the discs between the vertebrae have become weight-bearing, and it is this continual strain which can cause back pain and related problems.

Many people find it hard to distinguish between osteopathy and chiropractic and, certainly nowadays, there is little to choose between them. Daniel David Palmer, the originator of chiropractic, did visit Still's school, and the philosophies of the two systems were almost identical – i.e. God created man perfect, and if bodies are in alignment and are functioning well, then they can express their best potential.

The main difference was that the chiropractors treated the problem joint directly, often with the classic high-velocity thrust techniques which make the large crunching sounds and put the joint back in its correct alignment. Osteopaths, on the other hand, tended to treat indirectly: rather than popping the joint and putting it back into place, they would work on the muscles, the ligaments and the supporting structure (the fascia) to enable the joint to regain its function. The end result was the same, but the techniques were different. Over the years, however, there has been a lot of cross-fertilization, and now there are plenty of osteopaths who do the cracks and the bangs, while many chiropractors have incorporated the gentler techniques.

Modern osteopathy uses a wide variety of techniques: manipulation and stretching, massage and gentle touch. In addition, your osteopath will often advise on posture, diet and exercise. The spine is obviously of paramount importance: it protects the major part of the nervous system which, in turn, controls movement and registers sensations throughout the whole body. If the spine is badly aligned, then symptoms might appear in any number of far-flung corners of the body.

However, important though the spine is, the therapy does not end there. Muscular tension also needs to be relieved – any tension (whether physical or psychological) will make muscles less elastic and more prone to damage. In addition, tension in the muscular system slows down both the circulatory and the lymphatic systems, inhibits heart function and can worsen respiratory conditions.

The session

Osteopaths vary enormously. Some specialize in sports injuries, some in pregnancy, some in treating children and babies, while others have a more general practice. All osteopaths, however, will begin with a case history, by asking precise details about your past and present health, any accidents or operations, any medication or remedies you are currently taking; your life at home and work and at leisure. Obviously, you will also be quizzed on your specific problem: when did it start; what makes it worse; what makes it better? Sometimes, the questions seem endless.

Finally, you will be asked to demonstrate your mobility and posture: standing, sitting, walking up and down, leaning in all directions. Many osteopaths will ask you to strip to your underwear so that they can see your body structure more clearly. Once they have determined the cause of your problems, the work begins. Some movements will be carried out while you sit on the edge of the couch; others while you lie down. Although you may well find yourself being massaged, osteopathy isn't really a 'pamper' remedy – everything is performed swiftly and functionally, quite clinically. At times, it can seem as if nothing much is happening at all, while on other occasions treatment can be quite dramatic.

I'll never forget my very first osteopathy session – or rather, my first osteopathic 'crack'. The osteopath took my neck between her hands and, without any warning, gave it a sudden twist to the side. There was the most hideous crunching sound and, for one ghastly moment, I thought my neck had been broken. It didn't exactly hurt but it was a most peculiar sensation. Then she repeated the procedure the other side. The blood rushed to my face and neck, a result of the freeing of the connective tissue, allowing better blood flow, and I lay gasping with shock. I've never had that move performed again but have had plenty of other cracks and crunches. They sound hideous, but the feeling of release and regained flexibility make it all worthwhile.

CRANIAL OSTEOPATHY AND CRANIO-SACRAL THERAPY

WHAT IS IT?   A very gentle technique that uses tiny manipulations on the skull and sometimes the rest of the skeletal system.

USED FOR   A wide variety of conditions respond. It is excellent for post-accident trauma and for babies following a difficult birth. Migraines and headaches respond well. Success has been had with some cases of osteoporosis and tinnitus.

SUITABLE FOR   Anyone who wants the benefits of osteopathy without the crunches. Cranio-sacral therapy will appeal to those who like a more esoteric approach to manipulative therapy. Babies and small children benefit enormously.

NOT SUITABLE FOR   Very few people cannot take this gentle therapy.

PERFORMED   Fully clothed (for cranio-sacral); an osteopath may ask you to strip to your underwear.

ANYTHING TO TAKE ORALLY?   No.

STRESSBUSTER Yes, both these techniques are wonderfully relaxing – particularly cranio-sacral therapy.

COST Medium.

NUMBER OF SESSIONS REQUIRED Depends on your problem. Once a week, or more frequently with cranial osteopathy for serious problems. Once a month is more likely with cranio-sacral.

DIY Yes. Some techniques can be taught for home use.

IF YOU LIKE THIS, TRY MCTIMONEY CHIROPRACTIC is still very gentle but slightly more perceptible in its techniques. METAMORPHIC TECHNIQUE may well appeal with its gentle transformative focus.

The key to health and happiness may lie hidden in your head – not in your mind, but in the tiny joints that make up the skull. A new breed of osteopaths and bodyworkers are now focusing on the cranium or skull as the key to their work, and they are getting intriguing results.

There are two schools of cranial work: one practised by osteopaths as a part of their wider repertoire, and a sideshoot known as cranio-sacral therapy, which is either performed as a therapy on its own, or incorporated into other forms of bodywork, such as shiatsu or massage. Both cranial osteopathy and cranio-sacral therapy work by manipulating not just the standard joints in the back but also the infinitesimal joints, known as sutures, in the skull itself.

The results are impressive: cranial work can help everyone from acute accident victims to babies who have suffered a traumatic birth; it can ease migraine and soothe painful sinuses; phobias can vanish and energy levels can rise. Even notoriously difficult conditions such as osteoporosis and tinnitus can often be alleviated.

The history

Both forms of cranial therapy originate from the same source – the work of William Garner Sutherland. Sutherland trained as an osteopath in the early part of this century. He learned, like all students at that time, that there was no point studying the cranium, or skull, because there appeared to be nothing in it to manipulate: the early osteopaths believed that the bones of the skull were fixed solidly together. However, Sutherland found, through minute observation and examination, that the cranium was actually a moving structure. Certainly its movements were minute but, like any other joint, the sutures of the skull ran the risk of becoming traumatized, restricted or stiff. Equally, like any other joint, they could also be manipulated back into balance.

His other great discovery was that there were certain rhythms in the cranium, a pulse which echoed the fluctuation of the cerebro-spinal fluid (the watery liquid that bathes the tissues of the brain and spinal cord). He called this the cranial rhythmic impulse and found that in a healthy adult it should pulse at ten to fourteen beats a minute. When there was a problem or illness, the pulse would not beat at this optimum level. By very gentle manipulations of the head and lower spine (the sacrum), he was able to correct the pulse and cure the problem.

Cranio-sacral therapy developed out of cranial osteopathy and has now become a discipline in its own right. Unlike cranial osteopathy, its practitioners do not need any training in osteopathy or chiropractic. Its founding father is Dr John Upledger, an American osteopath and physician who found that a large proportion of cranial work could be taught easily and effectively to people with no background in osteopathy, and he commonly gave the family and friends of his patients movements and exercises they could perform between sessions. In addition, he became increasingly fascinated by the psychological and emotional aspects of cranial work and came to the conclusion that, for true healing, there had to be some form of psychological – as well as physical – release. Consequently, many practitioners who use cranio-sacral therapy combine the work with regression, counselling, guided imagery or visualization.

The lowdown

The touch is so gentle that most people who experience cranial work can hardly feel it. Osteopath Peter Bartlett explains that many of his colleagues avoid cranial techniques because they simply cannot work at such a subtle level. 'Put a hair under a page of a telephone directory and most people would be able to feel where it was,' he says. 'However, the best cranial osteopaths could feel that hair through the whole telephone directory.' However, those osteopaths who do use the technique find that they can have incredible results – without all the spectacular (and often quite traumatic) cracks and twists of the more conventional side of osteopathy.

Bartlett works a lot with babies who have had difficult births and says a wide variety of behavioural and developmental problems can be ironed out with the treatment. He tells of one baby who cried incessantly, only sleeping for half an hour at a time. The parents were exhausted and worried sick. After half an hour of treatment, the baby became quiet and immediately slept for two whole hours. A few treatments later, his behaviour was perfectly natural.

And, although osteopathy is generally considered a 'bone' treatment, it can help in seemingly quite unrelated ailments such as asthma, migraine and allergies. Some of the cures sound like magic but Bartlett's colleague, Corina Petter, is quick to point out that cranial work is nothing mystical. 'People think it's magic or faith healing,' she says, 'but it's not. This is firmly based on anatomy and physiology. It relies on fundamental science. If you know your anatomy, you can feel the stress traumas within the body and release them.'

The session

A session with a cranial osteopath starts with a detailed case history, minutely detailing every knock and fall, every serious illness. Any ache or pain is subjected to intense scrutiny: how *precisely* does it hurt; when *exactly* does it hurt; is it better for heat or cold, morning or evening? And so on. I saw Corina Petter at the Hale Clinic and, after the case history, she asked me to strip down to my underwear and stand with my back to her. She spent some time simply looking at my structure – how I stood, where I held tension. Her first observation was that I needed a new bra! 'It's amazing how many people have ill-fitting bras,' she said, 'and it can cause a lot of postural problems, plus neck pain or back-ache. Get yourself professionally measured.' She also advised I take up yoga or stretching exercises.

Next, I was asked to lie down on my back on the couch and she started to work on my body. The touch is gentle and the manipulations minimal – a slight twist here, a gentle pull there. At first she worked on my knees and hips and then she moved to my head. As she cradled it gently, I could hardly feel anything at all except for a light tingling all over my body. However, whatever she was feeling gave her quite precise information: she was able to pick up incredibly accurate details about my health and even my emotions.

Although cranial osteopathy may seem a little intangible, it is admirably suited to anyone who likes a straightforward, no-nonsense approach to complementary healthcare. Sessions are often quite short (thirty to forty minutes), and the approach is very single-minded: to correct the presenting problem.

When it comes to cranio-sacral therapy, although the basic techniques are the same, the approach is very different. I met Monica Anthony, a cranio-sacral therapist, at Violet Hill Studios, a healing centre in north London. Whereas the osteopaths' rooms were clear and clinical, Monica's treatment room was warm and cosy, with large comfortable chairs and paintings all over the walls. She too asked for a case history and stressed the importance of describing any old or new injuries or illnesses which could affect treatment. However, this time I only took off my shoes and socks before lying on the couch.

Monica combines cranio-sacral work with holistic foot massage, colour therapy and guided visualization. Sometimes she will ask her clients to monitor their dreams; occasionally she advises them to 'borrow a child and play in a sandpit' by way of homework. It's a far more alternative approach, far looser in structure and far more focused on the psychological.

She began by gently massaging my feet and then moved slowly up the body, spending a short time on my ankles and knees before holding first the sacral area, then the diaphragm, the thoracic region and finally the cranium. The touch was very similar to Corina's but she relied as much on intuition as on what she was feeling through her hands. At one point she asked me to visualize parts of my body linked together; at another she asked me to focus on a particular colour. Like Corina, she was remarkably accurate about both physical and emotional symptoms. I quickly found myself falling into deep relaxation, and surprisingly clear images would flash briefly through my head. After the eighty-minute session (cranio-sacral sessions are often much longer) I stepped off the couch feeling as if a huge weight had been taken from my shoulders. I felt relaxed but clear-headed and very calm.

Monica Anthony treats people for very much the same range of problems as the osteopaths. However, she does find that the people who are drawn to cranio-sacral therapy rather than cranial osteopathy are often looking for something more than physical relief. 'It's a little like playing a musical instrument,' she says. 'First, you tune it, but then you have to teach someone how to play it for themselves. Cranio-sacral therapy often helps people find out more about themselves.'

Whether you choose the osteopathic approach or plump for cranio-sacral therapy is very much a matter of choice. Both have good track records, and both are now becoming accepted by the standard medical profession – Monica Anthony has been demonstrating her techniques to nurses at the request of the local health authority. Whichever you choose, be prepared to change: once you work on your head, your body, mind and emotions might never be the same again.

CHIROPRACTIC

WHAT IS IT?   Chiropractic seeks to correct disordered joints, particularly those of the spine, by manipulation.

USED FOR   A vast number of problems – especially mechanical problems with the spine (which can cause lumbago, sciatica, headaches etc.) and rheumatic conditions. Chiropractic can also give relief in many other conditions including asthma (helps mobility in the chest), Parkinson's, multiple sclerosis and some cancers. It can ease pregnancy.

SUITABLE FOR   Virtually everyone. Although many people are scared of the idea of sharp, sudden manipulations, chiropractic is very rarely painful.

NOT SUITABLE FOR   If you are taking certain drugs (anti-coagulants for example), manipulation could cause bruising or bleeding to joints – discuss with your chiropractor.

PERFORMED   Generally in underwear or wearing an open-backed gown.

ANYTHING TO TAKE ORALLY?   No, although some chiropractors work alongside medical doctors who prescribe drugs.

STRESSBUSTER   Yes. Can relieve tension.

COST   Medium. You have to pay extra for X-rays or blood tests.

NUMBER OF SESSIONS REQUIRED   A few weeks to a year depending on the problem. Sometimes a chiropractor will suggest daily sessions but weekly is more likely to begin with. The average course is between six and ten visits.

DIY   None.

IF YOU LIKE THIS, TRY   If you are scared or worried about the sudden strong adjustments of CHIROPRACTIC or OSTEOPATHY, try CRANIAL OSTEOPATHY or MCTIMONEY CHIROPRACTIC. A gentle introduction to back work is the BOWEN TECHNIQUE. ZERO BALANCING works at the bone level but in a very gentle, energetic way.

Chiropractors like to say that they practise bloodless surgery. Their aim is to maintain the spine and the nervous system (and hence the entire body) in good health and harmony without recourse to surgery or drugs. Sometimes the results can seem like miracles – the chiropractor cracks a joint in the spine, and a pain somewhere quite different simply vanishes. The name sounds dramatic, but it simply means 'done by the hand' – although what a chiropractor can do with his or her hands is certainly not simple in its effects.

Alongside osteopathy, chiropractic is probably the super-therapy most accepted by the orthodox medical world. Doctors quite happily refer patients to both osteopaths and chiropractors, recognizing that their manipulative skills will treat the root causes of pain that doctors themselves can only numb with drugs: low-back and other pains, slipped discs, certain migraines and headaches, some cases of asthma and even indigestion.

The history

The first treatment using chiropractic in its present form took place in 1895, in Davenport, Iowa. Its originator was Daniel David (known as D.D.) Palmer, a Canadian schoolmaster turned storekeeper turned healer. Like many healers, he was driven to find the actual cause of sickness, believing that there was one fundamental reason why we become ill. Alongside his spiritual enquiries (he read the Bible and spiritualist texts with equal enthusiasm), he became fascinated by the spine and how it affected disease. He learned that the ancient Egyptians had known how to replace displaced vertebrae and that Hippocrates had also used manipulation of the spine to give relief in a wide variety of illnesses. Here, he thought, was perhaps the key to his search.

What happened next was quite dramatic: Palmer found that a man who had been deaf for seventeen years had a displaced vertebra. He put the vertebra back into position, and the man's hearing returned instantly. Another case shortly followed: this time, once the displaced vertebra was replaced, Palmer found he had miraculously cured heart trouble.

Palmer was fascinated. If deafness and heart trouble could both be cured by putting back displaced vertebrae, what else could this form of treatment do? He started to theorize that all disease could be caused by an imbalance of tension in the nerves running through the spine. Quite convinced that he had found the one true cause of all illness, he opened a training institute. His son, B.J. Palmer, became one of his students and eventually took over the school and put it on a firm footing. The word began to spread. However B.J. did not escape controversy. At one point, he took his father's idea of the one cause even further, insisting that all disease could be cured by a thrust on one particular bone. Meanwhile, others had taken up the chiropractic baton. One, Willard Carver, incorporated additional support into his sessions, supplementing the straight manipulation of the spine with massage, nutritional advice and heat therapy.

However, both approaches met with suspicion from the authorities in the USA. D.D. Palmer was imprisoned for practising medicine without a licence, and hundreds of chiropractors followed him right up to the 1960s.

Chiropractic came to Britain before the First World War and has slowly and quietly grown in popularity. Now chiropractic is a well-established and respected therapy both in Europe and the USA.

The lowdown

Chiropractors deal with spines. They are looking for a balanced spine which moves and functions harmoniously. If any of the individual joints move less or more than they should, or move in an abnormal way, then the spine as a whole will not work correctly. Adjustments and manipulations help the mechanical function of the spine which, in turn, helps muscles, nerves, joints and ligaments to work better. Chiropractors don't 'put bones back' as many people think – a bone only 'comes out' if it is dislocated. Instead, they prefer the word 'subluxation', which means that the bone is out of alignment relative to the one below. There are several causes of subluxation: an unbalanced muscular-pull on the bone, lack of harmony within the surrounding bones, awkward movement in a nearby joint.

Although D.D. was over-optimistic in his idea that all disease could be traced to distress in the spine, it is certainly true that a problem in this area can cause difficulties all around the body. Nerves proliferate all down the spine, and so pain felt anywhere in the body can have its origins in the spine.

The chiropractor mainly tries to free joints which have become fixed or limited in their mobility. To bring movement back to the joint they use 'adjustments', applying force across the joint to separate the joint surfaces. The effect can be dramatic – not only does the joint 'free up' but the surrounding muscles and joints will be affected too.

The session

Chiropractic is practised in a highly professional, clinical manner. Every chiropractor I have seen has worn a white coat and worked from a pristine treatment room, usually equipped with a desk and chairs plus a large treatment couch. Don't expect soft music and wafting incense here – it's all very down to earth and practical.

The first chiropractic session starts, as do many other supertherapies, with an interview. Expect to talk about your medical history, any past illnesses and, in particular, any injuries to joints or bones. You will also be quizzed on your present problem: your symptoms, when it's worse, when it's better, how long you've had it.

Then you will be asked to strip down to your underwear (some chiropractors will provide a robe as well) so that the therapist can examine you. Expect intense scrutiny, even while you are just standing still – a chiropractor can tell a lot from your posture. Then you will be asked to lie down on the couch. The mobility of your joints will be tested – the chiropractor may well lift your legs or move them around to gauge how flexible you are. Then he or she will feel your spine, touching, probing and prodding to see if any joints are impaired.

It's possible that your first session may not include any treatment. Chiropractors use X-rays quite commonly and may want to see the results of these before starting your treatment. Occasionally, if they suspect bone disease, infection or rheumatic diseases, you may be given blood or urine tests. Again, you will have to wait for the results of these before treatment starts.

However, once treatment begins it's quite noticeable. I don't think you ever forget the first 'crack' from either a chiropractor or an osteopath. The basic chiropractic adjustment is a sharp thrust across the joint which snaps the joint open. It makes a loud, distinctive crack which, when you first hear and feel it, is somewhat terrifying. But it doesn't actually hurt – it's just the shock that's painful. All that is happening is that the joint surfaces are parting. While your spine is being adjusted you will probably be asked to move into different positions to enable the chiropractor to make the right adjustment.

Results can be immediate if the problem is mechanical. It's not uncommon to tiptoe painfully into the chiropractor's office and stride out as if you've never felt a moment's pain in your life. While the initial examination and treatment can take an hour, follow-up visits are normally much shorter. It is often not advisable to do too much in one session, and you may spend no more than ten minutes with the chiropractor.

MCTIMONEY CHIROPRACTIC

WHAT IS IT?   A whole body form of manipulative treatment that uses gentle techniques.

USED FOR   Primarily back pain and joint problems, although it also often helps headaches; period pains; digestive problems; and can ease symptoms in many chronic diseases.

SUITABLE FOR   As McTimoney is so gentle, it can be used on virtually anyone, even those who are quite traumatically ill. It is also recommended for people who are worried about the 'cracks and crunches' of conventional chiropractic and osteopathy.

NOT SUITABLE FOR   Patients are advised to wait six weeks after post-surgical convalescence. McTimoney can be used throughout pregnancy, but great care is taken through the first semester.

PERFORMED   In underwear.

ANYTHING TO TAKE ORALLY?   No, although some practitioners refer to nutritionists. They also often work alongside orthodox doctors who may well prescribe drugs.

STRESSBUSTER Releases old tensions caused by stress and can ease stress headaches. The treatment itself is very relaxing.

COST Medium. Unlike conventional chiropractic, X-rays are not taken so there are no extra costs.

NUMBER OF SESSIONS REQUIRED It depends on the problem, but the standard is six sessions – one a week for six weeks. Many people return for 'MOT' treatments every three, six or twelve months.

DIY None.

IF YOU LIKE THIS, TRY ZERO BALANCING works at the bone level but in a very gentle, energetic way. CRANIAL OSTEOPATHY is another very gentle technique. If you want to move into personal development try CRANIO-SACRAL THERAPY.

Although many chiropractors now work very gently, there is only one sure-fire way to make certain that your chiropractic treatment will never ever hurt, and that is to insist on a McTimoney chiropractor. The McTimoney way seems to offer all the benefits of traditional chiropractic and osteopathy without the trauma. It's a whole body form of manipulative treatment which uses a gentle technique to achieve harmony in the body. Like conventional chiropractic, it is superlative for treating any form of joint pain or back problem, but patients often find that other problems, such as headaches, period pains and digestive problems also tend to clear up.

The history

John McTimoney, the originator of the system, started his working life as a silversmith and an illustrator. However, one day, in the 1950s, he fell from a ladder and lost the use of one arm. He went to a standard chiropractor in Banbury called Mary Walker, received treatment and rapidly recovered. Highly impressed by the cure, he willingly switched career, trained with Walker and swiftly turned into an extraordinary healer. He loved the effects of chiropractic but considered that the system could be even better.

Firstly, he was convinced that the whole person should be treated, not just the part that was causing problems and, secondly, he didn't see why the treatment should be uncomfortable or stressful in any way. By experimenting, he found he could achieve the same, if not better results, by very gentle techniques and, in 1972 he started teaching his form of chiropractic to students. John McTimoney died in 1980, but his students took up the baton and in 1982 opened their own school to teach his work. Now there are over 200 practitioners in the UK.

The lowdown

As with many other systems of complementary medicine, McTimoney teaches that our bodies are always striving to regain their health, that they are always working towards healing. The problem is that, over the years, we force our bodies into unnatural patterns. We have falls or accidents, wear crippling shoes, sit all day cramped over desks or slumped in a car seat. Emotional factors take their toll too: hurts and embarrassments, grief and anger can all be stored uncomfortably in the physical structure of the body. However, whatever strains and stresses we put on them, our bodies are always desperately trying to keep in a line with gravity. Say, you always carry a heavy bag on one shoulder. The shoulder moves up and the muscles will pull over. However, your head will move over so that it still sits in the centre of gravity. To compensate for that shift, your pelvis will shift the other way. Hence, many of us are walking round with curves in our spines. These are slight, but sufficient to cause the odd twinges and pains. The McTimoney chiropractor aims to release those old patterns of holding, to wipe out the bad habits that have been overlaid on our ideal structure so that our bodies can return to their healthy blueprint.

The main technique used is called the toggle recoil. Basically, this involves the practitioner using one hand as a nail and the other as a hammer. The hands are held over the precise spot that needs treating and the 'hammer' is brought down sharply on the 'nail' with a slight twist. It's rather like spinning a top and flicking it at the same time to set it moving. The effect is to change the tension surrounding the joint that has been 'toggled'. In a split second, the joint is freed: the adjustment is so fast that it outwits the surrounding muscle which doesn't have time to clamp fast into a protective spasm. The result is that the muscles are able to relax and then take up a more normal tension. Because many of our holding patterns have been in place for years, most people tend to see practitioners for around six sessions to really allow the joints to settle back into their natural balance.

The session

A session always starts with a very full case history. My McTimoney chiropractor, Jacquie Thomas, worked through several pages of questions, about past accidents and illnesses, operations and falls. Had I had any breaks or fractures, sprains or strains? Was I on any medication and did I have any current medical problems? She also asked for the name and address of my GP. Like standard chiropractors and osteopaths, McTimoney practitioners often work closely with orthodox doctors and consultants. And, although McTimoney is, sadly, not available on the NHS, many private healthcare insurance plans will now cover treatment.

The questioning didn't stop at standard medical queries: she also wanted to know about my sleep, my stress levels, my working conditions and my sleep patterns. 'We look at the body as a whole,' says Jacquie. 'McTimoney looks at all aspects of health, not just the fact that you may have a back pain.' She often sends her patients off with homework – postural exercises to correct bad habits and, if she feels it is necessary, she will refer patients to a nutritionist because, as she says, 'there is no doubt that diet does affect some musculo-skeletal problems.'

While we talked, Jacquie was marking potential problem areas on a diagram of the human body. In my case, she pinpointed the neck, pelvis, knees and ankles but stressed that, although she would focus on these areas, she would be checking me from my skull right down to my toes.

Theory over, it's time for the bodywork. Jacquie asked me to strip down to my underwear, remove any jewellery and to sit on the couch for a preliminary scan over my spine. Then, I lay on my left side for the first adjustment. As she worked just behind my ear, I felt her hands come down on my skin with a clapping sound. It didn't hurt at all – it felt rather like being lightly swatted.

She moved on over my neck and then the pelvis – the two extremes of the spine are always worked first. Next, she worked down to the knees, ankles and toes, then up to the arms. McTimoney has special techniques to ease problems like RSI (repetitive strain injury), tennis elbow and carpal tunnel syndrome. Then she moved on to my collarbone where one of the costal cartilages (which attaches the rib to the sternum) had popped free – Jacquie popped it back again totally painlessly. She finished off by checking my face and skull. Treatments end with a swift rubbing down to bring you back to earth and, as I sat up, Jacquie appraised me once more. A couple more toggles – a bit like an artist adding the final finishing touches to a painting – and I was allowed to dress.

Some people, apparently, find the McTimoney touch too gentle; almost as if 'if it doesn't hurt, it can't be working'. But as I walked out, I could certainly feel that something had happened to my body – it felt more relaxed, easier in itself.

ZERO BALANCING

WHAT IS IT?   A system combining hands-on bodywork (working at the level of the skeletal structure) with energetic healing.

USED FOR   Primarily neck and back pain; stress, migraine.

SUITABLE FOR   Excellent for sportspeople and those who are interested in bodywork but nervous of deep manipulation or taking their clothes off.

NOT SUITABLE FOR   People with hip and knee replacements, those with epilepsy, ME or a history of cancer.

PERFORMED   Fully clothed.

ANYTHING TO TAKE ORALLY?   No.

STRESSBUSTER   Yes, excellent for stress symptoms.

COST   Low.

NUMBER OF SESSIONS REQUIRED   Varies. For serious problems, initially one a week, becoming less frequent. Many people see a Zero Balancer every month or three months for a top-up.

DIY   Not generally, although some practitioners will give postural exercises.

IF YOU LIKE THIS, TRY   If you would like something more down to earth try BOWEN TECHNIQUE. If you feel you could go deeper, investigate ROLFING or HELLERWORK. If the concept of working with more direct manipulation on the bone appeals look at CHIROPRACTIC or OSTEOPATHY. Gentle alternatives are CRANIAL OSTEOPATHY and MCTIMONEY CHIROPRACTIC.

Zero Balancing aims not merely to soothe and relax your physical frame but also to stretch and balance your energetic body as well. It's a hands-on treatment which works physically at the deepest level of the body – the bone structure – and then moves even deeper still, influencing the body's innermost energetic levels. More than a massage or osteopathic manipulation, Zero Balancing seeks to balance you on all levels – body, mind and soul – and coax you back to optimum health. It's a system which works like esoteric engine oil, lubricating your body on every level, allowing your energy to flow steadily and easily. And it's not just your body which will appreciate a smoothly running energy system. Tone up your vital energies, say the Zero Balancers, and your mind and emotions will undoubtedly follow suit.

In many ways it is an ideal therapy for people who feel nervous of having to reveal too much of themselves, either by taking off their clothes or telling their deepest secrets. Treatment is given with the client fully clothed and there are no questionnaires to fill in, no need for painful soul-baring.

The history

Many therapies rely simply on bodywork; others look solely at the energy part of the equation, but Zero Balancing believes that better, faster, deeper healing can take place when the two are treated in tandem. It was developed by Dr Fritz Smith, an American physician, acupuncturist and osteopath who investigated a wide range of bodywork therapies and ancient energy systems before concluding that in order to bring people from sickness to health, from imbalance to balance, he needed to combine the two approaches. The result was Zero Balancing, which came into being around 1973. Smith calls it, 'a blending of Eastern and Western ideas in terms of body and structure. It brings energy concepts into touch, or body handling.' He believes that by working on the points of the body where the body energy meets its structure, Zero Balancers can bring clearer, stronger force fields of energy into the person.

Zero Balancers are all professional, highly trained bodyworkers. Before being accepted for training, they must already hold recognized qualifications in other forms of healthcare such as osteopathy, acupuncture, physiotherapy, chiropractic or Rolfing.

The lowdown

Zero Balancing views energy with clear precision. While most natural therapies would accept the importance of the energetic body, Zero Balancing actually differentiates between different kinds of energy, recognizing three distinct kinds of energy surrounding the body and a further three levels of energy circulating within us. Firstly, there is a background energy field (akin to the aura). Secondly, we have a vertical energy-flow that connects us to the world around us – it is this that gives us that distinction in feeling between a low-ceilinged room and a lofty pine forest. Thirdly, there is the internal energy flow which circulates within the body.

Within this internal flow lie three further distinct levels. The deepest runs through the bone and bone marrow, bringing the skeleton together as a complete functioning whole. The middle level flows through the muscles, nerves, blood and organs and corresponds directly to the Chinese concept of meridians – energy pathways connecting the soft tissue of the body. The superficial level controls the sweat glands and the energy in the tissue beneath the skin and acts as an insulation against the outside environment.

With so much energy flying around the body, it's no surprise to hear that problems can arise as easily in the energetic body as they can in the structural. Apparently almost anything – from physical accidents to emotional traumas – can affect our 'energy' body. A blow to the knee can cause physical damage, but long after the bruising has gone, the energy could remain twisted or stuck. And an emotional shock, such as bereavement, can equally remain caught in the energetic web, causing not just psychological stress but possibly physical stress and strain.

Zero Balancing is often successfully used to treat headaches, neck and shoulder pain and lower back problems. But equally, although practitioners make no claims about its ability to treat serious disease or dysfunction, it appears that when you balance the deep physical and energetic structures of the body, there is usually a beneficial effect on most forms of disease.

Aside from its physical benefits, Zero Balancers find their therapy has a remarkable capacity to help people through times of change or difficulty. It takes people very deeply into themselves, and the minor chit-chat of the mind drops away: often the clarity of an issue will become apparent and can even resolve itself. Many people say that they come off the table knowing what they want. Its effects have been described as akin to deep meditation.

Zero Balancers are cautious people, loath to claim too much for their fledgling therapy. They insist that Zero Balancing is far too young a therapy to claim to heal serious illness. However, if this is Zero Balancing in its childhood, it will be fascinating to see what this therapy will achieve once it grows up.

The session

I visited Jeff Lennard, a Zero Balancer who is also trained in shiatsu, polarity therapy and T'ai-chi. He has been practising bodywork for fifteen years. Quietly spoken and gentle, he first asked me if there was anything in particular that needed attention; whether I had any pain or stress. Zero Balancers don't ask for any deep disclosures – if you want to talk, that's fine; if not, they will simply get on with the work.

Then he requested I take off my shoes and jewellery and sit on the couch while he touched my spine with his fingers to gauge my energy. After a few minutes, I was invited to lie down on my back and relax for the duration of the forty-minute session. The Zero Balance touch is fundamental to the therapy – the practitioner seeks to get into a 'dialogue' with the client's energy system and together to balance the problem. The person undergoing treatment has as much to contribute to the process as the therapist. Lennard describes the touch as the 'Donkey-donkey touch – it's like two donkeys walking up a hill. If they're on a steep slope they will lean into each other to help get up the hill. Within this work we are doing it together.'

Starting at the lower back, Lennard worked down my legs and into my feet, then up to the upper back and neck, and finished off back at the feet. His fingers worked deeply into my spine, using the weight of my body to provide further pressure on the joints. While working on my legs he rotated the hip around, supporting my leg all the time with his hands. Sometimes it felt like acupressure, shiatsu or osteopathy, at others, akin to Rolfing or Hellerwork, but the touch *is* quite distinct. It goes deep, down to the bone, but is not at all painful. Lennard says one of its prime aims is to get people back in touch with their bodies, and I could see what he meant. After a few minutes of his working on my lower back I realized just how much stress and strain I hold there. And when he worked on my right knee, I felt almost a buzzing in my head and recalled an old horse-riding accident which had left my right knee weak and liable to twist. More than anything, I felt very deeply relaxed. The Zero Balance touch is firm but comforting – it was as if my body took a deep breath and simply decided to give in and flop into Lennard's hands.

My second session could not have been more timely: I had been involved in a car accident and my whole body felt jarred, particularly my lower back which was quite painful. I felt aware of it almost all the time. Lennard hit the spot almost instantly, carefully questioning me to ascertain exactly where I felt the pain. When I sat up after the session, I felt stiff and uncomfortable; I thought the Zero Balancing had in fact made it worse. However, after a few minutes walking around, the pressure eased and the pain had vanished totally. It didn't come back.

Lennard has seen a singer who was told she would never sing to her full potential while she was only using the muscles in one side of her neck. He found that trapped energy had caused her to hold her head undetectibly to one side. Now, after treatment, her singing has improved tenfold.

Another client was a dancer suffering with a bad knee. To her surprise, as Lennard worked on her neck, she suddenly felt a release in the injured knee. Lennard was quite unfazed: 'You don't ever know which part of the body will hold pain or trauma,' he commented.

The Manipulation Therapies: Working on the Fascial Structure

THE BOWEN TECHNIQUE

WHAT IS IT?   A gentle, non-invasive form of bodywork that works on the fascia, the connective tissue of the muscle.

USED FOR   Primarily sports injuries; low-back injuries; chronic tension headaches; and even for more complex problems such as asthma and bedwetting.

SUITABLE FOR   All ages. Particularly useful for those who are nervous of complementary treatments or prefer a down-to-earth approach.

NOT SUITABLE FOR   There is one move which is not performed during pregnancy.

PERFORMED   Fully clothed.

ANYTHING TO TAKE ORALLY?   No, although dietary advice may be given.

STRESSBUSTER   Yes, can relieve stress symptoms.

COST   Low.

NUMBER OF SESSIONS REQUIRED   Varies.

DIY   Sometimes you will be given home remedies.

IF YOU LIKE THIS, TRY   If you would like to go deeper but still keep your clothes on try ZERO BALANCING. Deeper still are ROLF-ING and HELLERWORK. If the non-invasive nature of the therapy appeals but you would like something less pragmatic, try REIKI.

The Bowen technique is, quite simply, the most down-to-earth bodywork therapy in the book. There's no need to wind your head around any complex philosophy; no call for mystic mumblings or deep emotional encounters; and no-one expects you to devote an inordinate time to a long drawn-out course of treatment. Quick, cheap and effective, it manipulates the muscle and connective tissue, leaving you walking tall and feeling relaxed, free and remarkably supple.

The history

With these characteristics it's no surprise to find that Bowen hails, not from the loony fringes of California, but from the clean-living, no-nonsense, bright and breezy reaches of Australia. Antipodean doctors have appreciated the effects of the technique for many years and use it widely for sports injuries, low-back injuries, chronic tension headaches, and even for more complex problems such as asthma and bedwetting. Its popularity is growing fast in Canada and the USA, and now Bowen is nudging its way into Europe too.

The originator of the technique was Tom Bowen, a great intuitive modern healer. He studied medicine prior to the Second World War and then saw service in the Middle East. When he came back home he switched career and became an industrial chemist. But by the 1950s, he was practising as a therapist, without any formal training. He had developed a system of very precise, highly specific moves mingled with a liberal splattering of home remedies and almost folkloric advice. In 1974, he came under investigation by the Australian federal government which discovered, to its frank amazement, that he was treating far and away the greatest number of patients on the continent – some 13,000 a year with cases responding to one or two treatments in 80–90 per cent of cases.

Bowen never advertised and never talked about his work – he certainly had no pretensions about calling what he did the Bowen technique. But he did allow one person, Oswald Rentsch, to study his technique and it was Rentsch who, after Bowen's death in 1982, began to train therapists in the procedure.

Bowen did not explain how his approach works, although Rentsch says he did describe energy as being temporarily trapped in one area. Releasing this energy appears to reduce muscle spasm while increasing blood supply and lymphatic drainage, resulting in the clearing of debris and the release of tension. Having cleared this form of blockage, he found, the body could get on with healing itself.

The lowdown

The technique can be used on anyone – from the newly born to the elderly and immobile – and its practitioners reckon it is state of the art, the future of bodywork. A Bowen treatment takes just twenty minutes; you don't even have to take off your clothes. There's no counselling, no emoting, no small talk and no chit-chat. Bowen is very straightforward, very down-to-earth. There is no great chanting or any tradition going back five thousand years. Best of all, it is almost totally painless.

Like Rolfers and Hellerworkers, Bowen practitioners work on the fascia (the connective tissue that covers the muscle), but in a quite different way. Bowen involves taking the slack across the muscle and moving over it. The touch is firm but not painful – no more than the pressure you could take on your eyeballs. There are around eight or ten prescribed moves that are given during the first session – on the back and around the neck. Other moves can be used at later sessions.

There is no mystery to the procedure, the practitioner simply makes the moves and then leaves the patient's body to deal with them. It may be simple, but Bowen claims to be highly effective: practitioners promise that 80–90 per cent of people need only one or two sessions to sort out their woes. However, if you have had pain for six months or a year, practitioners would say it is unrealistic to expect the pain to have vanished in one or two days. Generally, people do walk out feeling much better, more flexible and in less pain. The main concern of a Bowen practitioner, however, is that *something* has changed. If a client walked out after the first session in as much pain as before, a practitioner would not be worried, but he or she *would* be concerned if that person did not feel different. In the Bowen book, a change is as good as a cure.

Take the case of a woman who was having radiotherapy and chemotherapy and whose right leg was badly swollen; it felt solid and was purple in colour. After a couple of Bowen moves she felt terrible and continued to feel exhausted, drained and generally ghastly for forty-eight hours following. But then, suddenly, the swelling in the leg went down and completely vanished.

Numerous clinical trials are being carried out to try and pin down the secret of Bowen, but the results are some years away. For the meantime, suffice it to say that it seems to work. Bowen therapists have seen impressive results with frozen shoulders, tennis elbow and other sporting injuries. Not only does movement come back, but keen golfers have also even claimed that the technique has improved their swing. It seems to give greater flexibility.

But Bowen isn't just confined to sorting out sore knees and aching backs. Aside from the precise moves of the technique, Bowen therapists arrive with arm-loads of advice that, while smacking of old wives' tales, are in some instances now being proven by science. There are cures for bunions and suggestions for how to cure children of bedwetting; there is advice and treatment for hayfever sufferers. And, although practitioners are nervous of mentioning it, they occasionally see remissions from cancer. Practitioners are naturally wary of making any claims in this area and clearly point out that Bowen isn't universally successful. Nonetheless, there are cases which have responded very well.

Therapists put this down, partly to the actual Bowen but also in part to Tom Bowen's insistence that cancer patients take regular baths of washing soda and Epsom salts. He said it raised the temperature, and left it at that, but now American cancer researchers are experimenting with heat to shrink tumours, since they have found that the body's immune cells seem to produce antibodies faster at high temperatures. Bowen practitioners are not surprised: they are quite convinced that some day all of their founding light's curious remedies will be acknowledged by science.

The session

One of Bowen's prime advocates is Julian Baker who organizes the training of therapists in the UK. Smartly dressed in a neat suit and tie, Baker doesn't look like a typical therapist but then, he promises, Bowen isn't a typical therapy. As luck would have it, a weekend's hard gardening and an uncompromising tree stump a few days before my visit to Julian Baker had contrived to leave me feeling decidedly woeful, with a considerable pain in my lower back. Baker tried to look sympathetic but there was no disguising the glee on his face. 'Perfect. That's something Bowen can really help,' he promised confidently.

I edged gingerly onto the massage table and lay face down. As he moved across my neck and back, I could feel first a subtle resistance and then a giving-way as he 'rolled over' each muscle. Bowen practitioners describe the movement as similar to 'rolling a ball up a hill and then popping it over the top'. When he reached my tortured lower back there was a wonderful sense of 'hitting the spot'. But it's nothing like the continued pressure of massage, nothing like the deep probing of Rolfing and Hellerwork, and nowhere near the short sharp shocks of acupressure or shiatsu. More to the point, there is none of the impending sense of terror you get with an osteopath or chiropractor, wondering just when you're going to have your back or neck 'cracked'. In fact, Bowen seems so gentle, so *negligible* in its outward manifestation that you wonder whether it is really doing any good. 'Everybody says that,' agrees Baker. 'A lot of people get up and say "Is that it? How can *that* work?"'

When it comes to explaining precisely how Bowen *does* work, things become a little less straightforward. Julian Baker puts it like this: 'Bowen is a language and we're talking to the body, asking the body to start communicating with the brain to get the channels working properly.'

Along with most people, I found it hard to see how the tiny moves of Bowen could affect anything – especially something as clear-cut and obvious as my badly pulled back. And I must say that, if you are into the more sensually satisfying side of therapy, stick to massage. Yet, although Baker explained that it's not uncommon to feel initially *worse* after the first treatment, I have to say I felt better the moment I stepped off the couch. My back was simply easier, more fluid: I could bend down without wincing. The next day only the faintest memory of the stiffness remained and my whole body felt lighter and more flexible. In short, it *worked*.

Bowen home remedies

For bunions Soak your feet in warm water containing about three tablespoons of Epsom salts every night for at least three weeks. Tom Bowen said that the Epsom salts would break down the calcification that causes bunions.

For swollen knees or other joints Put crushed washing soda in a handkerchief, wrap it in a tea towel and fasten to the joint with a stocking. Go to bed and the washing soda should draw out the fluid and the swelling should go down.

For bruises Apple cider vinegar applied onto bruises or sprained wrists should take away the pain and tenderness.

For bladder problems, dizziness Take two slices (no more than 50g/2 oz) of raw beetroot daily, put through a juicer.

For bedwetting Bowen stressed that often the problems are psychological, but suggested children who bedwet should avoid dairy produce, apples and apple juice and go on an 80 per cent alkaline/20 per cent acid diet. He believed apple juice weakens the bladder.

For arthritis Epsom salts in the bath can help.

For rheumatism Try taking regular doses of honey mixed with cider vinegar.

ROLFING AND HELLERWORK

WHAT IS IT?   A form of bodywork that goes deeply into the fascia to restructure and balance the body.

USED FOR   Predominantly to improve postural problems; to relieve old injuries and release trapped emotions. Neck pain and back problems benefit.

SUITABLE FOR   People who want to improve their posture and appearance; their athletic performance and ease of movement. It is also prized as a facilitator of personal growth.

NOT SUITABLE FOR   People who are HIV positive, have ME or certain forms of cancer.

PERFORMED   In underwear.

ANYTHING TO TAKE ORALLY?   No.

STRESSBUSTER   Yes, an excellent stressbuster – although some people say the discomfort of the treatment itself is stressful!

COST   High.

NUMBER OF SESSIONS REQUIRED   A series of ten (Rolfing) or eleven (Hellerwork).

DIY   Possibly some postural exercises.

IF YOU LIKE THIS, TRY   CHAVUTTI THIRUMAL – a very deep massage using the feet. If you want something lighter which will still release memories held in the muscles, look at ZERO BALANCING, OSTEOPATHY or CHIROPRACTIC.

One and a half hours with a Rolfer or Hellerworker will transform the way you stand and alter the way you move. It could change patterns you have held for years, even since childhood. And, more incredible still, it could shift your whole emotional being. And that's just one session. After a course (Rolfing has ten; Hellerwork eleven) people's bodies, quite literally, look different – more upright, more centred, more relaxed. Graduates of these therapies report physical benefits such as release from long-term aches and pains; chronic headaches often vanish and there's a general consensus that energy levels soar. Minds follow close behind: on the emotional plane people swear it has given them increased confidence, a greater feeling of poise and balance, the ability to deal with people and to confront issues. It seems to make people more whole.

The history

At first sight, Rolfing and Hellerwork appear little more than a form of deep massage. So how do their practitioners achieve such deep effects? The answer, apparently, lies in the fascia. Deep-tissue bodyworkers bypass muscles and head instead for the connective tissue which contains and links the muscles. Not only does fascia house every muscle and muscle fibre, but it also thickens to form the tendons and ligaments. It keeps our whole structure, muscle and bone, in place.

Yet the fascial system had been generally ignored until around fifty years ago when American biochemist Dr Ida Rolf discovered that the fascia would adapt to support whatever patterns of movement and posture the body adopted. It you put more weight on one leg than the other, the fascia will bunch and shorten to compensate; if you hunch your shoulders, the fascia will knot to accommodate and hold your posture. If we put our bodies into imbalance, the fascia will obediently change to hold us in that position. But, as Dr Rolf soon discovered, if the fascia can change once, they can change again. And by manipulating and stretching the fascia back into their original position, she could reprogramme neurological pathways and return her patient to alignment.

However, it didn't stop on the physical level. Rolf also found that when she changed the body on a physiological level, her patients changed on a mental and emotional level as well. The technique became known as Rolfing.

The other major deep-tissue technique is Hellerwork. Its founder, Joseph Heller, trained with Ida Rolf before leaving to found his own form of bodywork. He wanted to concentrate more on movement and on the emotional side of treatment. But, as most Hellerworkers and Rolfers will admit, nowadays the differences between Hellerwork and Rolfing are very few.

The lowdown

Rolfers and Hellerworkers believe (along with the majority of bodyworkers) that memory isn't just held in the brain but in the muscles and tissues as well (Zero Balancers would go further and say it is held in bone as well). If you fall over and twist your ankle, your body will compensate for the injury by holding the whole body in a slightly different way. Even when the injury is quite repaired on a mechanical level, the muscles and tendons will 'remember' the incident and will always hold tension – until the ankle is stretched back into its original position. Equally, an emotional hurt or shock will be contained within the muscles, to be held there until it is given a chance to release. So when you change someone's body on a structural level, you will affect their being on an emotional level as well.

It's quite common for people undergoing deep-tissue bodywork to spontaneously remember incidents that happened years ago. Touch one point and nothing will happen; touch another area and the patient might scream and say it reminds them of when they were hit by their little brother decades before, or when they fell off a bike or had a terrible argument. The tissue actually seems to retain memory, so by releasing structural holding you release emotional holding.

A classic example involves a man who had been in a car crash as a child. He had lost a couple of ribs and his parents had both been killed. When the Hellerworker began to work on his chest the man started hyperventilating and went into a clear memory of the accident. He needed to talk about it and have a cry, but it allowed a profound sense of release. After the session he reported that he felt much better, calmer and more accepting.

Changes can be quite marked. Physically, people say they notice a difference in their posture and their skin tone. More subtly, there can be distinct changes in the way people present themselves, their vitality, confidence and energy.

Both Rolfing and Hellerwork have a quite rigid structure of treatment. A course of sessions is recommended – to be taken in sequence and, preferably, with a week to a fortnight's gap between each session. Each session deals with a different part of the body; plus, with Hellerwork, each session looks at a different emotional issue as well.

Although emotional issues can (and generally do) come up during the work, deep-tissue bodyworkers insist they are not psychologists and that, if any really deep emotional issues come up in the course of the work, they will refer the client to a trained counsellor. In America, Rolfers and Hellerworkers have had very effective results with shock and trauma victims – both from accidents and from rape and severe abuse.

The session

I was slightly nervous when I appeared for my appointment with Rolfer Jenny Crewdson: Rolfing has a reputation of being remarkably painful. Somewhat self-conscious in bra and pants, I stood as Jenny scrutinized my body and posture. 'You hold yourself up with your shoulders,' she noted. 'You have a rotation of the left hip and your left leg is shorter than your right.' She then asked me to lie on the couch and started to work on my body.

Sometimes the Rolfing touch feels like a strong pressing movement; at others the hands seem to push inexorably into the body.

It's insistent and sometimes very tender, but it's certainly not unbearable. In fact, if anything, I found it curiously releasing as old strains and stresses were stretched and straightened. But as Jenny worked around my shoulder blade she suddenly hit a sore point I hadn't even realized was there. And, clear as a movie, I suddenly 'saw' the bright green grass of my childhood back garden. I was learning to ride a bike and kept falling off. It was a scene I had completely forgotten.

After my session I felt deeply relaxed but, otherwise, not that much different. However, when I looked in the mirror at home my shoulders had noticeably moved several inches away from my ears to a more civilized position. And, over the next few days, I noticed emotional changes too: memories of old hurts and disappointments would suddenly pop into my head as if to let me take a last look before they disappeared again. And, as I ran up the third escalator on the tube, I suddenly realized my energy levels were higher than they had been for years.

I visited Hellerworker Terry Petersen to try out the other side of the deep-tissue coin. At the start of the session I spent about twenty minutes learning how to sit, stand and walk in a more balanced way. Wearing just my pants, I felt rather exposed and was very relieved to hear that Terry has not yet started to video her clients. However, both Rolfers and Hellerworkers take 'before and after' pictures to show how rounded shoulders can straighten and how protruding bottoms can tuck in following a course of treatment.

The Hellerwork touch is almost indistinguishable from Rolfing, although I found it slightly more painful in places. The main difference is in emphasis. Rolfing seemed more of an internal experience, with Jenny only making the occasional supportive comment or asking the odd question. Hellerwork demands far more participation. Each session has a 'theme', and the practitioner will engage the client in a dialogue while working on the body. The first session is called 'Inspiration' and while she was probing into my back, Terry asked me questions like 'What inspires you?' and 'What would you like to be doing that you don't have time for in your life?'

The sessions that follow have wonderful names like Standing on Your Own Two Feet; Reaching Out; Control and Surrender (a very powerful session which focuses on the pelvic floor muscles); The

Guts; Holding Back; Losing Your Head; The Feminine; The Masculine; Integration (in which all the work of the previous sessions is put together) and finally Coming Out which sends you, hopefully, out into the world with a spring in your step and a completely different way of standing, moving and looking at things. 'It's an incredible personal development experience,' says Terry. 'You're working very deeply on three levels: deep-tissue massage that unblocks the body; movement re-education and postural correction; and then the verbal dialogue, looking at emotional holding patterns. We're introducing people to areas which are blocked or not recognized; areas that are really holding them back.'

Unfortunately, as yet, there are very few Rolfers and Hellerworkers working in the UK, which is a great pity. Although the treatments do involve a fair commitment of time and money (regular weekly appointments for the whole ten or eleven weeks), the benefits really do seem worth the outlay and slight discomfort. As Terry Petersen puts it: 'The changes are quite noticeable. Physically you see it in the posture, the fascia, the skin tone. More subtly you notice changes in presentation, vitality, confidence and energy. When people start they look as if they are just hanging in there; by the end there is a sense of vitality and energy. It's very exciting.'

Re-educating Reflexes

INTEGRATION THERAPY

WHAT IS IT?   A system that aims to retrain the central nervous system via a series of exercises.

USED FOR   A host of problems: from headaches, migraine, shoulder tension and back pain, to fears, phobias, lack of confidence, dyslexia, depression and poor concentration.

SUITABLE FOR   Can be very useful for children with developmental problems. Also adults, particularly those suffering fears and phobias.

NOT SUITABLE FOR   The few people whose reflexes are quite perfectly developed.

PERFORMED   Fully clothed.

ANYTHING TO TAKE ORALLY?   No.

STRESSBUSTER Yes, one of its major claims – albeit over a period of time.

COST High.

NUMBER OF SESSIONS REQUIRED Approximately twelve to fifteen months of treatment for children; slightly more for adults. Sessions are usually at six-weekly intervals.

DIY Series of exercises to be performed daily at home.

IF YOU LIKE THIS, TRY OSTEOPATHY might suit. Osteopaths, particularly those who practise cranial work, believe in re-programming reflexes and could offer a less structured approach.

Integration therapy claims to stress-proof your world. Its therapists believe they can alter your life both physically and emotionally, not only by removing back pain and tension, easing headaches and migraine, but also by removing anxiety attacks and bouts of depression. This is one of the few therapies that actually professes to cure lack of confidence, banish shyness and conquer phobias. It is also used to help children who are hyperactive, dyslexic, clumsy or unco-ordinated, asthmatic, fearful or highly strung.

The history

The work started in the 1960s when American neurologists researching our balance mechanism became convinced that malfunctions were the root cause of stress. British researchers who took up the baton included Dr Peter Blythe, at the Institute of Neurophysiological Psychology in Chester, and Roger Bennett, who in 1985 set up the Institute for Developmental Potential to conduct further research. Out of this grew what Bennett calls integration therapy, a comprehensive process of testing followed by treatment to correct imbalances in the central nervous system by teaching it to replace baby reflexes with adult reflexes.

189

The lowdown

Psychologists would argue that the root cause of conditions such as depression and shyness lies in the dark depths of our subconscious, in early childhood experiences and long-submerged traumas. Stress, they would say, is simply a fact of modern life. Integration therapists think otherwise. They are totally convinced that a vast array of behavioural difficulties and stress-related problems are firmly grounded in the physical – that most of our psychological problems can be blamed, not on our parents or the strains of urban living, but on our central nervous system.

It all comes down to reflexes. Basically, a reflex is an action that occurs automatically in response to a certain stimulus, generally quite independently of our will. Each reflex – and there are countless numbers – is controlled by the central nervous system. Many are inborn – we shiver if it's cold, and our pupils contract if exposed to bright light – and they stay with us all our lives. But, as babies, we have a set of reflexes specifically designed to get us through the first months of life and, once that time is passed, those reflexes should gradually disappear, to be replaced by a more adult coping mechanism.

Integration therapy says that many of our problems occur because (generally due to a less than perfect, natural birth) the primitive baby reflexes simply do not disappear. And, if the baby reflex stays in place, there is no room for the adult reflex to take its place. We become stuck in an adult world, with the coping mechanism of a newly born baby. The problem, which apparently affects a large percentage of us to some degree, is called neuro-developmental delay.

For an example, take the reflex known as the Moro reflex. Watch any baby respond to a loud noise or alarming situation and it will fling out its arms and legs and throw back its head before it starts bawling – that is the Moro. By six months, the reflex should have gone but, unfortunately, the world is full of adults whose natural reaction to a shock is to throw out their arms and gasp or shriek. Although modified, it is still the Moro and it serves to keep us in a state of anticipatory anxiety. It's often the culprit behind fear of exams, of driving tests, of making a fool of yourself. It can be seen in people who feel threatened by situations, who are highly sensitive to light and sound, people who can easily be emotionally hurt and people who are terminally shy. There are often feelings of loneliness, lack of trust and even relationship difficulties.

If baby reflexes do not disappear and adult reflexes do not take their place there are still further knock-on effects: eye-movement problems can occur; balance problems can develop, leading to feelings of lack of confidence or insecurity; and, lastly, laterality (leftedness or rightedness) can be impaired, which can bring about severe learning difficulties in children and marked stress problems in adults.

Integration therapy uses a battery of tests to gauge reflexes and then utilizes precise exercises to coax adult reflexes to replace the outmoded childish responses. Results seem impressive: integration therapy has cured agoraphobics, conquered chronic shyness and blushing, and ameliorated everything from sleep disorders to low energy, low-back pain to depression, dyslexia to clumsiness. Unlike many other therapies, practitioners say, the results are permanent. Permanent, because this is a process of growing up – and, by its very nature, growing up is permanent.

The session

Integration therapy always starts with the filling in of a detailed questionnaire, which analyses whether or not you have central nervous system dysfunction. Most people send it in as a precursor to treatment, so the therapist can ascertain whether integration therapy would be suitable. One part deals with your personal history – your birth, childhood, schooltime experiences, adolescence – asking questions such as, 'Did you suffer car, coach or sea sickness as a child?' 'When playing ball games in the playground were you the "butterfingers" who missed or dropped the ball?' The second part looks at your feelings and attitudes now. The questions cover virtually all aspects of your physical, developmental and psychological life.

I visited Roger Bennett, who started his working life as a primary school teacher before retraining as a psychologist and psychotherapist. It was then that he came across the concept of neurodevelopmental delay and wondered whether he might see better results with his clients if he examined their neurological profile rather than their subconscious angst.

Integration therapy uses a sophisticated barrage of tests to look at your reflexes. After an hour with Bennett I felt like a performing monkey. He had me balancing on one leg and then asked me to close my eyes. I wobbled precariously. Next, I had to stand with one leg in front of the other. 'I'm checking your eyes, brain, muscles and balance – they are always firing messages to each other,' he explained. Eye exercises followed: mine veered all over the place. Then down onto the carpet on all fours: Bennett asked me to turn my head as far as I could in one direction and then in the opposite. He noted that, as I turned my head, my neck bent slightly and my arm straightened.

'You're very good at controlling your anger, aren't you?' he stated, 'and you probably have terrible neck and shoulder tension, grip a pen tightly and have a fear of heights. You also probably startle very easily.' All true, but how did he know? 'It's your reflexes,' he explained. 'You probably didn't crawl long enough to get your proper sense of balance.'

The upshot was that I have a whole battery of problems. I have two pronounced baby reflexes, a balance problem, eye-movement difficulties and, to cap it all, although I'm right-handed, apparently I am left-footed so I have impaired laterality to boot. 'Don't worry,' soothed Bennett, 'you're in good company. Most people have at least some difficulties.' He then taught me a few very gentle, slow and precise movements that I would need to perform every day for around twenty minutes. Back to childhood, back to homework: makes sense somehow.

Testing reflexes

The following questions form part of an extensive questionnaire compiled by the Institute for Developmental Potential. Answering positively to a large number of them does not automatically mean you have neurodevelopmental delay, but it could indicate problems with the central nervous system.

1. Was your birth unusual or difficult in any way (e.g. cord round neck, forceps, breech, Cesarean, cowl, prolonged labour)?

192

2. During the first few months did you have difficulty keeping food down? Did you have regular projectile vomiting accompanied by excessive screaming?

3. Were you early in learning to walk (i.e. before sixteen to eighteen months), and were you a 'bottom hopper' or did you crawl for just a short while before walking early?

4. When playing ball games in the playground or at games lessons, were you the 'butterfingers' who missed or dropped the ball?

5. If the teacher turned to you in class and asked you a question, did you hesitate even if you knew the answer, worried about getting it wrong? Do you still tend to plan what you will say or do before actually proceeding?

6. When you are a passenger in a car or coach, do you find it difficult to read a book while travelling?

7. Do you tend to overreact to sudden loud unexpected noises?

8. Do you experience frequent neck/shoulder tension or pain?

9. When you are very tired, do you tend to become clumsy or unco-ordinated?

10. Do you sometimes have problems differentiating between left and right? If directing someone using a street map, do you need to turn the map around to follow it successfully?

The Pressure Point Therapies

REFLEXOLOGY

WHAT IS IT?   An ancient technique of treating the whole body by pressing reflex points in the foot (or less commonly in the hand).

USED FOR   General health, particularly effective for digestive disorders; constipation; menstrual problems; stress and fatigue; migraines and skin conditions.

MOST SUITABLE FOR   Those who would like a lovely non-intrusive introduction to the bodywork side of natural health. Reflexology will get you accustomed to being touched in a thera-peutic way and will show you how effective touch can be. It's safe for children and even babies, in trained hands, and elderly people benefit greatly.

NOT SUITABLE FOR   Anyone who hates having their feet touched – reflexology isn't ticklish, but if your feet don't like being handled, forget it. Reflexologists are not supposed to treat specific diseases, although they can often combat a host of disorders by bringing the body back into balance.

PERFORMED   Fully clothed, except for feet.

ANYTHING TO TAKE ORALLY?   No.

STRESSBUSTER   Yes, can hit stress very effectively.

COST   Low to medium.

NUMBER OF SESSIONS REQUIRED   Varies enormously. Often the effect is cumulative and many people have weekly or fortnightly sessions over a long period of time.

DIY   You may be taught some simple techniques to carry out at home but, although there are many books on reflexology, it really is advisable to see a professional. The effects can be deep and you might inadvertently press the wrong point.

IF YOU LIKE THIS, TRY   If you find reflexology too painful, try MORRELL REFLEXOLOGY which works more energetically. META-MORPHIC TECHNIQUE also works on feet (and hands and head) but again works energetically. If you feel safe with your feet being touched and want to move further, trust yourself to a practitioner of SHIATSU or ACUPRESSURE – they will work with your whole body.

How can a simple touch on your toes affect your whole body? How can a treatment that seems little more than a foot massage possibly improve your health, kick-start your vitality and, above all, boost your self-confidence? Reflexologists are the first to admit that their method stretches the imagination to the limit, yet now even the most pragmatic doctors and surgeons are beginning to acknowledge the benefits of this most curious of therapies.

Reflexology is much much more than just a foot massage. It may look simple, but this ancient technique should be treated with deep respect: it can bring your whole body back into balance, and, practised properly, it can have deep, effective results on a large range of health issues. Not only is it great for your health but also, once you get used to having your feet prodded and poked, it is quite simply wonderfully relaxing. After a session, you will find yourself either bursting with energy or (in my case) so relaxed you feel an instant urge to hurl yourself into bed: the treatment works at the deepest levels of your body, clearing the channels so that the body can almost ask for what it needs. Another fascinating aspect of this therapy is its seemingly miraculous diagnostic powers. A skilled reflexologist could tell you your medical history and current woes, purely by feeling your feet. Unfortunately, however, according to law, reflexologists are not allowed to diagnose.

The history

The concept behind reflexology may sound bizarre and new-fangled but it's no new philosophy: over 5,000 years ago the Indians and Chinese were using a similar technique, and evidence suggests that the skill goes back further to ancient Egypt and even beyond. Pictographs found in a tomb of an Egyptian physician dating back to 2500–2330 BC show a man being given a form of reflexology. It is also a strong part of the traditions of many African tribes and Native Americans. Amongst the Native American tribes, the Cherokee say that, for centuries, they have understood the importance of the feet in maintaining balance in the body. Unfortunately, no-one thought to ask them about their techniques, or the Western world could have had the reflexology experience much earlier.

Instead, the Germans began to look at the treatment of disease with massage and developed techniques which became known as reflex massage. As with most therapies, there is a wonderful tale of how it all began: it runs that a Dr Alfons Cornelius was ill with an infection in 1893. During his convalescence at a health spa he had regular massages, and the masseur seemed to work longer on the areas that felt painful. Cornelius started feeling better, put two and two together and asked the masseur to concentrate solely on the painful bits. He recovered in record time and went on to use the treatment in his own practice.

However, it fell to Dr William Fitzgerald, an American ear, nose and throat specialist to really popularize a 'new' therapy, which he called Zone Therapy, in the Western world in 1902. He first realized the importance of pressure on parts of the body by watching how pain could be relieved during operations by pressure on certain areas of the body. He started to research the phenomenon and found that, by pressing firmly or massaging certain areas of the body, effects were noticed in other parts. This wasn't just confined to an anaesthetizing effect; healing appeared to follow too.

This was then developed by another American, Eunice Ingham, who concentrated almost totally on the feet: it became the reflexology we know today. A pupil of hers, Doreen Bayly, brought the treatment to the UK in 1966, and now it is flourishing. Reflexology is one of the best-known and loved of natural therapies. Many reflexologists now run practices alongside NHS clinics, and some hospitals use these services to help patients.

The lowdown

Fitzgerald divided the body into ten zones, from the head down to the toes and fingers. He taught that the body's essential energy flowed through these zones and ended up in reflex points in the feet and hands. The theory is similar to the Chinese concept of *chi* flowing along meridians. Six major meridians (those which cover the liver, spleen and pancreas, stomach, gall bladder, bladder and kidney) all end in the feet. The remaining six do not, but reflexologists who work on the concept of meridians explain that the meridian cycle is one continuous flow of energy; meridians are penetrated by other meridians and so, albeit maybe one step removed, all are grounded in the feet.

As the process became refined, reflexologists discovered that different areas of the foot and toes corresponded to different body systems: for example the big toe relates to the head and brain; the rest of the toes represent the sinuses; the lungs spread across the ball of the foot, while the lower back is down in the heel. By massaging the relevant point on the foot, the reflexologist is loosening tension and relieving blockages in the flow of energy to the corresponding body part of the system.

On a more general level, the massage works to stimulate blood circulation and the lymphatic system, increasing energy and helping with the process of elimination of toxins. The theory may sound fanciful until you realize that even orthodox medicine recognizes that the internal organs of the body are represented on the surface of the body, often in a quite different place but linked by the same nerve supplies. A pain in the left arm can warn of an imminent heart attack, while problems in the diaphragm can often present themselves as a pain in the shoulder tip. However, science is a long way from proving precisely how reflexology works.

Doctors are often sceptical, because reflexologists say they feel blockages in the form of crystallized nodules in the feet. It is breaking up these nodules that often causes the pain many people experience in reflexology. And yet no crystals have ever been found in post-mortems.

The session

I will put my feet into almost anyone's lap for a quick (or preferably long) foot massage, but I am very choosy when it comes to reflexologists. Why? Simply because, in my experience, reflexology can be very very painful. However, find a good practitioner who is willing to work within your pain threshold, and you're on to a winner. I try to make time for reflexology sessions at least once a month – they somehow clear away the debris and give me a renewed spring in my step.

Most introductory sessions last about an hour and a half and include a detailed consultation. The therapist will want to know all the usual details about your life and medical history – any past accidents and illnesses, any operations or recurring conditions. He or she will also quiz you on your lifestyle: your diet, exercise, any smoking or drinking, and your stress levels. If you are taking any medications, your therapist will need to know and you should also be sure to state if you are pregnant (certain points are not used during pregnancy). Mental illness is treated with caution as well: again, certain points have to be avoided or used with great care if treating anyone with psychosis or schizophrenia.

This over, you will be invited to take off your shoes and socks and bare your feet. Most people's first instinct is to apologize for their feet – don't worry, to a reflexologist your foot is not a horrible, calloused, smelly thing (although, please do wash your feet before you go): it is a guidebook to your body, an encyclopedia of knowledge just waiting to be opened up and read. Comfort is paramount. You generally take off any tight or restrictive clothing and sit (or more rarely lie) on a very comfortable reclining chair or couch. First, your feet are generally gently disinfected and the therapist will begin by gently stroking your feet to get you used to the touch and the therapist used to your feet.

Your feet are giving off all kinds of signals to the therapist even at this stage: she or he will be noticing their temperature and colour (cold feet could indicate poor circulation); the feel of them (dry skin might again be poor circulation, while sweating could indicate a glandular imbalance). Callouses, bunions, corns and irregular bones are also noted.

Then the practitioner will begin the examination, feeling the reflex points for any tenderness (do say if a particular point is sore – too many people suffer in silence) or for the crystal build-up that indicates stuck energy. Having felt the problems, the massage begins. Believe me, it isn't ticklish, it's too firm a touch for that. The therapist uses the thumb mainly to apply pressure to the reflex points. If an area is congested, it will feel sensitive, sometimes it feels as if you've had a sharp pin driven into your foot; at others as though you've got a bad bruise. Theoretically, treatment shouldn't be agony, it really shouldn't. But I've had more than a few painful sessions. However, quite equally, I have had plenty of wonderful sessions that were simply delightful, perfect pampering.

Some lucky souls find they literally bounce out of sessions, feeling totally rejuvenated. I generally find the opposite happens – I feel utterly relaxed and ready to curl up and sleep. But the next day I'm bouncing and raring to go. Another really common after-effect is that you will want to go to the toilet far more – the kidneys are stimulated, which naturally produces more urine. Equally, you may find you have more bowel movements, and the therapy may start to shift mucus. Also your skin may erupt in spots and pimples and you might perspire more. Sometimes your symptoms can even seem to get slightly worse. Don't be alarmed – your body is trying to throw out toxins and to get itself back into balance. If you are worried, however, get back in touch with your therapist and ask for advice.

MORRELL REFLEXOLOGY

WHAT IS IT?   A very gentle form of reflexology which uses massage, primarily to the feet. Morrell reflexology uses a particularly light touch.

USED FOR   Almost anything – from ME to frozen shoulder. Many people say it also helps them mentally, increasing self-confidence and relieving the ill-effects of grief and shock.

SUITABLE FOR   Everyone – from tiny babies to the elderly. However, great care is taken with pregnant women and people with psychosis.

NOT SUITABLE FOR   No contraindications, providing the practitioner is experienced and given a full medical history.

PERFORMED   With feet and ankles bare.

ANYTHING TO TAKE ORALLY?   No.

STRESSBUSTER   Very soothing and relaxing – some people find themselves in a quasi-meditative state afterwards.

COST   Medium.

NUMBER OF SESSIONS REQUIRED Varies. To begin with, treatments are once a week, usually swiftly tailing off.

DIY It is not advisable to practise any form of reflexology without formal training. Although it is generally safe, stimulating certain points could trigger miscarriage or overstimulate the brain which could be potentially dangerous for people with mental disorders or epilepsy.

IF YOU LIKE THIS, TRY If you love having your feet touched in a gentle way try the METAMORPHIC TECHNIQUE. For a complete change but still on a foot theme, look at CHAVUTTI THIRUMAL, an all-over body massage which is performed with the masseur's feet!

If you find standard reflexology difficult to grasp, then Morrell reflexology will really bend your mind. Practitioners hardly deal with the physical body at all and concentrate on feeling for disturbances in the energetic field surrounding the body and then treating them at a highly subtle level.

The history

Morrell reflexology uses the same reflexes as traditional reflexology and follows its basic philosophy. However, the original heavy pressure is replaced with an extremely light touch. It came into being just under ten years ago as a result of reflexologist Patricia Morrell's soft heart. Hating to inflict pain on her patients, she felt instinctively that there had to be a better way.

'I realized that the very act of touching the foot was affecting all the cells in the body,' she says, 'and I started to think that the talk about breaking down the crystals in the foot [crystals of uric acid which traditional reflexology says need to be broken down to stimulate the nerve endings] didn't really hold together.' She thought that something else had to be going on and began to think in terms of affecting a person not just on a gross physical level but on a more subtle, energetic level. She discovered that, by employing a soft, gentle touch, she not only made her patients more comfortable but, surprisingly, the results were even better than before. 'They were extraordinary,' says Morrell.

201

The lowdown

Reflexology teaches that every part of the body, from head to toes, heart to gall bladder, is mapped out in miniature on the feet. By touching the correct reflex point on the foot you can affect the corresponding organ, gland or area of the body. Although it sounds far-fetched, it does seem to work and reflexologists have had remarkable success with a wide range of ailments.

However, unfortunately, reflexology has suffered from having a reputation as being painful. Many traditional reflexologists can use up to 5.4 kg/12 lb of pressure per square inch and can easily dig into tender toes and knead thin-fleshed soles into sheer agony. Although not all reflexologists are quite so brutal and most would insist that a good reflexology treatment should *never* hurt, Morrell reflexology with its insistence on no pain is a distinctly welcome addition. It promises all the good effects and more – without any of the agony.

When Patricia Morrell started to lighten her touch she discovered she wasn't just getting the same results; they were better. The treatments weren't just relieving stress and making people feel relaxed, Morrell found she could have a profound effect on even the most mechanical of problems. While other practitioners said reflexology surely couldn't treat anything like a dislocated shoulder, Morrell disagreed. 'If we can go right into organs [through the reflexes], we can go right into a shoulder. Why shouldn't we adjust it?,' she reasoned. 'If we can't do it, then reflexology is a fake.' Since then, she has successfully treated dislocated knees and shoulders and even a crack at the base of the coccyx.

Other reflexologists soon heard about her work and asked to be taught her gentle technique. Now, there are two schools teaching Morrell reflexology and around 150 practitioners in the UK. Practitioners of the Morrell technique say that this new way of using reflexology provides the missing link. Sue Ricks, a practitioner and trainer in the technique puts it like this: 'We are a vibrational body and, by working on the outer edges of the foot the impact affects all levels of our being. It's like dropping a pebble into a lake and watching the ripples spread deeper and deeper.' In other words, instead of merely affecting the physical, Morrell reflexology balances, not just our physical body, but also its more subtle energy fields. It's a little like massaging your very essence.

Patricia Morrell adds that, by working so subtly, the practitioner becomes very intuitive, almost telepathic. 'It's as if there were a higher sort of intelligence that knows everything that is wrong with the person. When you work at a certain level you start to pick up this information.' She calls one of her patients the 'custard lady' because of a bizarre instance of this intelligence. A woman had come complaining of severe migraines and, after several treatments and a revised diet, they had quite vanished. Then one day the woman returned in agony: the migraine had returned. Morrell asked her whether she had eaten anything untoward and the patient said emphatically no. Yet, as Morrell worked on her foot, she found the liver area was very soft and she received the distinct impression it was connected with sugar. Suddenly it came in a flash: 'It was instant custard,' Morrell said. 'You ate instant custard which you've never had before. That's what did it.' The woman was stunned – Morrell was perfectly accurate.

The diagnostic powers of reflexology have always been uncanny, but the traditional technique usually depends on the patient indicating where there is pain before the practitioner can diagnose. In the Morrell method, the patient just lies back and enjoys the ride leaving the practitioner to feel the problem. Morrell says she can even tell if a woman is pregnant by feeling her foot – she says there is an almost magnetic feel.

However, just because it is so gentle does not mean that this treatment is not powerful. Morrell is keen to point out that, in untrained hands, even this subtle form of reflexology could potentially be dangerous. She is concerned that lay people might try to learn reflexology from a book or from a weekend course and then simply jump in. Trained practitioners insist on a detailed medical history and will treat certain people – in particular those with mental disorders and pregnant women – with very great care. 'We do treat psychotic patients but only with their own psychiatrist close at hand. If you didn't know what you were doing, you could make them suicidal or murderous. And we are very careful with pregnancy: you don't touch certain points at all for the first three months,' she says. 'If a pregnancy wasn't very stable it could have bad effects. Also, if you were to plunge into the pituitary point it would produce hormonal changes, so you have to be careful.'

However, pregnant women can derive huge benefits from the Morrell touch. Back pain is alleviated, and the babies of women having regular treatment are always calmer, gentler, more confident and less aggressive.

The medical profession is beginning to take notice of Morrell's work. An initial trial at hospitals in Cardiff yielded impressive results. Five reflexologists worked with two sets of patients: those in the trauma unit and those who had had replacement hips and knees. The trial looked at joint flexion, length of stay in hospital and need for medication: it concluded that patients having the reflexology all went home from three to five days earlier and needed less medication. The surgeon involved was thrilled with the result, not least because it represented a huge saving for the NHS. Now funding has been obtained for a longer, stricter controlled trial.

Both Morrell and Ricks have wonderful stories of incredible recoveries: of an ME patient who came in a wheelchair and left on her own two feet; of a baby needing bowel surgery who escaped the surgeon's knife; of the man who went into spasm and responded instantly to their gentle touch.

Despite such results, practitioners are modest about their skills. They are keen to work with the medical profession and would love a greater chance to use their diagnostic skills and procedures to help more patients but, as Morrell points out, 'We are not gods, we don't think we have all the answers.' However, they certainly have quite a few.

The session

Just lying back on the thickly padded treatment chair was relaxing enough. Patricia Morrell asked for my medical history and took a detailed case history before asking whether there was anything in particular I needed addressing. Then she took my feet in her hands and looked, just looked. 'The visual aspect is very important,' she explained. 'Looking at your toes, there is a problem with your neck and shoulders, and your lower back looks unhappy. Your jaw is not perfect and you've got vulnerable sinuses. Also your knees are a little weak.' Ten out of ten: I've always had weak knees and have a congenital problem with my jaw. Colds hit me in the sinuses and, hunched all day over a computer, I inevitably have neck and shoulder tension and odd twinges in the lower back. Although Morrell could have guessed the latter, knowing what I do, I found the other diagnoses uncannily accurate.

Then she took my feet in her hands – it was like being sent to Heaven first-class. I lay back, surrendered my soul and sank into bliss. It feels as if her hands are gently questioning your feet and your whole body is replying in some language you cannot quite hear. As she stroked and gently pressed, I felt nerves tingling in my head, my shoulders, my back.

But perhaps the greatest benefit of all is not physical, but psychological. I left Morrell and Ricks feeling like a three-year-old who had spent an hour being cuddled by its mum. The sensation of deep relaxation and profound peace lasted for several days.

Regular sessions go even deeper and, says Morrell, many patients find their lives subtly change. Self-confidence often improves, people find they can suddenly tackle difficult situations, have the confidence to go for a new job, even the ability to say no to friends and family.

ACUPRESSURE/SHIATSU

WHAT IS IT?   The use of pressure on acupuncture points to stimulate and rebalance the body's energy.

USED FOR   Stressbusting, all kinds of emotional and mental tension. Many chronic conditions such as back pain, migraine, rheumatic and arthritic conditions, asthma, insomnia, sciatica, constipation and even impotence can benefit greatly.

SUITABLE FOR   With an experienced practitioner, everyone can benefit. Particularly useful for stress relief.

NOT SUITABLE FOR   An experienced practitioner can treat most people, although treatment would be modified in pregnancy, in the existence of any tumour activity and problematic joints.

PERFORMED   If acupressure is incorporated into massage or other techniques, you may be asked to remove clothing and have treatment on a couch. Shiatsu is always performed fully clothed, generally lying on the floor.

ANYTHING TO TAKE ORALLY?   No. Some practitioners give advice on diet.

STRESSBUSTER   Yes, wonderfully relaxing. A supreme stress-buster.

COST   Low to medium.

NUMBER OF SESSIONS REQUIRED   Many people have regular (once a week or once a month) sessions to keep their energy balanced.

DIY   Yes, you may well be given stretching exercises to practise at home or be shown certain points for home use. Some practitioners may also advise on diet and exercise.

IF YOU LIKE THIS, TRY   JIN SHIN JYUTSU also comes from the same root. ZERO BALANCING is an interesting alternative from a different perspective. TRADITIONAL CHINESE MEDICINE works well alongside this therapy.

Acupressure is generally known as acupuncture without the needles. So, if the idea of turning yourself into a human pincushion turns you green but you still love the idea of balancing your body's energy via pressure on the acupoints and meridians, then acupressure is perfect for you. It can be gentle enough to be used on even the smallest babies or the frailest of elderly people, and yet its effects are undeniably powerful.

Acupressure can vary enormously according to who gives it to you. When I was living in London I had regular acupressure massages from a wonderful Westerner who combined acupressure with aromatherapy – I used to walk out on air. However when I had 'Chinese therapeutic massage', sometimes also called Tui Na, from a Chinese practitioner, it was totally different: much deeper and more 'medical'. Many beauty therapists now use elements of acupressure in facials to relax and tone the muscles of the face – a kind of facelift without surgery.

Shiatsu is more dynamic in its approach. I think of it as passive yoga – your body is stretched into wonderful positions without you having to do a thing. And, of course, you don't even have to take your clothes off for shiatsu, which is a bonus if you feel uncomfortable with normal massage.

The history

Acupressure is old, very old – a form of it has been practised for perhaps over 5,000 years. Although its origins are hidden in the mists of ancient time, it is thought to have originated in India and then come to Central Asia, Egypt and China. But it was the Chinese who took the system and made it their own.

In *Acupressure* (Headway), which is a useful introduction to the therapy, Eliana Harvey and Mary Jane Oatley tell a delightful legend of how the Chinese came to understand the power of pressure points. Apparently, extraordinary beings, known as the 'Sons of Reflected Light' arrived in China around 10,000 BC. These beings were seven feet tall and great healers who founded incredible healing schools. Their most amazing feat was their ability to see both the aura and the meridians of people, with the acupoints showing up as tiny points of light. These strange healers could literally 'see' what was wrong with the body and its energy field, and they healed by directing their own life force at the sick person from several feet away. The authors surmise that, over the centuries, this sensitivity and power was gradually lost and, as the healers needed to work closer with the body, they started to use pressure: at first they used pressure from their fingertips; eventually they graduated to the needles of acupuncture. While acupuncture became the medicine of the nobility, acupressure became the province of more intuitive healers who travelled from village to village offering basic medical knowledge and the power of acupressure. They were known as the 'barefoot practitioners'.

Shiatsu came to Japan around the sixth century AD when Buddhism was introduced to that country. Delegations went from Japan to China to bring back learning and, in particular, the Chinese skills in medicine. Inevitably, the practices changed subtly over the years, and the Japanese tradition, although always close to that of China, took on its own characteristics.

One interesting footnote in the shiatsu story came during the Edo Period (1603–1868), during which it was decreed that massage as a profession should be taken up by people who were blind, as they had such developed powers of touch. However, sadly, massage, known as *anma*, became devalued by this measure. Blind practitioners could not follow the other forms of medicine, which primarily involved the prescription of herbs, and so massage slowly became less highly regarded – a poor person's health system. Until 1919. Then a revival came about, fostered by the publication of a book called *Shiatsu Ho* by Tamai Tempaku, a practitioner of various massage forms who was also well versed in Western anatomy, physiology and massage. His adaptation of the traditional Japanese massage technique became popular. Others took up the baton, and one of his students, Tokujiro Namikoshi, established an Institute for Shiatsu in 1925. In 1964, shiatsu was recognized as a therapy in its own right.

The lowdown

Acupressure and shiatsu work in very much the same way as acupuncture, by stimulating the pressure points and so allowing the correct flow of *chi* or *ki* (vital energy) throughout the body. By stimulating the pressure points (acupoints), therapists say that, physiologically, they are able to shift and diffuse the lactic acid and carbon monoxide that tend to accumulate in muscle tissue. It is this, they say, that causes stiffness in the muscles and a general sluggishness in the blood. In turn, this stiffness and sluggishness puts pressure on the nerves, the blood and lymph vessels which, again, then affects the bone system and the internal organs. However, most acupressurists look on their therapy in less medical terms – they think in terms of easing the energetic system of the body. By clearing blockages in points, the meridians (or lines of energy that run through the body) are able to flow clearly – much like smooth-running traffic on a motorway, rather than the clogged congestion of a traffic jam in the city.

The session

All acupressure and shiatsu sessions start with a case history to make sure that the practitioner can adapt the treatment to your precise problems. Some masseurs simply use acupressure as part of their standard massage or incorporate it into an aromatherapy or therapeutic massage. In this case, you can expect to take your clothes off and lie on a couch, covered by towels. Such practitioners will usually follow a set pattern of points to either relax or revitalize you. If you are being treated by a practitioner with

Chinese medical training, the treatment will be more intense. Your pulses will probably be taken, as in an acupuncture session, and you may well be asked to show your tongue. Generally, you will be asked to undress and lie on a couch while the practitioner works along specific meridians and on specific points. In my experience, this kind of acupressure can be very deep and, on occasions, quite painful. But you do get a wonderful sense of release.

Shiatsu, on the other hand, almost always follows a set pattern. First, you will be asked for a full case history. Then your pulses will probably be taken and you will be asked to lie down on a mat. Here, the therapist will palpate (diagnosis by touch) your back and abdomen. *Hara* diagnosis, as it is known, is a fundamental part of shiatsu – the *hara* is the abdominal area which can be read almost like a map. Just as a reflexologist can tell about your health by touching your feet, so a shiatsu practitioner can gain vital information by the feel of your *hara*. This, together with the case history, gives him or her the information needed to decide on your treatment.

The shiatsu practitioner's aim is to free the meridians so that your energy (known in Japan as *ki*) flows smoothly and clearly. However, shiatsu uses stretches to stimulate or soothe the whole length of the meridian as well as concentrating on individual points. Expect to find yourself being moved and held in various positions, not just with the therapist's hands but also with their elbows and arms, feet and knees. Every so often, you get a wonderful sense of 'that's it' when a muscle or joint frees up. Sometimes it's subtle; sometimes your whole body seems to be creaking, cracking and groaning. Your entire body will be worked on – after the large body stretches, the therapist will often use long, slow pressure on points along individual meridians. Again, it's not uncommon for old thoughts and memories to be released although, personally, I find this happens less with shiatsu than with other forms of bodywork.

JIN SHIN JYUTSU

WHAT IS IT? A Japanese system of bodywork which works on 'energy locks' in the body, allowing energy to flow freely.

USED FOR A wide variety of ailments. It has been particularly successful in cases of ME. Also helps depression, asthma and digestive problems.

SUITABLE FOR Everyone. Children react well to it, particularly those who are hyperactive or autistic. Great for anyone who feels lacking in energy.

NOT SUITABLE FOR No contraindications.

PERFORMED Fully clothed, except for shoes and jewellery.

ANYTHING TO TAKE ORALLY No, although practitioners often advise on diet.

STRESSBUSTER Yes.

COST Medium.

NUMBER OF SESSIONS REQUIRED   Around four to six, plus homework.

DIY   Lots of homework – around ninety minutes of exercise a day for best results.

IF YOU LIKE THIS, TRY   The other Eastern bodywork systems of SHIATSU and ACUPRESSURE. If the idea of balancing vital energy appeals, you could try ACUPUNCTURE.

Jin Shin Jyutsu is hardly a household name. This Japanese bodywork system is hardly known in the UK and, until recently, there was only one practitioner. Now, that is changing as more people become fascinated by this Eastern cousin to acupressure and shiatsu.

Roselyn Journeaux brought the therapy to the UK after finding that it cured her of ME, a virus that affects the mid-brain, muscles and nerves. She had been disabled for over three and a half years: confined to a wheelchair, and even the slightest task such as peeling potatoes left her totally exhausted. By chance, she stumbled across Jin Shin Jyutsu and, after just one treatment, her life began to change. After her first session, she was able to get up and make a cup of tea for the first time in years. Ten weeks later, she had left her wheelchair behind and was so impressed that she decided to study the healing system for herself.

The history

The history of Jin Shin Jyutsu is hard to discover. All that seems clear is that the system developed either side by side with, or out of, the Chinese traditions of working with the body's internal energy flow – the *chi* (known in Japan as *ki*). However, Jin Shin does not follow the meridians of Chinese medicine but works on another level of pathways between the various organs. The art had almost been lost back in its native land, but there are numerous practitioners in the USA, Germany and France. Now, doctors in Japan are being taught the system and it is returning home.

The lowdown

Jin Shin Jyutsu works, like other Eastern systems such as acupuncture and acupressure, by balancing and harmonizing the body's vital energy. Its difference, however, lies in its theory of 'safety energy locks'. The locks, of which there are twenty-six on each side of the body, are unseen regulators of our body's energy; they act almost like gears in a car. When the body is under strain, the locks can become congested and sore: the aim of Jin Shin is to clear the locks so the energy can flow freely and the body can be helped back to optimum health. When we are assaulted by stress or pollution, the locks in our bodies become jammed and – rather like traffic lights stuck on red – our vital energy becomes congested, it just can't get through. The result, if the stresses continue, is the equivalent of a city-wide traffic jam throughout our bodies. Jin Shin goes in like a traffic-light electrician, clearing the locks, re-circuiting the body and allowing the energy to flow smoothly and freely once more.

It sounds fanciful, and practitioners cannot physiologically explain exactly what an energy lock consists of, but the curious thing is that you *can* feel them. When a Jin Shin practitioner gently holds particular points on your body, you can feel distinct tenderness. Sometimes practitioners say they can even feel a slight swelling. Whereas the medical profession are alarmed at high blood pressure and generally unconcerned about low blood pressure, the Jin Shin practitioner would not be happy until the blood pressure was quite normal.

Some of the theory of Jin Shin is decidedly strange. Practitioners will ask you at what age you had illnesses and accidents, because the age apparently indicates underlying weaknesses. Equally, they will say that different complaints are linked to different life issues: stiffness in the joints would indicate not allowing yourself to move; asthma relates to grief as does eczema and, to a degree, cancer. Asthmatics need to learn to receive more from people, instead of always giving. Rheumatism and arthritis are said to be connected to stubbornness, and throat problems indicate that you are not saying what you really think. It's an interesting theory and one that echoes in the New Age teachings of 'positive thinkers' such as Louise Hay, whose books *You Can Heal Your Life* and *Love*

Your Body, Heal Your Life (Eden Grove) link specific illnesses and ailments with particular character traits.

However weird its philosophy, Jin Shin does seem to have profound effects and, perhaps fortunately, it is not necessary to believe in the background theory to benefit from the treatment. Grateful clients sing the praises of Jin Shin for conditions as varied as depression, hiatus hernia, asthma and autism. Some practitioners even claim to have had success with cancer, and one patient has been cleared of 'fairly large lung tumours' to the amazement of her doctors. Research is being carried out in Belgium on its effects on children with leukaemia.

Like many other complementary health practitioners, those who give Jin Shin Jyutsu don't claim to *cure* anything: they say that what they do is harmonize the body and allow the body to heal itself. One hundred per cent perfect, brilliant health is the aim. Most of us, they say, quietly potter along, grateful to feel 50 per cent, or even 80 per cent. Not good enough, is their reply. With pure balance in your body, life should be a joy to live.

Unlike many other therapies, the philosophy of Jin Shin is very much DIY. Each patient is given a self-help programme to practise each day, and patients are encouraged to take responsibility for their new healthy lifestyle, backing up the Jin Shin with good diet, regular exercise and lymphatic drainage. Ninety minutes of home-help Jin Shin should sort out all your problems, say practitioners: your eyesight might improve; colds and flu will be consigned to memory; skin and hair will look healthier; and bowel movements will become more regular. Maybe, just maybe, your weight might balance itself out.

The session

The treatment starts like any complementary health discipline, with a detailed case history. Journeaux takes particular notice of the age that accidents and illnesses occur because, she explains, the age at which you became ill can affect different organs in the body. Having listened to my history (which predominantly involves careless accidents and bouts of bronchitis) she suggested, rather surprisingly, that she would probably have to work on my liver.

She then asked whether I suffered problems with my eyes (I do), whether I have weak knees (I have) and whether I slept lightly with vivid dreams (my nightlife is so active that it puts the days to shame). 'It's like being a detective,' she says to explain her curious accuracy. 'You might have ten symptoms which can all be linked to one safety energy lock. You have to link the symptoms.'

As I lay fully clothed (except for shoes and watch) on her couch she took my pulses. Jin Shin teaches the practitioner to listen, not only to the blood pulse but also the *ki* pulse, the subtle pulse of the organs and even the sound of the locks.

Having decided which locks were blocked, she then put one hand on a certain point of my body while the other reached to another point. The effect, she says, is like that of a car battery with jump leads: 'You are acting as a cable for the circuit to clear.' Once she felt the pulses in the two areas synchronize, she moved on, covering perhaps eight or ten pairs of locks.

Hauling myself off the couch forty-five minutes later, I felt very tired and a little disappointed to find that the headache I arrived with had still not dissipated. Journeaux pressed more points in my feet and the pain momentarily lifted, but then quite swiftly returned.

To get the true benefits of Jin Shin, she says, I would need to see her perhaps four to six times and, in addition, I would have to follow a stringent hour and a half self-help routine at home. Then, she promises, I would lose the headaches.

DIY – how to beat jet lag

Jin Shin Jyutsu has a host of home exercises. Some are so simple you can do them on the bus, watching television, anywhere.

The following is a simple exercise to help balance your internal organs – it will also help with jet lag.

Hold the thumb of your left hand with the fingers of your right hand and wait until you feel a steady pulse. It might take a few minutes but you will feel it eventually. Once you feel the pulse, do the same thing, holding on to the index finger of your left hand – again until you feel the pulse. Keep going, working your way through all the fingers, and then swap over and do the same thing with the right hand. The whole exercise should take around twenty minutes and should be done every day for maximum effect.

The Massage Therapies

AROMATHERAPY

WHAT IS IT?   The use of oils extracted from plants for healing. Essential oils are most usually used in massage, baths and inhalation, although medically qualified aromatherapists can also give the oils internally.

USED FOR   A wide variety of conditions. It is a powerful anti-stress treatment, deeply relaxing. Skin conditions respond well, the immune system can be strengthened, and it is useful for muscular pains; rheumatism; sinusitis; depression; anxiety; high and low blood pressure.

SUITABLE FOR   The deeply stressed. Anyone who wants an experience of sheer bliss!

NOT SUITABLE FOR   Some oils cannot be used during pregnancy.

PERFORMED The massage is generally performed with just your pants left on. However, most of your body remains covered by towels during treatment.

ANYTHING TO TAKE ORALLY? Very few practitioners would ask you to take essential oils internally – it can be very dangerous unless very carefully monitored.

STRESSBUSTER Perhaps the ultimate quick-fix stress buster; regular aromatherapy will certainly help with the effects of stress, if not catching the cause.

COST Varies enormously. Low to medium.

NUMBER OF SESSIONS REQUIRED Regular aromatherapy massage is ideal – every week is perfect. But even the odd massage will work wonders.

DIY Using essential oils very diluted in baths or for massage can safely be carried out at home, providing you use the right oils. If in any doubt, always check with a qualified aromatherapist.

IF YOU LIKE THIS, TRY Any of the other forms of massage for a different form of bodywork. If you want to take the therapeutic use of herbs further look at HERBALISM or the herbal traditions within TRADITIONAL CHINESE MEDICINE or AYURVEDA.

What can be more delicious than the combination of sweet-smelling oils and a deep, relaxing massage? Aromatherapy is the sybarite's natural first step into the supertherapies. But don't be deceived by its sweet smells and gentle exterior: aromatherapy is powerful medicine. Essential oils were some of the original medicines used by doctors in former times. They can treat quite serious complaints, from high blood pressure to chronic migraines. And the effects don't stop at physiological – the smell of essential oils can have profound effects on your mood and emotions as well.

The history

Essential oils have a long and respected history dating back at least as far as ancient Egypt. The Egyptians used aromatic oils in mummification, and pots of scented unguents were found in King Tutankhamen's tomb. In Tel-el-Amana, piles of aromatic herbs were burned in public places to purify the air and people perfumed themselves with animal fat mixed with aromatic oils. The Greeks took over the practice of this early aromatherapy, and Hippocrates, writing in the fourth century BC, said, 'the way to health is to have an aromatic bath and scented massage every day.' Given the money, I would certainly follow his advice – after all, it's hardly a miserable prescription for health. He recognized that burning certain aromatic oils offered protection against contagious diseases. Now, we know that they work because they have anti-bacterial and anti-viral properties.

By the seventeenth century, oils were used as a part of everyday medicine but, like their cousin herbalism, the use declined with the advent of modern chemical preparations.

Modern aromatherapy in the form we know it today originated in France with the research of René Maurice Gattefosse, a chemist working in his family's perfume factory. Gattefosse burned his hand in a laboratory explosion one day and plunged it into the nearest container, which was full of pure lavender oil. The hand healed in hours with no sign of scarring or infection. From here, he developed the use of essential oils in dermatology. His findings came out in a paper published in 1928 called *Aromatherapie* and, hence, the name was born.

About 300 essential oils are in use today. Aromatherapy is mostly synonymous with its divine form of massage, but if it's used in its fuller form, can be a highly effective and potent treatment for a wide range of illnesses and diseases. Aromatherapy oils are now freely available in chemists and health shops. But, although they can be used for DIY, extreme care should be taken. These are highly potent medicines and can be extremely toxic if taken in the wrong way or in incorrect amounts.

The lowdown

Essential oils are extracted from varieties of trees, shrubs, herbs, grasses and flowers. It can be a lengthy and expensive process, which accounts for the high prices of some oils. It takes sixty thousand rose blossoms to produce one ounce of rose oil. Lavender has more oil, and one hundred kilos can provide three kilos of oil.

The oils work directly on the chemistry of the body: an essential oil contains on average one hundred chemical components – terpenes, alcohols, aldehydes, ketones, and phenols. They are powerful substances: for instance, the essential oil of oregano is twenty-six times more powerful as an antiseptic than the active ingredients in many commercial cleansing materials.

Chemists now know that essential oils have myriad functions: they can be antibacterial and antifungal, antiseptic, anti-inflammatory, antineuralgic, antirheumatic, antispasmodic, antivenomous, antitoxic, antidepressant, sedative, nervine, analgesic, hypotensol, hypertensol, digestive, expectorating, deodorizing, granulation-stimulating, circulation-stimulating, diuretic etc. Not bad for substances that most people simply think have a nice pong.

They are particularly useful therapeutically because they enter and leave the body with great efficiency, leaving no toxins behind. The most effective way to take them is by external application or inhalation – body compresses, lotions, baths, inhalation, room sprays. Unlike chemical drugs, the oils do not appear to stay in the body but are excreted through urine, faeces, perspiration and exhalation. Expulsion takes up to six hours in a healthy body and up to fourteen hours in an obese or unhealthy body.

Although it is clear that essential oils work in a direct way on the body's physiology, they also have more subtle effects. Scent works powerfully on mood – olfactory nerves connect to the limbic system of the brain which regulates our sexual urge and our emotional behaviour. It also affects memory – in France there are psychoanalysts who use fragrance to bring out the hidden memories of their patients.

Several oils act as adaptogens, natural balancers of the body. Hyssop, for example, will normalize blood pressure, whether it is high or low; peppermint will either stimulate or relax, depending on what your body needs.

The session

A good aromatherapist will always take your case history and ask quite detailed questions about your health – past and present. If you have sensitive skin, problems with blood pressure or epilepsy, your aromatherapist will need to know. In particular, it is very important to inform the therapist if you are pregnant: certain oils are not used during pregnancy because they can induce miscarriage.

Most aromatherapists will use massage as the most effective way to get the oils into the body. Essential oils in the pure state are too highly concentrated to be used directly on the skin. Base oils (generally vegetable, nut or seed oils) are therefore used to dilute the oils.

The aromatherapist will then choose the oils. If you have no specific health problems, general relaxing oils are usually picked. Some aromatherapists work on the more esoteric theory that your body will know precisely what it needs and will ask you to smell a selection of oils and pick out the ones you like. However, many will look at your symptoms and problems and choose oils on a strictly therapeutic basis.

Aromatherapy is a discreet form of massage – you won't be expected to lie stark naked on the floor or couch. The therapist will usually leave the room for a few minutes and ask you to get undressed and put yourself on the couch, where you will be covered by a towel. Some people strip right off: I always personally like to keep my knickers on for modesty's sake!

Each aromatherapist has a different way of working, but a full-body massage usually includes plenty of time devoted to that key stress-holding area, the shoulders and neck. Most will include hand and foot massage and often your face will be included – oils can be wonderful for cosmetic purposes and most beauty salons will now offer an aromatherapy facial.

Many aromatherapists have also learned massage techniques which are therapeutic in their own right. It's far from uncommon to have acupressure or shiatsu techniques incorporated into the massage. Some practitioners have studied TCM practices and will choose particular oils because of their *yin* or *yang* properties – they may go very deeply into the underlying causes of your illness or stress. A good aromatherapist will not stop with oils. He or she will probe into your lifestyle in far greater detail. Changes in diet may well be advised and often you will be encouraged to take up exercise if you do not already do so. Other advice might well include taking up DIY self-hypnosis or creative visualization with tapes.

And, although massage is the commonest form of treatment, you might be given compresses to help with bruising, muscle pains and skin disorders or sent home with oils for inhaling (to clear coughs and colds, bronchial or sinus problems, headaches) or to use in baths. Your therapist might also recommend you use oils in a burner to spread the scent around the room. On the herbal front, herbal teas or supplements are often prescribed and patients are encouraged to introduce herbs into cooking.

So, it's hard to say what a typical session is like. It all depends on the aromatherapist. The best thing to do is decide what you want – whether it's simply a relaxing massage or a more complete form of holistic care – and check with the aromatherapy societies about which practitioner would best suit your needs.

The scented home – introducing DIY aromatherapy

Be very wary of essential oils. I can't say often enough how dangerous these wonderful therapeutics can be if not treated with care and respect. Follow instructions very carefully and never be tempted to put neat oil on the skin or take oils internally unless you have been specifically instructed by a medically qualified aromatherapist. However, there are some oils that every home should have . . .

LAVENDER

If you buy only one oil, make it lavender. It smells delicious and has a host of other properties. It's a natural antiseptic and is indispensable for soothing burns. Plus it's a wonderful anti-depressant and a great help in insomnia. A few drops of lavender in your bedtime bath (make sure the water isn't too hot) will help you relax. A few drops on your pillow will send you sweet dreams.

Scatter lavender bags liberally amongst clothes – they help to keep away moths. And if your dog suffers from fleas, try making your own natural flea collar. Mix one teaspoon of vegetable oil with one drop each of lavender, cedarwood, citronella and thyme. Add half a teaspoon of alcohol (e.g. brandy). Soak a soft material collar in the mixture and pop it on your pet. Some recipes say a couple of capsules of garlic added to the mix will give better protection. Re-soak the collar every month.

TEA TREE

I'm not quite sure how I coped before tea tree oil appeared in my life. Next to lavender, it's the one I use the most. A powerful anti-septic, I reach for tea tree the instant I feel a cold coming on. A few drops in a hot bath (along with a couple of drops of black pepper oil if you've got it) will often stop a cold in its tracks. In addition, I put it in an oil burner in my office to stave off germs.

It's also a subtle way of stopping colds spreading. If your visitors do that 'I do hope I don't give you my cold' routine, then simply put an oil burner in the room or, if you don't have one, a bowl of hot water with a few drops in it will help to antibacterialize the room. In addition, inhale it for catarrh and sinusitis and use it in a very dilute wash for acne or for those stubborn spots that appear round your nose and chin before your periods.

Another handy use for this wonderful oil is to build up strength before surgery. Pop it in your bath for the weeks prior to an operation: you're likely to find that healing is swifter and scarring not so bad.

ROSEMARY

Rosemary is the prime stimulating oil, an excellent tonic for the heart, liver and gall bladder. It also helps to lower cholesterol levels in the blood. Use it in a steam inhalation to ease colds, catarrh and sinusitis: add a few drops to a bowl of very hot water, then breathe in the fumes by putting your head over the bowl, using a towel to make a tent over your head and the bowl. Even asthma will often benefit.

If you suffer from rheumatism or arthritis or simply have over-worked or strained muscles, massage with a base oil which has a few drops of rosemary added. On a cosmetic level, a few drops of rosemary oil in a hair rinse will help bring a gloss to dark hair.

GERANIUM

My favourite good mood oil, geranium is an instant lifter for the spirits. A few drops in the bath or popped in an oil burner will help cheer you up on a dismal day – and many people find it helps them get to sleep at night. I usually add geranium to my bedtime laven-der bath – the two smell delicious together.

However, it doesn't just lift the mood: geranium has a stimulat-ing effect on the lymphatic system and can help the body eliminate fluids. It also tends to balance the hormones and can be very use-ful in cases of PMS.

LEMON

Bright, fresh and tangy, the scent of lemons brings a sharp clarity to the air. It's another lovely one for baths – not only does it smell wonderful but apparently it can help disperse cellulite and is said to keep wrinkles at bay. On a more serious note, it's a powerful bactericide and will help to stop bleeding, so use a drop or two in warm water, or alternatively fresh lemon juice, on cuts. A mouth-wash of lemon juice (not oil) is also good, providing a real tonic for the gums.

Be slightly careful with this oil because some people find it irritates their skin. Use just one drop in the bath to test your sen-sitivity: and don't go above three drops.

EUCALYPTUS

Well-known and loved as a decongestant inhalation for coughs and colds, eucalyptus is also a very powerful antiviral and anti-bacterial oil which should always be used when there is flu or infectious disease around the house. Use it in burners, vapouriz-ers or in a bowl of hot water.

It is also a very effective insect repellent (even better if you combine it with lavender and bergamot).

PEPPERMINT

The digestive tonic par excellence. If you've got a stomach upset, pour yourself a mug of soothing peppermint tea (made with the herb not the oil), and massage your stomach with a very well-diluted (one or two drops in a base oil) mixture of peppermint oil.

Peppermint is also a wonderful first-aid remedy for any kind of shock: put a few drops on a tissue and inhale or simply sniff the bottle. It will also help any nausea.

A couple of drops (no more) of peppermint in your early bath will set you up for the day as it stimulates the brain and makes you think clearer (I often put some in my oil burner when I'm working), but don't use it at night as it will stop you sleeping.

YLANG-YLANG

The sexy oil, ylang-ylang, has a reputation as a powerful aphrodisiac and, to be frank, I think it's true. If you want to enjoy a sensual massage you could do far worse than to add a few drops of ylang-ylang to your massage oil (don't be tempted to add more, you might end up with a very unsexy headache). If you really want the heavy seduction effect, add some sandalwood. And, if you're seriously made of money, you could add rose and jasmine (both hideously expensive – if they're not, they simply aren't pure).

Ylang-ylang is also a great relaxant, an antidepressant and it even reduces high blood pressure to boot.

CHAMOMILE

The great soother. Chamomile is wonderful for menstrual pain and PMS, it soothes sore muscles and inflamed joints and calms down sore, sensitive skin. If you suffer from allergic conditions, eczema or urticaria, regular baths with a few drops of chamomile can be wonderfully soothing – drink the herbal tea as well.

In fact, chamomile tea should be a staple in every cupboard: it's wonderful for stomach upsets, cystitis and as a soothing drink. Its action is so gentle, it can be used quite safely, even on children.

CLARY SAGE

The great relaxant. Any woman who suffers from period pains and menstrual cramps should make a friend of clary sage – massage the abdomen gently with a few drops of clary sage mixed with a base oil. The same treatment will also help digestive problems.

Some people swear by clary sage as another aphrodisiac oil but, in my experience, after you've had a bath or a massage with this oil, all you're fit for is deep sleep. It's just wonderful if you need to wind down at the end of a hideous day.

MANUAL LYMPHATIC DRAINAGE (MLD)

WHAT IS IT?   A gentle massage technique which encourages the elimination of toxins and the stimulation of the lymphatic system.

USED FOR   Oedema and swelling; for deep relaxation and to improve the appearance.

SUITABLE FOR   Anyone suffering from swelling, oedema, puffiness, tiredness due to sluggish lymph. Also useful cosmetically for cellulite, stretch marks, puffy eyes.

NOT SUITABLE FOR   Anyone who has suffered from tuberculosis; anyone with heart problems (particularly cardiac oedema) is also advised against the treatment; those with active cancer cannot be treated.

PERFORMED   In underwear, covered in towels.

ANYTHING TO TAKE ORALLY?   No.

STRESSBUSTER   Yes, wonderful.

COST   Medium.

NUMBER OF SESSIONS REQUIRED   Depends on the problem. Usually a couple a week until the problem abates, then a maintenance programme of one a month or so.

DIY   Yes, self-help routines are often shown.

IF YOU LIKE THIS, TRY   Other gentle techniques such as ZERO BALANCING or CRANIO-SACRAL THERAPY. REIKI may also appeal.

Manual Lymph Drainage (MLD) is one of the best-kept secrets on the health and beauty scene. MLD can actually get rid of stretch marks. It can banish cellulite and tighten up your skin. Puffiness can vanish from the eyes and chins miraculously lift. Old scar tissue dissolves, and burns heal. Not bad for a massage. Although MLD has been around since the 1930s, few people know what it is, and even fewer realize how far-reaching its benefits can be. It's not just a beauty treatment either: MLD is now being recognized as an essential part of treating oedema and is highly effective post-surgery.

The history

Dr Emil Vodder and his wife Estrid first developed MLD in France in the 1930s. Vodder noticed how people suffering from chronic catarrhal and sinus infections tended to have swollen lymph glands and, much against medical practice at the time, started to work with the lymph nodes. The massage he developed had a circular, pumping effect which increases the movement of the lymphatic system of the body. Medical tests have since proven his conviction that when you increase the flow of the lymph system, infection is dealt with more effectively.

The lowdown

Everyone can benefit from MLD because even the healthiest of us lives in a polluted world. Even on a superficial level, our skin contacts the outside world and if it starts to get clogged, then our looks will suffer, not to mention our health. What we need to combat this

227

is a healthy lymph, because the lymph is the one thing that can absolutely, thoroughly cleanse the system. There are microscopic lymph collectors throughout the body, which pull the debris from both the outside and the inside of your body. The lymph is your body's garbage bin, and lymph drainage will clear it all out.

At the very least, MLD will increase your resistance to colds and flu; will firm and improve the look of your skin and brighten and clear your eyes. Colds disappear in hours or days rather than dragging on for weeks, and sinuses drain as if by magic.

The medical establishment is beginning to take MLD very seriously. If the massage is given to burns victims soon after the accident, it can rapidly bring the burn down. Scar tissue can be encouraged to build up only where needed, getting rid of unsightly large scars. And now, the therapy is even being used following cancer treatment, to reduce the swelling that often occurs. However, where cancer is concerned, practitioners have to proceed extremely cautiously, and they are not allowed to work with people who have live, active cancer – although this might change in the future. There are two schools of thought at the moment: the first is that MLD would spread the cancer; the second is that MLD would strengthen the immune system and possibly help to cure the cancer. Obviously, there are not many people who are willing to test the theories, but some doctors are now beginning to think about the second scenario.

More and more people, however, are now visiting MLD therapists for less serious problems. MLD can have pretty spectacular effects as a beauty treatment. It draws the skin in and tightens it. Removing the garbage from the body gives the skin a chance to regenerate. And while it won't actually make you thinner, it will certainly make your face *look* thinner by tightening up all the little saggy baggy bits, all the puffiness. To a degree, it's like a face-lift without the surgery.

Stretch marks *will* disappear, but it takes hard work. In severe cases, clients are taught MLD techniques to use at home and have to studiously work on themselves for at least twenty minutes a day for about six months. It's the same story with acne and that scourge of modern life – cellulite. MLD *will* help, but you have to help yourself. That means learning the technique and clearing your lymph on a daily basis as well as following a diet programme and keeping up a regime of regular swimming. It's no instant cure – it takes time and commitment because you need to free the fat and the water that is trapped by proteins.

Practitioners, however, are keen to point out that there is no point in baling out a boat if you don't plug the leak. Draining your lymph can have miraculous effects, but it can only truly be effective in the long term if you are prepared to make changes in your life. Like most holistic therapists, MLD masseurs will ask you a battery of questions about your whole lifestyle and attitude to life and will make suggestions on how to keep your newly cleansed system in a detoxified state. As with any system aimed at long-term change, you need regular treatment. A one-off treatment is pleasant and great for stress – it will make a difference to puffy eyes immediately. If you have a blocked nose you'll notice a swift change as well. But if you want to build up your immune system or treat deep-seated problems, you will probably have to think about treatment three times a week for the first two weeks and then tail off after that. Thereafter, practitioners tend to see clients only every two or three months or if they have a particular problem.

Regrettably, there are some people who are not advised to attempt MLD. Anyone who has suffered from TB (tuberculosis) should avoid it, as there is a possibility that TB molecules stored in the lymph system could be reawakened. And anyone with heart problems (particularly cardiac oedema) is also advised against the treatment.

The session

MLD practitioners are highly professional and treat their therapy seriously. I visited Dee Jones, a highly experienced masseur who works in London. Her room was light, airy and pleasant with a couch in the centre. Dee herself was pristine, in gleaming white. First, you sit down for the consultation – Dee asked plenty of questions, not just about my medical history but also about my lifestyle in general. I was given a few lectures on diet and some recommendations for exercise: all sensible, practical advice. Then I stripped down to bra and pants and hopped onto the couch to be generously smothered in fluffy white towels. Only the part that is being worked on is exposed, and the therapists are expert at whisking towels around.

So far, it's much like any other standard massage. However, the MLD touch is quite, quite different. There is no pounding of muscles, no probing and pulling; an MLD massage feels like having your skin softly stroked by a child's gentle fingers. It's a light, repetitive movement that has an almost hypnotic effect. After an hour and a half I felt as if I were floating in a deep blue lagoon – I have never been so relaxed. Dee Jones explains that the relaxation comes about because the massage affects the nervous system, instigating a change from the normal stressed 'daytime' state of the nervous system to the 'night time' state we use when we're asleep.

My glands felt slightly swollen – showing that toxins were moving to the lymph nodes – but, otherwise, I felt wonderful. The puffiness under my eyes had gone and my skin somehow seemed brighter. The beginnings of a cold that had been lurking around my head and throat had completely vanished.

DIY ways to ease the load on your lymph

Walk and swim Exercise acts as a powerful pump for the lymph, but high-powered aerobics is not necessarily ideal. If you overuse the muscles, they create more waste, rather than helping the lymph. Dee Jones recommends swimming, walking and yoga.

Detox your diet High-fat diets slow down the circulation of lymph and encourage a build-up of waste – dairy produce and red meats are the main culprits. Detox specialists 'Stop the World' recommend a diet rich in alkaline foods with plenty of fresh fruits, vegetables and sprouted seeds. And drink loads of water (at least two litres a day).

Brush your skin Simple but effective, regular brushing moves the lymph and softens any impacted lymph mucus from the nodes. Use either a natural-bristle brush or a damp flannel with a bicarbonate and salt mixture, and brush smoothly, always moving towards the heart.

Put rosemary in your bath Aromatherapists use a variety of oils to help the lymph. Rosemary is one of the best. Put a couple of drops in a warm bath and relax. Then gradually add cool water until the water is quite cold – the change of temperature also stimulates the lymph.

Stand on your head All yoga positions (not just head-stands!) combined with deep breathing help the lymphatic system to keep pumping.

Drink herbal infusions Impacted lymph mucus can be shifted slowly with herbs. Echinacea is a supreme lymph cleanser. Many herbalists swear by fenugreek and suggest either boiling or steeping a tablespoon for around fifteen minutes.

CHAVUTTI THIRUMAL

WHAT IS IT?   A deep massage performed by the feet which originated in Southern India.

USED FOR   Stress, back pain, migraine, sports injuries, to stimulate the lymphatic system.

SUITABLE FOR   Sportspeople, particularly those who want to increase suppleness; stressed businesspeople.

NOT SUITABLE FOR   Anyone who feels uncomfortable totally naked. Anyone who doesn't like the idea of being trodden on. People with cancer or heart disease.

PERFORMED   Totally naked.

ANYTHING TO TAKE ORALLY?   No.

STRESSBUSTER   Yes, superlative.

COST   High.

NUMBER OF SESSIONS REQUIRED   Varies. Most people have one every two or three months.

IF YOU LIKE THIS, TRY   Deep-tissue massage such as ROLFING or HELLERWORK. If you love the all-over feel and want something even more mystical, try KAHUNA BODYWORK. Use Chavutti as a springboard to the total Indian healthcare system AYURVEDA.

Imagine a massage where the therapists walk all over their clients and yet the clients keep coming back for more. This is the Indian art of Chavutti Thirumal, a curiously named massage which is practised in a decidedly bizarre fashion, using the feet rather than the hands.

But while the idea of someone's toes probing your body might sound rather unpleasant, devotees of massage by foot pressure simply adore being trodden upon. Not only does it feel quite delicious but, they insist, its benefits are enormous: it soothes and relaxes; stimulates the circulation, immune and lymphatic systems; and can ease arthritis. Regular massage will apparently rejuvenate the body, liberate the mind and could even help you lose weight. Although, as yet, there are few practitioners outside India, this is quite certain to become one of the massage techniques for the future.

The history

The massage originated in Southern India and was developed primarily to keep practitioners of both the local martial art and dance supple and flexible. Before performances, dancers and fighters would be given a ten-day intensive course of the massage to allow them to perform in peak condition. It generally prevented injuries and strains, but if anything *did* go wrong, then Chavutti Thirumal would equally coax them back to health. It was even used to promote the healing of broken bones.

The lowdown

While most Western practitioners would draw the line at mending bones, they all say this form of massage has wide-ranging beneficial effects. A lot of people use it simply for stress relief; many find it very helpful for muscle spasm or back tension. And it's also ideal for sportspeople who need to keep supple.

Chavutti Thirumal helps improve body image and foster a sense of acceptance of your body, however imperfect. Practitioners say it helps people get to know themselves that bit better – it's rather like an education. However, the massage does appear to affect everyone in a different way. Some people find the effects are all physical, while others find it affects them psychologically as well: it can help emotions to clear and it can sometimes relieve psychological blocks.

Nevertheless, not everyone feels better immediately after the massage. Some people bounce away feeling on top of the world and others feel calm and centred; some people actually feel worse before they feel better. The latter happens, say practitioners, because the therapy draws things out. It can help to eliminate toxins, which means that people can sometimes suffer sore throats or headaches – these usually vanish quite quickly and people soon start to feel the true benefits.

Chavutti reaches every external muscle and ligament in the body while stimulating the circulation and the lymphatic system. Stimulating the lymphatic system inevitably helps push toxins to the lymph nodes to be eliminated. It is this elimination of toxins that leads people to claim that Chavutti Thirumal can be a factor in successful weight loss and even in rejuvenation. In addition, the deep kneading action is said to promote the breakdown of cellulite. Practitioners, however, point out that the massage alone won't make you drop the pounds but it will certainly give your body a nudge towards shedding cellulite.

The session

The Chavutti Thirumal experience is quite unique. Walking into practitioner Jessica Loeb's room in the heart of London's West End was like stepping into a sauna. A bank of electric fires kept the temperature up high, very high. There was no massage couch, simply rush beach mats laid on the floor with a large white towel in the middle. Across the room above head height hung a thick red rope, while a large bowl of sesame oil sat waiting on the floor. Loeb herself looked more as if she were about to do a workout than a massage, garbed in shorts and T-shirt. Her feet were bare and, she assured me, freshly scrubbed.

234

'Pop off your clothes and jewellery and lie face down on the mat,' instructed Loeb, politely leaving the room while I disrobed.

Chavutti is certainly not for shrinking violets. There are no discreet swathings of towels: you are left lying on the floor naked as the day you were born. I felt like a beached whale. On reappearing, Loeb asked a few questions: had I ever broken any bones; did I have any back problems; was I asthmatic or epileptic; was there anything else she should know about my health? 'The only contraindications are cancer and heart disease,' she explains, 'but it's good for me to be aware of any problems.'

Then she turned away to prepare herself. Although a massage by foot may sound about as down to earth a treatment as you could imagine, its practitioners look on it as an almost spiritual exercise. Before starting work, they will mentally salute their teachers, asking for help and guidance. They also believe that by opening up their minds in prayer, they will receive healing energy which can then be transmitted through them into the person being massaged.

'It sounds corny, but I'm like a channel for energy to come through,' says Loeb. 'There has to be a feeling of love.' Throughout the entire massage Loeb breathed in a particular way, a yogic form of breathing known as *pranayama* which she says helps to keep her open to healing energy.

I couldn't quite imagine how massage by foot would feel: my first thought was that it would seem rather clumsy. I couldn't have been more wrong. Loeb liberally doused my body with sesame oil and then, holding on to the rope for balance and to modulate her weight, she began. The first stroke ran right down the right-hand side of my body, starting at the tip of my outstretched fingers and sweeping down over my shoulders, back, hips and thighs and on to my very toes in one long smooth wave. It felt perfectly exquisite: firm, controlled and secure. My embarrassment fell away and I awaited the next stroke with unabashed pleasure.

Loeb's feet do everything a pair of hands can do – and more. They kneaded, probed, stretched and soothed every muscle and ligament in my body – starting with the shoulders and working right down to fingers and toes. Nothing was missed: even my face and head had attention.

It is one of the most satisfying massages you could ask for. Normally, I leave the massage table feeling that I need more; that my shoulders want more work or my back would have liked an extra ten minutes. There's a sense of incompleteness somehow. Chavutti Thirumal however leaves nothing untouched and nothing left crying for more. Although there is a formal structure to the massage, Loeb somehow picked up on where the really knotty bits lurked and every so often would return to those painful shoulders or that stressed lower back and probe yet deeper. It wasn't all uninterrupted bliss however: my calves felt decidedly tender and my poor buttocks were virtually wincing after Loeb had probed and pressed. No wonder cellulite is said to vanish.

However, the net effect after an hour and a half is that your body feels like singing. I felt totally relaxed, blissfully unstressed and, amazingly, I even felt happier about my body image. When Loeb says that many people find it builds self-esteem and helps them gain confidence I am not remotely surprised.

KAHUNA BODYWORK

WHAT IS IT?   An ancient system of bodywork developed by the Hawaiian Hunas, or healers.

USED FOR   Deep relaxation plus coming to an acceptance of your body. Its ultimate aim is a 'divine' experience, coming close to your idea of God.

SUITABLE FOR   Those who want to get back in touch with their bodies and emotions.

NOT SUITABLE FOR   Anyone who feels uncomfortable totally naked; anyone who dislikes New Age mysticism or talk of God.

PERFORMED   Totally naked, except for a brief loin-cloth.

ANYTHING TO TAKE ORALLY?   *No.*

STRESSBUSTER   Yes.

COST   High.

NUMBER OF SESSIONS REQUIRED   Varies. Most people have one every two or three months.

DIY   No.

IF YOU LIKE THIS, TRY   CHAVUTTI THIRUMAL – another all-over megabody massage. REIKI may appeal if you want something mystical but lighter. METAMORPHIC TECHNIQUE is also transformative but only works on feet and hands.

Kahuna, or Hawaiian massage, is a system of bodywork that has been practised in the Polynesian islands for centuries. Unlike traditional massages which simply aim to relax, the Hawaiian method has a much more profound purpose. Its practitioners believe they can put you back in touch with your body, teaching you to accept and love yourself, whatever your shape or size. And once you accept the beauty within, they say, you will start to recognize the beauty that surrounds you. It may sound implausible if you live in an inner city millions of miles away from the beaches of Hawaii, but practitioners insist that if you can find perfection even in tiny things, then your life will certainly start to change. Accept paradise in everyday life and almost anything can happen.

The history

Given the beauty of the world around them, it is hardly surprising that the ancient Polynesians should have developed a life philosophy, known as Huna, that sought to reproduce the outer beauty of their world on the inside. The Huna priests, known as Kahunas, were acknowledged not only as great spiritual leaders but as superlative healers. They taught that in order to achieve perfect health and true happiness you need to align yourself with the universal life-force, to become one with creation. For most of us, unable to attain such an elevated state at will, the massage acts as a gentle nudge, a reminder of how it is possible to feel at one with our bodies and, by extension, at one with creation.

The training of a Kahuna is arduous, long and steeped in mystery – few outside of Hawaii have ever completed it. However, now the Kahunas are allowing elements of their work to be taken outside the islands, teaching outer aspects, such as the massage, to enlightened Westerners. Although the massage is but the simplest manifestation of the Huna philosophy, its effects can be deceptively powerful.

The lowdown

Although most people would agree that a massage can be a wonderful experience, surely it is overly optimistic, even a little foolish, to expect it to change your life? However, although Kahuna bodywork may use a barrage of professional techniques, its power lies not in the performance but in the intent of the practitioner. Put yourself in the hands of Hawaii and you are absorbing centuries of the wisdom of Paradise.

Practitioners say that nearly everyone has a strong dislike of some aspect of their body or their life – some people actively dislike everything. Over time, the dislike turns into a deep self-hatred which can erode self-esteem and take a toll on health, happiness and success.

Hawaiian massage, apart from deeply relaxing the physical structure of the body, also affects the body on a vibrational level. It is said to accelerate the vibrational rate of the cells and the energy fields of both the physical and subtle bodies. As with many other forms of massage, practitioners believe that the action of Hawaiian massage is able to release trapped memories of old traumas and bad experiences – it's quite common for people to remember old hurts and wounds during the session.

However, the deepest difference between this and other forms of massage is its ability to make you feel your body as a whole. The smooth repetitive movements which cover the whole body induce the body into almost a hypnotic state. Meanwhile the practitioner's heart is concentrating on smothering you with unconditional love, acceptance and joy. The idea is that your body, cocooned in all this love and acceptance, will begin to believe that it is, indeed, lovable and beautiful. The length of the massage (often up to three hours) allows the message to be reinforced: this is not a quick pick-me-up but a lesson in love for the body, a chance to remember its worth.

The session

When you step into the world of the Kahunas, the first difference you notice is the heat. I visited Rosalie Samet, a nurse who learned the Kahuna technique in Hawaii and now practises in Glastonbury. In her treatment room a bank of fires took the temperature up to tropical levels. Light incense scented the air and candles spread soft pools of light. Alongside the familiar massage couch was an unusual addition – a large, gilded mirror leaning against the wall.

'Sit in front of the mirror and really look at yourself,' suggested Samet. 'See what emotions, what thoughts, emerge. Try to accept yourself just as you are.' She then left me for what seemed like an eternity; at least long enough to catalogue every imperfection in my much maligned body. By the time she returned I was feeling fat, ugly and totally disgruntled.

'We really need to be able to stand naked in front of our mirrors and see our bodies as just beautiful,' said Samet. I winced at the idea – it was bad enough scrutinizing myself fully clothed. She smiled and added: 'But isn't that hard? We have so much judgment and very few people really like their bodies. Very often, when people finish the massage they feel very good about their bodies, they have a total transformation in the way they feel and see themselves. It will last as long as they allow it to last.' I've had plenty of massages in the past and I couldn't quite see my body image changing after a massage, however skilful, but I dutifully stripped off and laid myself on the couch.

For someone whose body image is pretty poor, this simple act was far from easy. Because the Huna experience seeks to teach us to see our bodies as a unified, beautiful whole, there is no chance to cower under layers of towels. Instead of covering up the majority of the body and leaving exposed just the part that is being massaged, Hawaiian 'performers' (as they are called) leave the whole body uncovered (save for a brief loin-cloth). You feel very exposed and, initially, I found the experience exceedingly uncomfortable. Using light scented oils, Samet started massaging my back, sweeping down from my head right through to my legs in long fluid movements. The movement is rhythmic and repetitive and, after a few minutes, it became hard to remember where one

240

stroke ended and the next began. Samet threw her whole body into the work, often using, not just her hands, but the whole length of her forearm. As she pulled, twisted and stretched me, it felt as if we were partners in some strange dance.

As times I noticed elements of shiatsu and acupressure, at others the firm but gentle feel of therapeutic massage, but the whole is far more than the sum of its parts. Throughout the time she worked on me I was continually forced to think about my body, there was no escaping, no possibility of lurking behind clothes or denial.

I drifted into a sense of total timelessness, as if I were floating in an eternal sea. And, from a distinct feeling of discomfort and embarrassment I shifted slowly towards a surprising feeling of acceptance, of connectedness. I didn't have any flashbacks to early experiences (although people often do) and I didn't become over-whelmed with any intense emotions (although it's not uncommon for people to find themselves either crying or laughing). However, after almost two hours, I had the strangest sense of being coaxed back into my body, of feeling almost kindly towards it.

Samet seemed satisfied. 'When people get a good experience of themselves, they can go away with new inspiration and new enthusiasm and new perspectives,' she says. 'As a result, they can start to look at the assumptions, the beliefs that have caused some of their problems – ill health, unhappy relationships or whatever.' The Huna experience, she promises, allows you to differentiate between what is important and what is not, what allows you to experience each moment and what ties you to expectations of the future and regrets of the past. At the time it sounded like a lot of New Age spirit-babble. However, I truly did experience a new acceptance of my body that almost amounted to love. A few hours later, someone offered me a bar of chocolate and I couldn't bear to eat it. Somehow I found myself filling my shopping basket with wholemeal bread, tons of vegetables and fresh fruit. I scorned my usual tipple of wine and returned to the gym after a lengthy absence. I even looked at myself naked in the mirror and didn't feel sick.

How long the effects will last I really don't know. Samet says that many people often come for just one or two massages and then she won't see them for some time. Others pop back every few months for a top-up of bliss.

INDIAN HEAD MASSAGE

WHAT IS IT?   A neck, shoulder, scalp and face massage using a variety of techniques for health and beauty.

USED FOR   To promote hair growth and keep it lustrous; to ease stress and tension; useful for headaches and eye strain.

SUITABLE FOR   Almost everyone – from the very young to the elderly. Stressed businesspeople benefit greatly. So do those who want to improve the quality of their hair – or even those who simply want to keep it.

NOT SUITABLE FOR   Anyone with weeping eczema or head injuries; psychotics or people with epilepsy.

PERFORMED   Fully clothed.

ANYTHING TO TAKE ORALLY?   No.

STRESSBUSTER   Yes, deep stress relief.

COST   Low.

NUMBER OF SESSIONS REQUIRED   In an ideal world, once a
week.

DIY   Yes, weekend courses teach all the techniques.

IF YOU LIKE THIS, TRY   Indian head massage is a great introduction to massage. From here, maybe try a full body massage –
if you feel nervous about taking your clothes off, go for SHIATSU.
Otherwise, ACUPRESSURE keeps up the Chinese connection, or
AROMATHERAPY is a delight to the senses.

Narendra Mehta has a mission to bring the beaches of Goa into the
homes and offices of Britain. Sadly, he can't import the sun, sea
and sand of the Indian region – but he *can* impart a large slice of
relaxation and revitalization, thanks to his technique of Indian
head massage. On Indian beaches it's quite common to see roving
masseurs plying their trade. They rarely have to hunt far for willing clients, and that's no great surprise. Regular doses of this
sunshine massage can make your hair shine, your face glow and
your stress levels dive. And, promises Mehta, it could even
help your marriage and increase your chances of promotion.

The history

If you've ever wondered how Indian women always seem to have
such lustrous hair, this is the secret. Head massage, using a variety
of oils, has been a feature of Indian tradition for thousands of
years. Originally it was part of the ancient healing system of
Ayurveda and practised therapeutically, but over the years the
techniques were watered down and altered. Before the advent of
barbers' and hairdressers' shops, the barbers used to visit the
family homes of Indian families. Among their techniques they
included head massage, which not only improved the quality of
their clients' hair but also gave them deep relaxation. Sometimes
they rather misused the deeply relaxed state of their clients, and
some barbers were renowned as spies who extracted secrets from
their clients when they were utterly relaxed after the massage. On
a lighter note, the barber knew the families so well that he would
often act as a marriage broker.

The colourful tradition of head massage has continued up to this day. Now it's quite common to see masseurs offering head massage on the beach, on street corners, even in busy markets. Within the family, most babies are massaged from birth and, by the age of seven or eight, most children can perform massage. It's considered an essential part of family life, keeping everyone close and in touch. Women spend hours tending each other's hair to keep it shining and glossy; men use head massage to prevent them going grey or to keep them from turning bald.

Mehta was born in India and grew up having regular head massages. When he came to this country in 1973, he missed the massage and looked around for a practitioner. But he couldn't find a soul. 'The head was totally neglected,' he laments. So, armed with his knowledge of osteopathy, beauty therapy and body massage, he went back to India to learn for himself. Everyone, he found, had a different technique. 'It was like Chinese whispers,' he smiles, 'as it had been passed down through the generations it had changed.'

Eight years later he was satisfied that he had extracted all the best elements and had evolved them into the ultimate massage. 'I wanted a massage that was good for the hair but also relaxing. I extended it to the neck and shoulders because they are truly the most vulnerable part for tension accumulation. I also wanted to include Ayurvedic principles, so I work on the energy centres, the *chakras*, to balance the subtle energy of the body. And I finish off with a face massage which is a lovely part of beauty therapy.'

The lowdown

Almost everyone can benefit – from the very young to the elderly. The only people Mehta can't treat are those with weeping eczema or head injuries, the psychotic or people with epilepsy. The whole treatment takes just half an hour and can be performed anywhere. You don't need to take your clothes off, and it's not even necessary to use oil, so you don't end up messy and mucky. All it takes is a chair and a pair of hands. Mehta can teach the technique in a weekend and, although many of the people who attend his workshops are already therapists, masseurs or hairdressers, he is delighted when the lay public come along too. He especially likes to teach husbands and wives because he firmly believes that a regular dose of head massage can help cement a marriage.

'Touching makes us feel nurtured, cared for and relaxed,' he says. 'If husbands and wives could massage each other, even just on the top of the head, it would bring them closer.'

Mehta would also love to see the massage incorporated into the working day. 'If everyone had a massage once a week it would help employers as well as the employees,' he insists. 'It helps people work better, concentrate better. You become more alert and single-minded and yet relaxed. Absenteeism would drop immediately.'

But until the Mehta method becomes more widespread in the workplace, the workers have to go to him. He finds many of his clients are solicitors and barristers, doctors and stockbrokers who work under continual stress. People who use computers find it helps eye strain and tension headaches as well. But, above all, people come to Mehta because they want to look and feel better. The massage stimulates the circulation of the scalp which nourishes the hair roots. The oil (generally an Ayurvedic preparation containing five herbs) improves the texture of the hair and gives a wonderful gleam. Massage can help to prevent hair turning grey and can even stop it falling out. The face massage leaves tired, tense faces looking relaxed and calm.

The session

Mehta never sees the changes he produces. Blind since the age of one, he feels his way. But once you're in his chair, his fingers do all the seeing he requires. The treatment starts off with a deep kneading and probing of the neck and shoulder muscles. He ferrets out taut painful muscles and almost shakes them into submission. Some of his techniques seem almost osteopathic (and he *is* a trained osteopath) but he never cracks or crunches – rather he coaxes the muscles to give up their stranglehold and relax. Then he moves on to the head. My scalp was squeezed, rubbed, tapped and prodded; my hair was tugged and then 'combed' with his fingernails. My ever-taut jaw was gently persuaded to unclamp and my ears were given a thorough overseeing ('ears are very neglected too,' says Mehta, 'but they contain so many acupressure points').

245

Finally, he moved on to my face, first pressing firmly on the acupressure points to relieve sinus pressure, stimulate blood circulation and increase alertness, and then he moved into the final relaxing mode, gently stroking my face with his fingertips and the palm of his hand. The sensation was one of utter gentleness, almost of love. At first, I felt slightly uncomfortable – this seemed a very personal kind of touch. Mehta understands: he grieves that we have lost the ability to touch and be touched safely and innocently. This, he says, is a tragedy for our society and he sincerely hopes that his form of massage which can be performed without taking any clothes off in full view of all, might lure people back into the therapeutic power of touch.

I hope so. As I got up from his chair I felt a curious mixture of exhilaration and calm. If we all had half an hour of this a week, I'm quite convinced life would seem brighter and sunnier.

Get a head start at home

The following exercises are all totally safe and can be practised at home. For all these exercises your 'patient' should be sitting upright in a straight-backed chair.

For tension in the neck   Stand to one side of the person you are massaging and put one hand on their forehead and the other at the back of the neck. Keep their head slightly tilted back and then start to massage with the heel of your hand one side of the spine and your fingers the other. The action is pulling the muscle up and then out. Press firmly but not too hard.

For tension in the shoulders   The action here is as if you were ironing the shoulders, using the heel of your hand to roll forward over the shoulder from the back towards the front. Start from the outside edge of the shoulder and move in towards the collarbone. If you are doing the massage on someone much taller than you, use your forearm to press across the shoulder, using your body weight for pressure.

To relax and warm the muscles   This movement is known as the 'windscreen wiper', which should give a clear idea of the technique. Support the head with one hand. Using the palm of your other hand, employ a swift rubbing motion as if you were buffing a window. Start behind the ear, go round it and then away from the ear. Then do the other side of the head.

To soothe and relax Support the head with one hand while the other gently strokes the top of the head. First, use long sweeping movements, then 'comb' the hair, running your fingernails through the hair in long strokes.

For headaches Put both hands around the head like a cap. Then squeeze, lift and let go. Do several repetitions.

For insomnia Stroke the face very lightly with your whole hands (palms against the face), moving gently down from the forehead to the chin. Repeat as much as necessary.

Energyworking

We are not just skin and bones, organs and muscles: we are more, far more, than mere flesh and blood. It's true we are physical beings but, just as importantly, we are energetic ones as well. Although we cannot generally see our energetic bodies, that doesn't mean they don't exist.

For centuries, the ancient healing systems have known about the vital energy that circulates through the body. The Chinese call it *chi*, the Japanese *ki*, the Indians know it as *prana*. They mapped it clearly: the Chinese saw the body as a shimmering mass of organized energy, flowing along subtle lines – the meridians. The Indians talked of the *chakras*, the swirling masses of energy that ran through the body.

More modern systems such as Zero Balancing, discussed in the Bodyworking section, see energy as a complex web, existing in a vast complexity of forms and on many distinct levels. It may all sound like mystical mumbo-jumbo, but our energetic system is as much a part of our anatomy as the physical body. It just hasn't adequately been charted by modern medicine – yet. And it's sad but true that most modern physicians won't treat what they can't see under a microscope – the energetic, the psychological, the spiritual are simply not considered in medical schools because they can't be dissected.

248

Yet we ignore our energy bodies at a high cost. This subtle energy, this life-force is the very stuff that animates us, that turns us from lumpen masses of flesh into intelligent, feeling, thinking creatures. It has only been very recently in the history of modern medicine that scientists have acknowledged that our minds can influence the physiological mechanics of our bodies. Mind is simply one aspect of energy; what we loosely term soul or spirit is another.

However, for most supertherapists, the energy body in all its complex glory is the linchpin for health. In fact, the vast majority of the supertherapies in this book could accurately be labelled 'energyworking'. They may differ in the way they treat energy but they all follow the same basic tenet: if you can get the energy flowing freely, easily and smoothly through the body, then the physical frame simply doesn't have the opportunity or the desire to be ill. Our bodies are always striving towards health – ill-health is simply the body's way of telling us that something is wrong on a more subtle level.

As I write this, I am suffering from a hideous cold – I've got a headache, my sinuses are blocked, my nose is running and my stomach sounds like the rhythm section of an orchestra. You could simply say that I picked up a bug. However I know very well why I'm ill. I've been working too hard, racing to get this book finished and, consequently, I have simply not been spending enough time on myself. My mind wants a rest: it wants the odd hour spent out in the garden, quietly thinking, it wants time to recoup some stamina. Imbalance occurs first in the energetic body – stress, unhealthy thought patterns, negativity, pollution can all throw its delicate mechanism out of sync. If the cause is not treated, the imbalance will spread and eventually the body will suffer.

However, treat the subtle energy of the body, and quite incredible things can happen. Doctors are at a loss to understand how a homeopathic pill which contains not a single molecule of its original substance, can cure a person of migraine. They just don't believe that a healer can simply lay their hands on a person's head and ease their pain. They scoff at the idea of beaming colour at a person suffering from PMS or projecting sound at a tumour. In the future this form of therapy will most probably be the norm. We still don't understand precisely how many of these supertherapies work but, in time, the answers will all undoubtedly become clear.

HOMEOPATHY

WHAT IS IT?   A form of alternative healthcare which treats the whole individual by giving them infinitesimal doses of a remedy which most closely matches their symptoms.

USED FOR   Virtually all conditions respond to homeopathy, from acute conditions such as bee stings, colds and cuts, to chronic longstanding complaints such as arthritis and schizophrenia.

MOST SUITABLE FOR   Those who are prepared to delve deep into their physical, emotional and psychological history and current feelings. Those who are prepared to slowly unearth old symptoms and gently bring themselves back to optimum health. When used constitutionally (to treat the whole person rather than the odd acute symptom), it is not a quick fix by any means.

NOT SUITABLE FOR   Under a qualified and experienced homeopath everyone can be treated – from the newly born to the dying. However, although very gentle, homeopathic remedies can bring about potent changes, so the very young, elderly or infirm should never be treated by DIY remedies or the inexperienced. It is not a system for people who want instant, easy answers or those who cannot be bothered to spend time and effort in self-monitoring.

PERFORMED   Fully clothed.

ANYTHING TO TAKE ORALLY?   Yes, tiny tasteless pills or powders.

STRESSBUSTER   Not an instant fix, but deep-rooted stress will eventually be alleviated.

COST   Varies enormously. Low to medium.

NUMBER OF SESSIONS REQUIRED   Again, varies enormously. Acute conditions can be treated in one or two sessions, chronic cases can take months or years.

DIY   DIY homeopathy can be used as first aid quite safely but it's a very complex science and far better left to the professionals.

IF YOU LIKE THIS, TRY   FLOWER AND GEM REMEDIES work on a similar energetic level. As homeopathy is very much a 'talking' therapy, why not get in touch with your body with some form of bodywork (*see* BODYWORKING section) as well? Note: many homeopaths advise that you don't combine homeopathy and aromatherapy, as the essential oils can antidote the remedies.

A tiny tasteless white pill that contains not even one molecule of the original substance from which it was composed is at the heart of homeopathy. It sounds like complete medical madness. And yet homeopathy is one of the fastest growing, and most trusted, systems of natural healthcare. There are well-established homeopathic hospitals in several cities around the UK, and many GPs are now using homeopathy as an adjunct to their more conventional treatments. Although this sounds wonderful in principle, unfortunately many doctors have but a passing knowledge of homeopathy, garnered from a weekend's course in prescribing. A classical homeopath, on the other hand, will have spent upwards of three years studying this precise science. In skilled hands, homeopathy can seem like a miracle: results can often be very swift in acute illnesses; chronic cases take longer, but improvements can be sweeping.

The history

Samuel Hahnemann founded homeopathy back in the eighteenth century. It was revolutionary then and even now is still firmly at loggerheads with modern scientific and medical belief.

Hahnemann trained as a doctor but was also a fine chemist. After he graduated from medical school he felt so uncomfortable with the medicine he had been taught that he actually stopped practising, terrified that he might do more harm than good to his patients. His main concern was the way that traditional medicine (which he termed allopathy) looked for a remedy to produce the opposite effect to the illness. In other words, a doctor would (and still will) give a patient suffering from fever a medicine which would cool them down; an itchy cough would be soothed. He felt this was entirely the wrong approach.

'We should imitate nature,' he said, 'which sometimes cures a chronic disease by another and employ in the disease we wish to cure that medicine which is able to produce another very similar disease, and the former will be cured; similia similibus.'

Although his ideas seemed to spring out of nowhere, it is most likely that he was harking back to much earlier physicians. Hippocrates wrote of the law of similars (curing like with like), and Paracelsus, a sixteenth-century healer, also appeared to be aware that within each disease lay the key to its cure. 'There where diseases arise, there also can one find the roots of health,' he wrote.

These ancient masters of medicine also understood the essential point that, to effect a long and lasting cure, you should not seek to cure the disease but to cure the whole person, then the disease would, of necessity, cure itself.

Hahnemann's breakthrough came with his observations on the effects of cinchona bark which, when given to healthy individuals, produced symptoms very similar to that of the dangerous intermittent fever in malaria. When given to actual sufferers, it appeared to cure the fever. Out of this, Hahnemann developed the main principles of homeopathy, testing numerous substances on himself to find out what symptoms they caused. He found, quite curiously, that the more dilute the form of the remedy, the more effective it became and, consequently, he began to dilute remedies more and more. He also discovered that there was no point in precisely matching a remedy to a particular disease or condition. Five patients with flu might well require five different remedies because they would all have slightly different symptoms.

In addition, he realized that he needed to look beyond the merely physical: when he tested different remedies he found his mental and emotional state would change just as clearly as his physical being. He concluded that the physician needed to take into account all aspects of the patient: their mind, emotions, body and even spiritual feelings. Thus homeopathy can be considered a truly holistic science.

When Hahnemann died in 1843, his work was eagerly taken up by others, and research continues today. Remedies range from common plants and trees; minerals and metals; poisons such as arsenic and snake venom; narcotics like opium; and even quite esoteric compounds such as sunlight and moonlight. On a more mundane level, homeopaths have potentized everyday substances such as petrol and chocolate. And people with severe allergies can get relief from a potentized form of the allergen, whether it be grass pollen or dog hair. Some people are even experimenting with homeopathic potencies of wheat and dairy produce to ease food intolerances. Although homeopathy still perplexes doctors and scientists, it is probably one of the most established alternative therapies with several homeopathic hospitals and a quite considerable body of GPs who are also trained in homeopathic prescribing. It even has royal approval: the Queen has had her own homeopath for many years and other members of the Royal family have relied on the gentle powers of homeopathy to keep them healthy.

The lowdown

How does homeopathy work? At first sight it seems obvious – the homeopath prescribes the remedy which most exactly matches the patient's symptoms. But when you realize that the remedy has been diluted so much that not even a molecule of the original substance remains, the cure seems more improbable, even impossible.

Sceptics have attempted to dismiss the effects of homeopathy as mere placebo, but the homeopaths will point to their work with animals and babies who surely have no conscious knowledge that the remedy is supposed to cure them.

However, scientists are slowly discovering that homeopathy does have a solid base in science, although it seems to be following rules that are still very much in the realm of the unexplained. At the moment, the thinking is that water (in which the remedies are initially diluted) can extract and store a type of subtle energy which can affect the human body and psyche.

The clearest indication of how this works has come from Dr Bernard Grad of McGill University in Montreal, who tested psychic healers. Wanting to avoid the placebo effect, he used barley seeds for his experiments and set them to germinate in salty water which is known to retard the growth of seeds. Before setting the seeds to germinate he asked a healer to simply hold a sealed container of salt water. One set of seeds were then placed in 'healed' water, while the other was placed in salt water untouched by the healer. He was quite surprised to find a significant difference in the growth of the two sets of seeds. Those grown in the 'healed' water had grown stronger and taller, were heavier in weight and had larger leaves than the 'unhealed' counterparts.

He then extended the experiment: psychiatric patients with severe depression were given the water to hold. The seedlings grew even less than those in the neutral water. Intrigued, Grad carried out a chemical analysis of the water to see whether the healer had caused any measurable change that could be physically measured. He found that there were significant changes in the molecular structure of the water and also in its surface tension. Other laboratories duplicated his experiments and found the same results: it seems that it is possible to 'charge' water with some form of subtle energy – whether of a beneficial or detrimental nature – and then store it.

Having proved this fact, it becomes more feasible that homeopathy can work by means of subtle energy being stored and released into the patient. As the homeopathic remedy is being prepared and progressively diluted, the physical elements of the substance are removed, leaving the energetic qualities behind. Hahnemann believed that the remedies were working very much like a classic immunization, by creating an artificial illness in the patient which has very similar characteristics to the illness the physician wants to remove. The artificial illness stimulates the body's natural defences which then rise up to cure the original ailment. In the light of Grad's experiments, it seems that the remedy, rather than producing a physical reaction at a structural cell level, is producing a vibrational reaction, a vibrational illness to stimulate the body to heal at a vibrational level.

The session

Homeopathy involves talking, a lot of talking. You will spend the whole session answering questions – many of which seem quite irrelevant to your condition. The first session usually lasts for one and a half to two hours with the homeopath taking precise details of your medical history. Expect to provide exact details, including the age at which you had illnesses, operations and accidents.

There isn't usually any need to take off your clothes for examinations, but your homeopath will be minutely observing you the whole time, taking notice of the condition of your skin and hair, your eyes, how you sit and talk, how you express yourself. Generally, these observations are very subtle, but you can feel quite scrutinized.

After the medical history, you will be asked to describe your specific problem in quite precise terms. When is it at its worst? What makes it feel better? Sometimes the minute detail can seem irritating, but it is all essential information – if your pain is worse at two in the afternoon or four o'clock in the morning it could mean the homeopath choosing a quite different remedy.

Every homeopath has a slightly different approach. I have seen homeopaths who are interested simply in the purely physical symptoms and will only quiz you on purely practical details. On the other hand, many homeopaths take more interest in your emotional and psychological profile. I have frequently found myself talking to a homeopath about my dreams, my fears, my sexuality, even my thoughts about God. Sometimes it can go very deep, almost akin to psychotherapy; sometimes sessions can even be quite painful as you discuss long-forgotten hurts and disappointments. An unrequited love affair in your teens could be quite as important as the bout of tonsillitis you suffered last month.

At the end of the session, you either leave with a remedy or the homeopath will arrange to send the remedy to you within a few days – a pill or a powder to be taken. Sometimes results come quickly; sometimes it takes a little longer, but there is almost always a change of some kind. You might find that your condition simply improves. However, if you are being treated constitutionally (seeking long-term better health, treating your chronic complaints rather than short-lived acute symptoms), all manner of changes might occur. Classically, old symptoms will reappear, in a much reduced manner. I found myself with the odd mysterious sore throat which suddenly appeared and then just as suddenly disappeared (I had suffered badly from strep throats as a teenager). Old dreams will often resurface and then frequently vanish for good.

Sometimes results can be quite drastic – on one occasion I found myself suffering from terrible diarrhoea after a remedy: it was as if my body was getting rid of years of accumulated waste. However, most usually changes are subtle. There are no set rules, but the one thing that almost always happens is a wonderful increase of energy.

The homeopathic first-aid box

If you can see a qualified homeopath, please do. Many clinics will offer shorter sessions for acute problems at a much-reduced rate and you will be far more likely to get the right remedy at the right potency. However, there are some remedies that every home should have. For first-aid purposes, obtain your remedies in the sixth potency (often labelled 6c) – they are readily available now from most chemists and health shops. Keep them away from perfumes or essential oils. Please note these remedies should not take the place of a qualified physician.

Arnica   The great shock remedy. Give it immediately after any kind of accident or shock, whether physical or emotional. It is very useful after visits to the dentist, after operations and after childbirth.

Ars alb   Actually arsenic, but don't let that put you off. It's wonderful for any form of food poisoning, when you've eaten food that's off or tainted. The classic symptoms are restlessness and irritability; a feeling of desperation; feeling thirsty but only wanting small sips; intense burning pains.

256

Belladonna Another old poison – deadly nightshade. Wonderful for fevers when the face is brightly flushed; for bursting headaches when the face is red; for sunstroke and sore throats when the tonsils are enlarged and red.

Calendula Used generally as a lotion or ointment (again, easily available). It is absolutely wonderful for any kind of wound or sore or for soothing rough or chapped skin. It promotes healing and lessens scarring.

Cantharis The great cystitis helper. Useful for any kind of burning pains, especially in the bladder or urethra when connected with urination.

Chamomilla Wonderful for teething children – the kind who are fractious and always asking for things and then tossing them away. It can help if you've drunk too much coffee and is also useful to combat insomnia after a mental upset.

Gelsemium The great flu remedy – suitable for the typical variety of flu with shivers up and down the spine, aching back and limbs, tight headache, thirstless.

Ignatia The great grief counsellor. Give ignatia after any form of emotional shock, fright or grief. It is wonderful for helping with bereavement, not just for humans but pets as well (children particularly often grieve terribly for lost pets).

Ledum Useful for old bruises and for puncture wounds such as insect stings, splinters or nails.

Nux vomica A classic remedy for today. Helps with the ill-effects of overeating or eating the wrong kind of food, overindulging in alcohol or drugs, overstudying and overwork.

Petrol Useful for travel sickness – car, train or sea. Also useful for this is **Tabacum**. One may be more effective for you than the other, so experiment.

Rhus tox Helps sprains of joints or tendons, any form of physical overexertion or strain. Helps after surgical operations.

A NOTE ON VACCINATION

Should you vaccinate your child? Should you pump yourself full of vaccinations before you go abroad? More and more reports of the side effects of vaccinations have to make us stop and think. It's a very complex subject – one which I do not have the space to cover fully here – but very important to your health. Homeopaths are working on alternatives, and I would recommend anyone who is concerned – particularly about their children and vaccination – to consult a homeopath. Many homeopaths are highly experienced in children's issues – when you seek a practitioner in your area, ask for someone with expertise in this field if this is your main concern.

FLOWER AND GEM REMEDIES

WHAT IS IT?   A subtle form of healing using the vibrational healing power of flowers and gems to affect primarily the personality.

USED FOR   Any form of problem that has an emotional element.

SUITABLE FOR   Absolutely anyone – from babies to the elderly, even animals and other plants. Most suitable when there is an emotional state that is preventing healing.

NOT SUITABLE FOR   You don't have to believe in the remedies for them to work, but you do need to take them regularly for good results.

PERFORMED   Fully clothed.

ANYTHING TO TAKE ORALLY?   Yes, a few drops of essence either directly on the tongue (tastes slightly of the alcohol which is used to preserve the essence) or in any drink (when it becomes quite tasteless).

STRESSBUSTER   Depends on the remedy. Some are aimed specifically at the stressed personality.

COST Varies enormously. DIY treatment is, of course, free although you will have to buy the stock remedies and books. Practised on its own by a therapist: low to medium. Combined with other therapies: usually high.

NUMBER OF SESSIONS REQUIRED Varies. For example, combined with nutrition, generally once a month for two or three months; combined with hypnotherapy, once a week for a month.

DIY Yes, the flower and gem essences can be safely self-prescribed and used.

IF YOU LIKE THIS, TRY If you like the principle of the flower remedies but would like physical problems treated try HOMEO-PATHY. Any of the other therapies in ENERGYWORKING would probably also appeal. If you would like a therapy based on touch, METAMORPHIC TECHNIQUE might prove interesting or REIKI.

I first came across the Bach remedies by chance around fifteen years ago. Armed with a little book describing the remedies and the negative states of mind they treat, prescribing became almost a parlour game. I spent hours choosing remedies for family and friends. At first I thought it was a bit of harmless fun, but I quickly realized that the remedies did have deep effects.

One instance, in particular, stays in my head. It was a bright sunny summer's day and I was sitting in a Covent Garden pub with a friend, cheerily chatting. Gradually, we became aware of a young man sitting at the next table, slumped over a glass of water. He emanated total despair. I'm not normally a prier but I felt driven to talk to him, to ask him if there was anything we could do. He could barely bring himself to speak, but from what he told us there was no doubt that he was suicidal. Suddenly, I remembered I had a bottle of rescue remedy (a combination remedy for all emergencies) in my bag. I asked him if I could pop a couple of drops in his drink – he barely lifted his head and nodded. I don't think he would have cared if I'd said I was going to pour neat arsenic in it.

We sat in silence and he sipped his drink. Over five minutes the change began. He lifted his head and began to talk, to unburden himself of all the grief and pain he was suffering. By the time we came to leave we felt confident that he would no longer take his life. 'I don't know what you put in my drink,' he said, 'but I can't thank you enough.' We left him the bottle and the name of a good counsellor whom he promised he would see and walked out quite humbled by the power of these flowers.

Now, the remedies are almost household names – you can even buy them in Boots. And alternative therapists are finding that the remedies are not only powerful in their own right but that they can also augment the healing potential of other therapies. Homeopaths, healers, chiropractors, even some medical doctors, use the Bach remedies.

The remedies are simplicity itself: thirty-eight essences of common British plants and flowers, diluted much like homeopathic medicines. They are totally safe and very easy to administer – just a few drops on the tongue or in a drink. And they are the ultimate DIY therapy: this is one of the few systems of natural healthcare which can be quite safely practised by complete novices.

But be warned: their effects can be so profound that they might just turn your entire life around. The Bach remedies (and the other systems of flower and gem remedies that have followed in Bach's footsteps) do not work on the body – they react directly upon your personality. They are not seeking to heal your physical ailments; rather they seek to cleanse your psyche. And, at their deepest level, the aim is deeper still: to soothe your very soul.

The history

Numerous ancient cultures, including the Egyptian, Malay and African, employed flowers to treat emotional states and imbalances. Some even go as far as to say that flower and gem essences were the ultimate healing systems in the highly evolved mythical cultures of Atlantis and Lemuria. Whether or not that is true, what is certain is that, in Europe, essences were being used in the sixteenth century by the great healer Paracelsus to treat his patients' emotional problems. Around sixty years ago, the British physician Dr Bach established his thirty-eight flower remedies based on common trees and plants such as oak, walnut, clematis and mustard.

Dr Edward Bach (pronounced Batch) was an extraordinary

man. A medical doctor, he had seen the very worst in physical and mental suffering during his time as a physician in the First World War. He was also a highly successful bacteriologist and had his own business preparing vaccines. Then he was introduced to homeopathy and became completely converted to the 'subtle' methods of healing – methods that worked not by acting directly on the physical body but by influencing the energy system of the body to bring about change in the physical.

As he put it, 'Disease is in essence the result of conflict between Soul and Mind and will never be eradicated except by spiritual and mental effort. No effort directed to the body alone can do more than superficially repair damage.'

Like the classical healers Hippocrates and Paracelsus and the founder of homeopathy, Hahnemann, he felt convinced that there were 'no diseases, but only sick people'. So in 1930, he gave up his lucrative Harley Street practice to search for a healing system that would heal the person, not the disease, reasoning that once the psyche and soul were healed, the body would simply follow suit. Although he was deeply impressed by homeopathy, he felt the need, in addition, for a simple system that would deal with what he saw as the main source of disease: disharmony in the soul caused by negative thought patterns. Inspired by homeopathy's use of natural substances and fired by his deep love of nature, he looked to the countryside for the answer.

Bach found that, like many other people, he felt at his best in nature. And, as Bach flower therapist Maurice Griffin explains, 'It wasn't just the bright sun and the beauty of nature – he realized there was an essence that could be harnessed and used to help human beings, and animals as well, to overcome any difficulty or distress. He only had to put his hand over a flower and he could detect if that flower had a virtue that could help to counteract a negative state of mind.'

The result was thirty-eight remedies which, to Bach's mind, adequately covered all the negative states of mind. In recent years, other people have sought to expand the Bach system: there are now Californian flower essences, Himalayan flower essences, Tibetan and Australian flower essences, to name but a few. There are also gem and crystal essences, said to capture the healing power of minerals.

Ian White, an Australian naturopath and originator of the Bush Flower system, believes that, wonderful though Dr Bach's remedies are, the world has moved on and now needs a new set of flowers for healing. 'In the last sixty years, numerous changes have occurred in our awareness of ourselves and our world,' he says. 'The essences have evolved as a form of healing to help us keep pace with the changes.' He argues that sixty years ago, Dr Bach did not have to deal with such problems as learning skills, sexuality, thwarted creativity and anguished spirituality – all too common today. He believes that the new flower remedies (such as his own Bush Flower essences) can go right to the core of modern dilemmas and modern ailments.

The lowdown

At first sight the idea of these essences affecting anything – let alone personality – seems far-fetched. Bach believed that the healing power of plants lies in their energy, an energy that can bring body and soul back into harmony. In order to take that energy into our bodies, he surmised, it was not necessary to ingest the whole plant (as in herbalism) but to merely take in the essence of the plant, captured by putting the flowers in a glass bowl of pure spring water and allowing it to stand in the sunlight for a few hours. The water then, he found, would be imbued with the healing signature of the plant.

But how can this vague essence of the flower actually heal a damaged personality or a traumatized mind? The essences work on a vibrational level, invigorating and balancing our psyche. While everything in life vibrates to a certain frequency, the essence of flowers apparently vibrates on a very high level and so affects our bodies at their most subtle level. Rather than dealing with the dense matter of flesh and blood, the remedies go straight to the core of our being, working from the very inner levels out to the denser fabric of the emotional and physical body. Ian White puts it this way: 'The only difference between dense matter, such as antibiotics or a piece of wood, and subtle matter, such as a flower essence, is the frequency at which they vibrate. Subtle matter vibrates at speeds exceeding the speed of light.'

The session

Although you can easily treat yourself with flower and gem remedies, many practitioners use them as part of their practice. At the Ultimate Health Clinic in south-west London they even use the remedies to help you lose weight. Maurice Griffin and his wife, nutritionist Nicola, find that results are swifter, deeper and longer lasting when they back up standard nutritional therapy with the Bach flower remedies.

'Most people realize that even nutritional problems have an emotional link,' he says, 'and once you realize that, you can do something about it.' So while Nicola looks for hidden allergies and intolerances in her clients, Maurice probes to find the emotional blockages that stop them losing weight.

Although the remedies themselves are so gentle, finding the right remedy can be a painful process, akin to psychotherapy. Consultations take well over an hour and you can expect to be gently grilled on all aspects of what makes you tick: not just your responses to food but your whole attitude to life. The weight generally shifts quite quickly, but patients also find other benefits. Maurice has seen several people who were chronically depressed, even suicidal: the remedies pulled them back from the brink. Quite a few people come when they suffer a loss of confidence, often after losing their job. Others seek help when their marriages break down – the remedies gently soothe them through the 'dark night of the soul'.

Serena Smith combines the Australian Bush Flower remedies with her original discipline, hypnotherapy and psychotherapy. A corporate psychologist and member of the National Register of Advanced Hypnotherapists, she had been working very successfully for several years, achieving good results. However, once she started using the Bush remedies in conjunction with hypnosis her results became 'quite startling'. 'Both therapies can stand on their own,' she says, 'but the combination of the two is very dynamic and it certainly cuts down the length of treatment.'

Forget any notion of years of analysis or even the usual five or six sessions needed for most hypnotherapy: Smith generally sees her clients just two or three times. Sometimes all it takes is one solo session to cure anything from fears and phobias, addictions, depression, stress and even learning disorders.

Serena Smith has coined the phrase hypno-flower therapy for her unique combination therapy and, if orthodox doctors and psychotherapists might scoff, her patients have no doubts of the efficacy of her methods.

'I've seen everything from hair pulling to nail biting,' says Smith, 'but I think the most common problem is lack of confidence, low self-esteem, a feeling of being unworthy, a dislike of self.' She considers such feelings are on the increase as parental, school and media pressure increasingly makes us feel that we can never be good enough, never achieve enough, never be beautiful enough. But, she insists, the flower remedies can help. 'They can change that feeling of lack of self-worth to a feeling of self-esteem, of liking yourself. If you dislike your physical body there are even remedies for that.'

Before starting treatment Smith asks clients to fill out a detailed questionnaire which asks such questions as, 'Are you nervous to speak in public?' 'How do you feel about old age/dying?' 'Are you stuck in the past?' And even 'Have you had any problems conceiving?' The questionnaire not only guides Smith into the areas needing to be addressed under hypnotherapy but also gives her indications of which flower essences to prescribe.

After agreeing on the aim of the session, Smith settles you into a comfortable chair and asks you to concentrate on your breathing. Within a few minutes I was deeply relaxed and totally focused on Smith's calm but authoritative voice. She uses a barrage of state-of-the-art techniques to weed out unhelpful patterns of thought and replace them with more positive images. At one point, she asked me to think about the changes I wanted to make in my life and then invited me to look five years into the future – firstly, as if I had stayed the same and, secondly, as if I had implemented all the changes. Switching from fat, contented but stagnant Jane to slim, wildly successful and elated Jane was a spine-tingling experience and I was still repeating the exercise with the same frisson weeks later.

She then spent some considerable time bombarding my subconscious with positive statements about myself. At first, it feels slightly uncomfortable and a trifle embarrassing to hear someone repeat statements like, 'You have perfect self-control' and 'You can achieve anything you want' but, after a while, they stop sounding corny and begin to feel just right.

Smith often makes up individual tapes of such affirmations for her clients to play throughout the day because, as she explains, the more you repeat statements to your unconscious mind, the more it begins to believe them. And, once your subconscious mind believes something, it will move hell and high water to manifest that belief into reality. It's the reason why people who always believe that 'my life is a mess' find they cannot shift out of the mire, while wildly self-confident types just go from strength to strength.

Hypnotherapy has always been one of the most effective means of turning negative thought into positive, and the flower essences reinforce the message. As Ian White insists, 'They not only resolve negative beliefs but also make positive qualities within us come flooding to our conscious minds.'

Serena Smith firmly believes that combining the gentle force of these exotic plants with the power of hypnotherapy can have quite incredible, fast-acting and far-reaching results.

I have only tried the Bach remedies and the Australian Bush remedies, but that does not mean that the other systems are not equally effective. To my mind, some of them seem a little vague but, as with all therapies, I would advise you go with a system that makes sense (whether logically or intuitively) to you. Personally, I find it easier to relate to flowers I know: you, however, might find yourself drawn to the more mysterious flowers of other countries or the etheric beauty of gems and crystals. Rest assured that none of them can do you any harm.

The Bach flower remedies at a glance

These are the main personality traits associated with the thirty-eight remedies.

For fear   Aspen (vague, undefined fears); Mimulus (fear of known things – heights, spiders etc.); Cherry Plum (irrational thoughts and fears); Red Chestnut (over-anxiety and fear for others); Rock Rose (sheer terror, sudden shocks and alarm).

266

For uncertainty   Cerato (doubting your self-judgment); Gorse (hopelessness, pessimism); Gentian (despondency, discouragement); Hornbeam (lack of energy, listlessness); Scleranthus (indecisiveness), Wild Oat (lack of direction in life, uncertainty about career).

For loneliness   Impatiens (impatience); Heather (self-obsession), Water Violet (aloofness, disdain).

For over-sensitivity   Agrimony (torturing thoughts hidden behind cheerful facade); Centaury (timidness, subservience); Holly (envy, jealousy, hatred); Walnut (difficulty adapting to change).

For despondency or despair   Crab Apple (self-disgust); Elm (overwhelmed by responsibility); Larch (lack of confidence); Oak (for struggling on against the odds); Pine (guilt, self-blame), Sweet Chestnut (extreme despair); Star of Bethlehem (for after-effects of severe shock); Willow (resentment).

For over-concern for others   Beech (intolerance, have to be right); Chicory (selfishness, possessiveness); Vervain (over-enthusiastic, fanatical); Vine (domineering); Rock Water (self-repression).

For insufficient interest in the present   Chestnut Bud (keeps repeating same mistakes); Clematis (daydreaming); Honeysuckle (nostalgia); Mustard (depression); Olive (exhaustion, 'burn-out'); White Chestnut (persistent worries); Wild Rose (resignation, apathy).

RADIONICS

WHAT IS IT?   A system of healing that works on a quantum level, enabling the patient to be treated at a distance.

USED FOR   Virtually any condition can respond to radionics.

MOST SUITABLE FOR   People who find it hard to visit their practitioner; anyone who has a persistent, difficult condition that nothing seems to sort out.

NOT SUITABLE FOR   No contraindications. However, radionics does require a leap of imagination to accept.

PERFORMED   Fully clothed. You don't generally need to see your therapist in person – most consultations are carried out by post or telephone.

ANYTHING TO TAKE ORALLY?   Yes, you will often be prescribed herbal or homeopathic remedies, vitamins and minerals or radionic preparations.

STRESSBUSTER   Not directly.

COST   Medium to high.

NUMBER OF SESSIONS REQUIRED Depends entirely on the condition. Many people only consult their radionic practitioner when something goes wrong. Others check in periodically as a preventative measure, balancing themselves to avoid serious illness.

DIY No, this is one that needs training.

IF YOU LIKE THIS, TRY HEALTH KINESIOLOGY seems to appeal to people who like radionics. Many people like the face-to-face contact with a therapist and go direct to practitioners of either HOMEOPATHY or FLOWER REMEDIES who often use the same remedies.

Imagine long-distance medicine: you need to consult your doctor, but you are in America on business while your doctor is in the UK. So you simply phone him, explain your symptoms, put down the phone and wait. Back in the UK your doctor takes out your file and scans a small piece of hair you provided several years ago. Popping it in a machine, he directs a light beam through a series of cards for a few minutes: end of treatment. Three thousand miles away, you start to feel better.

Wishful thinking? Lurid imagination? Apparently not. Radionics is a system of healing which, although it sounds like futuristic science fiction, is being practised right here and now. Satisfied customers claim they have been cured of asthma, eczema, irritable bowel and chronic fatigue, to name but a few ailments. And patients find their treatment goes way beyond the physical: they develop new interests, start new careers and generally become happier as well as healthier.

The history

Radionic systems of healing have been in use since the early part of this century. The founding light of radionics was Dr Albert Abrams, an American doctor, considered to be quite a genius. He found that by percussing (a form of tapping) the body when the patient was facing West, he could detect areas of dullness which corresponded to diseases within the body.

His next step was to place a container with a piece of diseased tissue on the head of a perfectly healthy person. Percussing again, he found the same hollowness: the close contact of the diseased tissue altered the patient's nervous system in a manner that changed the percussive note. His theory was that the diseased tissue was radiating an abnormal wave form which had an influence on the healthy man.

Abrams researched over years, refining his techniques: he was soon able to produce the same diagnostic results merely by using a spot of blood on a piece of filter paper. He felt sure that the blood spots were retaining what he called 'human energy'.

Abrams started to market his equipment, the infamous 'black boxes' of radionics, and trained doctors in their use. Tests showed that they had a remarkable degree of accuracy, but the Royal Society of Medicine wasn't so sure, and radionics fell into disuse after Abrams' death.

It was an American chiropractor, Ruth Drown, who took up the radionic flag and carried it further along. She modified and developed the equipment and also realized that she could treat people from a distance. She had a remarkable success rate but possibly overstepped her mark by taking on too many patients. One complained, the US FDA (Food and Drug Agency) leaped in and she was put on trial in 1951. Nobody quite understood how radionics worked – they thought it was something to do with radio waves. Ruth Drown was convicted of fraud and medical quackery and sent to jail. Her radionic equipment was destroyed and when she came out of jail she soon died of a stroke.

However, in the UK, radionics kept its head down and kept going. An English engineer, George de la Warr, set out to put radionics on a solid scientific level, refining and rigorously testing the instruments. He too, was taken to court for fraud but the charges were dismissed.

More recently, radionics has taken on a fresh lease of life, finally beginning to gain credibility with new advances in physics. Perhaps surprisingly, not all in the medical profession dismiss radionics as outright hocus-pocus. After twenty-five years of practice, one of the foremost practitioners of radionics in the UK, Keith Mason, gets frequent referrals from GPs, dentists and specialists who find that radionics frequently has success with cases their orthodox techniques just can't reach. Now, there are even plans for a large research project with a London hospital – the aim is to study the effects of radionics on patients with irritable bowel syndrome and chronic fatigue.

The lowdown

But how, just how, does it actually work? Mason explains that we have to look beyond the chemistry and biology of modern medicine to the shadowy world of quantum physics. Quantum physicists see nothing odd or alien about a system of medicine that takes no notice of time or place; that ignores physical examination and can choose whether or not to treat you with pills or potions. The theories are extraordinarily complex and shake our very concept of the world, teaching that, far from being reassuringly solid bundles of flesh and bone, we appear to exist as vibrating parcels of sheer energy.

Illness, according to the radionic consultant, occurs when there is a disturbance to our energetic frequency. It's a little as though we were radio stations – sometimes the signal becomes confused and you need to twiddle the dial a bit. The causes for such disturbances, says Mason, are pretty basic: mechanical injury to the body; environmental stress (pollution, poisons, toxin); trauma; mental or emotional anxiety; hereditary and genetic factors. However, he adds, the most important factor of all is our personalities and understanding our purpose and role in life.

'Often people are not on their correct path in life,' he says. 'Without goals and ambitions, a person's energy is not channelled properly. It makes sense: if a person is at peace mentally, emotionally and energetically, it is very difficult for the physical body to be sick. Your immune system will be working well and you will simply fend off all sorts of diseases and deal with all kinds of environmental pollutants.'

The mind factor, he points out, is increasingly being accepted by orthodox medicine. 'Doctors totally accept that a businessman who might eat a good diet and be emotionally stable can develop an ulcer simply because the stress in his work affects the chemistry of his digestive tract,' he says. And just as doctors can generally guess who will be at risk from ulcers by analysing their patients' reactions to stress, so Mason can detect with uncanny accuracy which illnesses and diseases a person will be prone to, purely by analysing in greater depth the strengths and weaknesses of their personality, alongside past history and genetic factors.

Some people say that radionics is merely a form of faith healing. Certainly, Keith Mason says that, in actual fact, all the boxes and equipment of radionics aren't really necessary: what actually lies behind radionics is the interaction between mind (of the practitioner) and matter (the patient's body).

The session

Not surprisingly, with such a mind-bending supertherapy, there isn't really a session as such. The radionic practitioner will usually send you a detailed questionnaire, asking for details of your medical history, past illnesses and operations alongside your present health problems. It also includes questions on your hobbies and pastimes and quizzes you on your temperament. You will be asked to send back the questionnaire along with a small piece of hair. The hair itself is not chemically analysed but acts as a 'witness', a way of tuning in to the patient's vibration. It doesn't matter that the patient is a continent away from the hair or that the hair was taken several years ago: according to quantum theory, it remains in energetic equilibrium with its source and, even more incredibly, its energetic characteristics will vary from moment to moment according to the energetic patterns of the patient.

If you can accept this (and it does, practitioners admit, take a radical lateral shift in thinking), then it becomes logical (if not perhaps understandable) that by correcting imbalances of energy within the hair witness, you will set up a ripple effect and bring the rest of the patient back into balance.

However, radionics practitioners don't always rely on such subtle means of energetic healing. Mason generally draws on an eclectic range of far more mainstream disciplines.

'Often we send people back to their doctors,' he says, 'because there simply hadn't been an accurate diagnosis. We refer to dentistry in some cases because there can be links between general health and your teeth. For example, cystitis sometimes happens to women with mercury in certain teeth: change the fillings, and the problem goes away. Then again, we often find dietary solutions: many children develop skin and asthma problems because they can't cope with milk products. Or the problem might be mechanical, and so we advise they see a chiropractor or osteopath. Some people might need a homeopathic remedy or vitamins. We accept all the other complementary therapies and the orthodoxy as well – we use them all.'

And if sceptics say his successes are all based on nothing more than placebo effect or coincidence, he suggests they talk to his wife, Chrissie, who works entirely with animals. She cites the case of a horse which was a regular and keen eventer. Then it started to become difficult and unwilling to participate in long, arduous events. The owner took it to the vet and to a trainer, but both found nothing wrong and suggested it simply needed harder work and training. However Chrissie diagnosed two problems, one with its spine, one with its teeth. Some chiropractic manipulation and a dental check later, the horse was back in peak fitness and keenness.

Both the Masons have no doubt that, in the future, we will all take their form of healing for granted. For them the idea of a world in which you never even meet your doctor but can receive effective healing and precise medical advice, however far away you are, is perfectly normal – and eminently practical. For the rest of us, at least for now, it takes a giant leap of faith – a quantum leap of the imagination.

HEALTH KINESIOLOGY

WHAT IS IT?   A system of diagnosis and treatment that asks the body what it wants by means of muscle testing.

USED FOR   Many illnesses that have proved immune to other forms of medicine – both orthodox and complementary – seem to respond to Health Kinesiology, including psoriasis, ME, candida, PMS, frozen shoulder and bronchitis.

SUITABLE FOR   Everyone. Even pets can be treated. However some people might find it simply too weird.

NOT SUITABLE FOR   No contraindications.

PERFORMED   Fully clothed.

ANYTHING TO TAKE ORALLY?   No.

STRESSBUSTER   Not directly.

COST   High.

NUMBER OF SESSIONS REQUIRED   Sometimes just one – rarely more than three.

DIY   Yes. Simple health kinesiology can be learned at workshops.

IF YOU LIKE THIS, TRY   RADIONICS is almost as mind-bendingly weird, but radionic practitioners will give explanations (even if the explanation itself is weirder than the treatment).

Health Kinesiologists talk to bodies. Give a practitioner an hour with your body and it will tell him or her exactly what it's allergic to, precisely what is wrong with it and then it will calmly give the prescription.

Health Kinesiology is a therapy which has developed a precise means of diagnosing health and emotional problems and a swift means of resolving them. It starts off with a simple procedure to test muscles to ascertain allergies and intolerances and then veers into decidedly weird and wacky ways of treatment which even its practitioners cannot quite explain. However, apparently this most bizarre new therapy can treat everything from hay fever, asthma and arthritis, to dyslexia, nail-biting and depression. It can even improve your golf handicap.

The history

Health Kinesiology was originated by a Canadian, Dr Jimmy Scott, who started working primarily with allergy. Irritated that most forms of allergy testing were not really accurate, he stumbled upon a system of muscle-testing called kinesiology which appeared to be swift, sensitive and reliable. Its principle is that the body, at some deep unconscious level, knows precisely what it needs. By asking the body direct, the practitioner bypasses the conscious mind which might *think* it knows what is best but which has really lost touch with the body.

The kinesiologist asks questions by applying light pressure to the patient's outstretched arm while the patient is trying to keep the arm held still. If the body answers yes, the arm will resist the pressure and remain strong; if the answer is no, the muscle slightly weakens and the arm will drop. It's rather like dowsing using the body instead of a pendulum.

The lowdown

As yet, there are only a handful of practitioners in the UK, and the vast majority of homegrown scientists and doctors would laugh them merrily out of court. But in Germany and Switzerland, Health Kinesiology is not so ridiculed. Alongside the numerous practitioners who practise it as an individual discipline, an increasing number of doctors, pharmacists and vets are also using it as a remarkably accurate diagnostic tool.

While the muscle-testing makes sense, the treatment is quite hard to get your head around. One frequent form of treatment is by 'tapping' – touching the body with little tapping movements. This is used to clear the body of intolerances and allergies. The problem allergen (e.g. milk) is placed in a small phial resting on the stomach, while the therapist taps the acupuncture points down the body to allow the body to take the energy pattern of the milk on board. Practitioners say that, with tapping, it's quite possible to rid the person of their intolerance altogether. Ann Parker, who practises in the north of England, describes an MS (multiple sclerosis) patient who came to her in desperation. She had been told she was allergic to virtually everything and was only able to eat about six things. Now, says Anne, she can eat almost anything except red meat, black pudding and tropical fruit. In addition, her MS is much improved.

However, Jane Thurnell-Read who practises in Cornwall, points out that tapping isn't the only technique they use. Sometimes magnets or crystals are placed on the body; at other times you will have a homeopathic remedy or an essential oil – not to take, merely to hold against your body. Sometimes, again, you will be asked to think a certain word or phrase while the practitioner touches you. It all sounds horribly close to a witch-doctor's hocus-pocus. Jane Thurnell-Read agrees quite merrily.

'I know how bizarre it seems,' she says, 'but even people who have been so sceptical are forced to agree it works.' She cites the bank manager who couldn't stop biting his nails. When she asked his body what he needed to do, it answered back 'work on relationships.' The bank manager thought his relationships were just fine and walked out feeling foolish and gullible. However a fortnight later he was back. 'I still don't think I have a problem with relationships,' he muttered, and then added with a helpless shrug, 'but I *have* stopped biting my nails.'

Thurnell-Read finds Health Kinesiology excellent for dealing with severe emotional trauma because feelings can be released without having to delve back into the past or dwell on painful thoughts. And, yes, it has even enhanced sports performance. 'I've improved several people's golf handicaps,' she laughs, 'and there was also a woman who wanted to improve her badminton game. We asked what was stopping her winning and found she had a problem with being aggressive. When she started to win she felt sorry for the other person and allowed them to beat her. Now, she wins all her games.'

Jane has successfully treated people with psoriasis, ME, candida, PMS, frozen shoulder and bronchitis, to name but a few. She says her success rate across an immense range of illnesses is 'up in the high 90 per cent range' and she rarely sees patients more than two or three times. 'Some people take just one session,' she smiles. 'One woman said she was able to breathe through her nose for the first time in thirty years. She hadn't even got off the couch.'

Another patient was losing his eyesight due to thrombosis in his veins and had been told nothing could be done to save it by either surgery or medication. However, he found that after three sessions his vision gradually improved and this continued for eighteen months. Now he can drive again and enjoys his hobbies of wood-turning and reading. A recent eye examination confirmed that his eyesight had indeed significantly improved. Another client was astonished to find that all her hay fever symptoms disappeared after one visit. 'I had given up on conventional medicine,' she says. 'I had learnt to live with it. Then it vanished. I was astonished.'

Thurnell-Read predicts that this most curious of therapies will grow and grow in the years to come. We might even find out precisely how it works, she laughs. For the moment however, she (and the people she treats) are happy to live in ignorance and wonder – and much improved health. Having a talk to your body might just prove the most meaningful conversation you have ever had.

The session

When I saw Jane Thurnell-Read for my session I had no pressing problems that I needed sorting, so I merely asked her to talk to my body and see what *it* wanted for a change. I sat next to her with my arm outstretched as she quietly muttered, seemingly to my arm, asking it a long string of questions, pausing imperceptibly between each to gauge my arm's response. 'Is the problem physical? Emotional? Psychological?' She was nodding – evidently my arm was answering back. 'It's something physical,' she told me. 'Is it a body system? A body part? Digestive? Respiratory? Immune?' She rattled on at breakneck speed before announcing that my body wanted us to work on my thymus.

Frankly, I was surprised – of all the various parts of my body that regularly misbehave, my thymus has never, to my knowledge, stepped out of line. I barely knew what it did. 'You could be feeling tired a lot, unable to relax,' said Thurnell-Read. Well, that was certainly true. She proceeded to go into another intimate chat with my arm.

By now, I was feeling a trifle excluded from this cosy relationship. Jane swiftly translated: my body needed to be held at certain acupuncture points; it was asking for magnets to be placed on my collar bone and for some kind of crystal contraption to be held on my chest. I sat while Jane pressed various points on my face and body and Sellotaped the magnets on. No doubt about it, I felt like a complete idiot.

Jane promised that within a week or so I would feel more rested and relaxed, my memory would improve and I would find myself far more tolerant to food, tea and coffee. All good news, but all rather vague. What I really wanted to hear was that I would miraculously lose two stone – but then, unfortunately, weight loss isn't Jane's speciality. Looking back after a fortnight, if there *are* any benefits they are hard to gauge but then, to be fair, I didn't ask her to deal with any specific problem.

ELECTRO-CRYSTAL THERAPY

WHAT IS IT?   A system that aims to 'tune' the body back to its healthy vibration using electromagnetic fields amplified by crystals.

USED FOR   Practitioners claim it can balance virtually any disease and even help heal mechanical injuries.

MOST SUITABLE FOR   Many people see electro-crystal therapy as a 'last-chance' therapy. Perhaps most useful for people who want to actually *see* the problem in their bodies and how treatment affects it.

NOT SUITABLE FOR   No contraindications.

PERFORMED   Fully clothed for treatment. You may be asked to strip to underwear for the examination.

ANYTHING TO TAKE ORALLY?   No.

STRESSBUSTER   Not directly.

COST   Low to medium. Some therapists will treat children or those with life-threatening illness free.

NUMBER OF SESSIONS REQUIRED Varies. Regular weekly sessions for some months for serious complaints or injuries. Every few months for general balance.

DIY Some people, convinced of the power of electro-crystal therapy, buy their own machines and gizmos for home use.

IF YOU LIKE THIS, TRY Perhaps working with FLOWER AND GEM REMEDIES would appeal. HEALTH KINESIOLOGY and RADIONICS are more mysterious, if that's possible.

Acupuncturists talk of meridians, the invisible energy pathways that lie beneath the skin. Healers worry about *chakras*, swirling centres of energy in the body. But no-one has ever seen a *chakra* or a meridian under a microscope or with an X-ray, so who's to say they're there at all? Harry Oldfield and his growing band of electro-crystal therapists do because they have seen them before their very eyes.

Oldfield is no psychic, 'seeing' auras with clairvoyant eyes: he's an ex-science teacher who doesn't just tell you about your inner secret energy self, he lets you see it with your own eyes. He has developed a means of filming the body's subtle energies. While he scans you with a camera, a multi-coloured image of your body appears on his computer screen. On it you can see what the mystics have known for years and the scientists have refused to believe: energy points (the acupuncture points), energy channels (the meridians), energy centres (the *chakras*) and the cocooning egg-like field of energy that surrounds us (the aura). Not only does he see the systems of your energetic body, he also sees the blockages that cause disease. And he treats them. Electro-crystal therapy is another one of the supertherapies that sounds like pure science fiction, but this is science fiction you can actually see before your very eyes.

The history

Oldfield began his healing journey over twenty years ago with Kirlian photography. He discovered to his amazement that he could detect illnesses and diseases from the patterns of energy surrounding the photograph. Doctors and scientists were impressed with his findings. But when he began to develop more precise diagnostic tools and then start to treat – and heal – people, the orthodoxy turned away almost en masse.

However, the patients started to come in their hoardes, their numbers swelling by word of mouth. They came and they kept coming back because they found Harry's treatment, however weird and magical it might seem, actually worked. And we're not just talking about the odd cut or bruise, the stray headache, the irritation of a bout of flu. Oldfield and his disciples do what very few practitioners of alternative medicine would ever dare suggest: they talk about remissions and cures for even the most serious and terminal of diseases. They don't promise cures and they admit that there are times when people simply don't get well but, even so, they will freely talk about what most people would term miracles.

There's the man who broke his neck and was told to expect to live life in a wheelchair as a quadriplegic: now he walks and drives his own car rather than a wheelchair. There are people who swear they have been cured of eye diseases: degeneration of the optical nerve, glaucoma, retinitis pigmentosa. There are the tales of cancer sufferers who have been given weeks to live: years later they are all still living and praising Harry Oldfield.

The lowdown

The system which Oldfield now uses to detect illness and imbalance is called a Poly Contrast Interface or PIP and it is being touted as the X-ray of the future. The camera looks at very high frequencies of light not normally detected by the human eye. A computer programme diagnoses the waves of light and gives each a different colour reading so you can literally see the shape of your own energy.

A trained therapist knows what to look for: energy centres that are weak or blocked; wavery meridians where the energy isn't getting through; dull patches that could indicate a physical swelling or tumour.

Based on the findings of the PIP, the therapist will decide which areas need balancing and how much energy needs to be 'beamed' at your body to correct the problem. The process is known as electro-crystal therapy and its name sums it up: electromagnetic fields are beamed at the patient, using crystals to amplify the energy. Oldfield found that, if disease showed up as a disturbance in the body's own force-field, then directing a correcting vibratory pattern back into the body would correct the imbalance.

'I'm like a piano tuner,' he says. 'All I do is get out my tuning fork of crystal and tweak the strings. Then they are able to play their Moonlight Sonata or whatever.' However, as he points out, how long the 'cure' lasts, depends on the patient. 'The only problem is how long will it stay in tune,' he smiles. 'The onus is now on the owner of the instrument, and if they go back and abuse it and play the wrong kinds of tunes in their life, they are going to get the same kind of pattern emerging again.'

The session

I met Harry Oldfield many years ago when he was the only person practising his brand of weird science. Now he has trained hundreds of people in his techniques, and there are practitioners all over the UK and Europe.

I decided to visit the Yantra Vibrational Energy Centre in west London, to see how electro-crystal healing has developed. Five years ago, Harry had correctly diagnosed my health problems, both past and present. I was keen to know whether I was in better shape now.

Julie Wood, the therapist at Yantra, first 'tuned in' with one of Harry's earlier tools, moving a meter that reads sound waves in the body around me, noting down any imbalances. Then she asked me to strip down to my underwear while she pointed the PIP scanner at me. Suddenly, there I was on the small computer screen, my body shape clearly visible but covered in swirling bands of colour. Julie pointed out interesting areas as she scanned. The straight lines of colours stretching down my arms were my meridians ('nice and straight'); the clear blue circle on my forehead was my brow chakra ('lovely and clear'). My organs all looked fine and I was generally pretty OK, except for slight blockages in the feet and wrists (I suffer from terribly cold hands and feet). There was some slight disturbance around a couple of teeth (I've been putting off a visit to the dentist). And my old back strain was there in multi-colour for all to see.

However a couple of things didn't make sense: firstly she said there was a lot happening in my throat, something viral going on now or about to come. Then she noted congestion between the eyes and congestion in the stomach. However, she said, all in all, I wasn't in bad shape but she would give me a short blast of electro-crystal therapy to give my immune system a bit of a boost. Perhaps this, she suggested, might ward off the throat problems. It appears that the PIP can detect illnesses and problems even before they happen.

A few short calculations and she had worked out what frequencies I needed for optimum balance. Sitting in a chair I was plugged into a small machine, with a kind of rod pinned over my thymus area and a headband of flexible plastic filled with crystals plonked over my head. Treatment is totally painless – in fact, you don't even feel a thing and most normal sessions would last for an hour.

To be honest, I didn't notice any difference after the session – although, to be fair, I was only on the machines for about a third of the normal time. But a few weeks later, I just happened to be reading through Julie's notes on my scan. Maybe it was sheer coincidence, but she had virtually predicted my present condition word for word: stricken with a miserable bout of gastric-like flu, I had a throbbing throat, congested sinuses and an upset stomach. It was all there in my PIP scan. Maybe in the future we will all pop in for a quick PIP to check out what nasty predispositions are lurking in our bodies – and zap them before they get a chance to play havoc with our health.

POLARITY THERAPY

WHAT IS IT?   A complete system that aims to balance the body's energy via bodywork, nutrition, exercise and counselling.

USED FOR General balancing of health; most conditions improve but consistent good results with migraine, digestive problems, allergies, ME, back pain and sciatica.

MOST SUITABLE FOR People who want to take a dynamic interest in their health; for those with stress-related illness and any debilitating conditions. Those who are fascinated by Eastern systems of healing but want a Westernized approach.

NOT SUITABLE FOR Cleansing diets are not advisable for people who are very ill or weak – or for the very young or old. Certain points are not used during pregnancy. Active cancer has to be treated very cautiously. For best effects, you need to be prepared to overhaul all aspects of your life.

PERFORMED   Mostly fully clothed unless you have a structural problem which can be seen more easily undressed.

ANYTHING TO TAKE ORALLY?   You will most probably be asked to adapt your diet. Quite frequently, polarity therapists recommend cleansing diets or juicing.

STRESSBUSTER Yes, polarity therapy will train you to deal with stress; the bodywork is stressbusting in itself.

COST Low to medium.

NUMBER OF SESSIONS REQUIRED Start off with once a week for a few weeks then once a fortnight – clear results are usually obtained within six to ten weeks.

DIY Yes. You will be advised on diet and given exercises to do at home.

IF YOU LIKE THIS, TRY Polarity therapy developed many of its concepts from AYURVEDA and NATUROPATHY, so these might appeal; so might other bodywork systems such as ZERO BALANCING.

The human body is simply a living magnet. Just like a magnet, we have electromagnetic currents of energy flowing constantly backwards and forwards between positive and negative poles. Polarity therapy teaches that, if we could only regulate a balanced flow of energy, we would all enjoy rude good health. The therapy is little-known in this country but, in America, polarity therapy is a popular form of complementary healthcare. It's easy to see why – combining nutrition, exercise, bodywork and counselling, it's a totally holistic therapy. And its insistence on DIY techniques provides a clear blueprint for healthy living. It is, quite simply, a very neat synthesis of Eastern and Western therapeutic techniques; a potted 'best of' natural healthcare.

The history

The founder of polarity therapy was an extraordinary man called Randolph Stone. Born in 1890 he studied to be a Lutheran minister and then, after recovering from a severe illness, worked his way around the west of America as a labourer. While getting his body fit he was also expanding his mind, studying a bewildering array of religious thought and philosophy. He practised fasting and meditation and then decided to train as a physician, studying osteopathy, chiropractic and naturopathy. He set up practice in Chicago and enjoyed considerable success.

However, he felt that he still did not have the complete prescription for health and began to study Eastern systems of medicine, including Ayurveda and yoga. With great excitement he found that other cultures felt, as he did, that the basis of good health lay purely in energy. Blocked energy was, to his mind, the root cause of all physical illness and mental unhappiness.

It took him fifty years to pull together strands from all these traditions into the comprehensive package that finally became polarity therapy. He continued practising in America, but increasingly took his healing art to India where he felt people needed him more. The treatment he provided there was free, and he took on only the most hopeless cases, those that would not respond to any other methods of treatment. He said, 'This I consider a fair test of polarity therapy.'

The lowdown

Dr Stone believed there was one, and only one, disease in the world – blocked energy. 'Disease is not an entity, nor a fixed thing,' he said. 'It is nothing but a blockage of the currents of life in their flow and pattern circuits. All pain is but an obstruction of that energy-flow. A cure constitutes reaching the life current within and re-establishing a free flow of its energy currents. Anything short of this is but a relief measure.' [*Health Building*, by Dr Randolph Stone (CRCS Publications)].

Stone believed the life-force in humans to be precisely the same as the life-force in the whole of creation: 'It whirls round in the smallest microscopic cell in the same manner that it spins in the largest galaxy.' All living things have a positive, negative and neutral pole. He taught that energy flows from the centre of any system to its circumference and returns by magnetic pull. It will flow from the top downwards, from within to without. The current is, he said, like 'a radio wave flowing out in every direction from the grand central broadcasting station. The wave has two aspects . . . it flows outwards from the central dynamo of all creation and it flows back toward that dynamo.'

Stone followed the Indian concept that energy comes down

through the third eye centre in three currents: the *pingala*, a positively charged current; the *ida*, a negatively charged current; and the *sushumna*, the vertical neutral current. These three currents spiral down the spine, creating five *chakras* or energy centres, where they cross over each other. Each *chakra* is governed by an element.

The throat *chakra* is governed by ether and creates stillness, harmony and balance. The emotions are centred here, particularly grief.

The heart *chakra* governs air in this system and is concerned with conscious desire, mental activity and thought. Dreamy or anxious people are often stuck in the air element. Air also governs the lungs and respiration, kidneys and nervous system. An imbalance here can show as tense shoulders and a congested rib cage, excessive sweating and excessive thirst.

The solar plexus *chakra* governs fire – the warmth of healing and the power of the intellect; sight and insight, hunger and digestion. Anger and resentment can be carried here and imbalance can cause digestive problems, poor circulation, energy slumps and tired eyes.

Water is attached to the genital *chakra*, it governs unconscious emotions and attachments, gut responses and deep feelings. It rules the generative system, the lymphatic system and the secretory systems.

The base *chakra*, at the sacrum, is linked with the element of earth. It governs the colon and rectum, and imbalance can manifest as constipation or diarrhoea. If the flow is blocked at this level the person will tend towards hypochondria and will not be 'grounded'.

The polarity therapist is looking for imbalances in the elements and stagnation of energy. Then, he or she will attempt to coax the system back to good working order with a combination of bodywork, exercise, nutrition and counselling. Polarity therapy follows the principles of the other complete systems, such as Ayurveda, TCM and naturopathy, and overhauls all aspects of life. It is quite unique, however, in its insistence on counselling as part of the total healthcare package. Few supertherapies include counselling as an automatic part of treatment. The only aspect missing from the polarity prescription is herbalism. While Ayurvedic and traditional Chinese physicians and naturopaths quite often use herbs to stimulate healing, Stone made no mention of them in his system.

The session

I visited Rosamund Webster, who trains polarity therapists in Cheltenham. The first thing she, and most other polarity therapists, will do is ask you to monitor your diet for around five days *before* you come to the first session. You don't adapt your diet in any way at this stage but simply write down everything you eat and drink. This allows the therapist to ascertain how your energy is balanced.

When I arrived at Rosamund's treatment rooms, we sat down opposite each other in comfortable chairs, and she spent some time simply asking me how I felt and what my problems were. Unfortunately, when I saw her I was deep in the throes of a vicious bout of flu: more or less everything was out of balance. 'Your throat infection shows the ether element out of balance,' she said. 'Sinus problems are a problem of air and water, and you have an air condition in your chest.' She decided I needed a good session of bodywork to try to bring everything back into line.

Bodywork is essential to polarity – indeed many people forgo the dietary advice and the counselling and just ask for the hands-on treatment. And, although polarity therapists might gently suggest you try other parts of their therapy, they will never insist – the responsibility for your health lies firmly in your own hands. As soon as Rosamund started to touch me, Stone's osteopathic and chiropractic legacy became clear. But so too did other concepts: the pressure point techniques of acupressure and reflexology, plus the energy-balancing of Indian and Chinese therapeutic massage.

Rosamund performed the first part of my treatment while I sat on a chair; then she asked me to move on to the couch. For the most part, polarity bodywork is performed through clothing although, if you displayed a distinct structural problem, you might be asked to remove clothing so the therapist could clearly see what was happening. The touch is firm and focused, pressing deeply into points of tension and manipulating stiff joints. However, the intention is not just to look at the physical body but also to balance the energetic or magnetic field of the whole person. Polarity sees the centre of the human body – from the top of the head down through the spinal cord – as the neutral pole. The right side of the body and head is the positive pole; the left is the negative. Therapists use their right hand to give energy; the left to soothe. Stroking downwards is reckoned to be soothing, while stroking upwards is stimulating. Standard techniques include gently rocking or shaking parts of the body to stimulate energy-flow, alongside more traditional massage and manipulation. It sounds complicated, but as the client (polarity doesn't use the term patient, instead believing that you are a partner in the healing process), you don't need to understand the theory – you just lie back and enjoy a very pleasant sensation of deep relaxation.

A typical polarity session will always include bodywork. In addition, you will be given clear guidelines on diet. Food is prescribed as medicine, and Stone believed firmly in cleansing diets and the power of fresh vegetables and fruit juice for healing. His original diet was purely vegetarian but now, says Rosamund, therapists feel meat in moderation is fine. Time is also set aside to just talk. Polarity insists that emotional wellbeing is an essential part of therapy and you will be encouraged to talk freely about your life.

The final part of the polarity equation is polarity yoga. Stone worked out his own form of yoga which consists of simple poses held either statically or while gently rocking. Rosamund Webster teaches clients the precise exercises which will balance or stimulate the various elements and says, 'It's a very neat system and it doesn't take long to do – five minutes for a great energy boost.'

Polarity therapy, she promises, is not only effective, it's very safe. There are certain movements which are not performed during pregnancy, and she would not give a stringent cleansing diet to anyone very weak, very young or very old. Aside from that, she claims, we could all benefit, although the conditions that respond most dramatically tend to be digestive problems and allergies, ME and debilitating conditions, stress-related illness and back pain.

Juicing for health

Polarity therapy strongly advocates the use of fresh natural fruit and vegetable juices to aid healing and general health. If you have a juicer try the following:

For constipation Cabbage, spinach, celery and lemon juice.

For skin conditions Carrot, beetroot and celery juice.

For arthritis Carrot, celery and cabbage juice.

For high blood pressure Celery, beetroot and carrot juice.

For asthma and catarrhal conditions Carrot and radish juice.

For low blood pressure Carrot, beetroot and dandelion juice.

To open up sinuses and air passages Horseradish and lemon juice (100g/4 oz horseradish and 50 ml/2 fl oz lemon juice, combined with one teaspoon of garlic juice and a tablespoon of honey – take a teaspoonful four times daily).

To help you sleep Celery juice.

To soothe the nerves Lemon and lime juice.

For sore throats and colds Lemon, lime and pineapple juice.

The famous polarity liver flush Three to four tablespoons of pure cold-pressed olive or almond oil with twice the amount of fresh lemon juice. Add three to six cloves of garlic, plus fresh ginger to taste. Said to clear the liver, the kidneys and the intestinal tract and to restore correct chemical balance if combined with a cleansing diet. The only problem is that it tastes disgusting and makes your breath smell foul as well.

The purifying diet

Polarity therapy is very fond of different cleansing diets. 'Stop the World' in Somerset use one very similar to Dr Stone's at their detoxing weeks (see TOXINS AND DETOXING in GOOD FOOD). The regime is tough but it does seem to clear out the body. If you are in good health, you could try this for a few days, but if in any doubt, check with your physician. Don't be surprised if you get the stray headache or excessive sweating – it's quite common as your body throws out toxins.

The following diet is supposed to be wonderful for constipation, high blood pressure, arthritis, rheumatism, congestion and toxicity. You will naturally lose several pounds and should feel cleaner and lighter. Try it for a weekend for starters. If you continue it for a week, it would be ideal to combine it with MLD and skin-brushing to stimulate the lymph, plus gentle stretching and yoga.

For the duration of the diet, cut out all dairy produce, regular tea and coffee, alcohol, all carbohydrates and starchy foods. Water can be drunk freely.

DAILY PLAN

First thing   Two or more cups of hot herbal tea made from equal amounts of licorice root, anise or fennel, peppermint and fenugreek. Add fresh ginger, lemon juice and honey to taste.

Breakfast   Liver flush drink (see page 290).

Mid-morning (two hours after breakfast)   225 ml/8 fl oz or more of fresh vegetable juice, made from cabbage, lettuce, carrots and beetroot. Add radish or onion if you like and ginger, lemon, honey and garlic to taste.

Lunch (noon)   Raw salad of fresh lettuce, cabbage, grated carrots, radishes, cucumber, tomato, onions and sprouts. You can use a little dressing of almond, olive or sesame oil with lemon, garlic, onion and ginger. A piece of fresh fruit makes for dessert.

Mid-afternoon   Glass of fresh vegetable juice (see above).

Evening meal (around 6 p.m.)   Fruit: choose from apples, pears, grapes, pomegranate, papaya. Plus herb tea. If you are very hungry, you can repeat the lunchtime salad.

MAGNETOTHERAPY

WHAT IS IT?   A system of treatment using electromagnetic fields.

USED FOR   To speed up healing of injuries; ease insomnia; give increased energy; possibly improve arthritis.

SUITABLE FOR   Those who like their therapies slightly more scientific and high-tech.

NOT SUITABLE FOR   Anyone with a pacemaker; pregnant women; those with cancer.

PERFORMED   Fully clothed but without shoes and jewellery.

ANYTHING TO TAKE ORALLY?   No.

STRESSBUSTER   Yes.

COST   Low to medium.

NUMBER OF SESSIONS REQUIRED   For medical conditions, ten days of daily sessions are recommended.

DIY   Yes, plenty: you can buy mattresses, pillows, inner soles, hand balls, personal packs, but they are quite expensive.

IF YOU LIKE THIS, TRY   There's nothing quite like it – however, for weirdness factor, HEALTH KINESIOLOGY could appeal.

Sometimes it feels as though you're running on worn-out batteries. You find yourself getting slower and slower until you virtually grind to a halt. You can blame it on lifestyle, eating habits, the school holidays or excessive workloads but, according to Japanese scientists, there could be a more prosaic cause. It might be that you simply need your batteries recharging. In other words, you need a dose of magnet power.

The history

The idea that magnets have remarkable properties is nothing new. Cleopatra is even said to have worn one on her forehead to keep her beautiful and young. But it is only in the last thirty years that the mythology has been proven as medical fact. In 1959, Dr Robert Becker and Dr Andrew Bassett were working on the regeneration of amphibian limbs when they realized the potential for using electromagnetic fields to heal human orthopaedic problems. Electromagnetic fields were used in last resort cases where gangrene had left amputation as the only option. The success rate was so outstanding that orthopaedic surgeons were stunned.

Meanwhile, in the USA, NASA (National Aeronautics and Space Administration) were finding that their astronauts were returning to earth feeling sick and debilitated. Intensive research revealed that they were suffering withdrawal from the earth's magnetosphere, which allows the blood to circulate properly and be thoroughly oxygenated. NASA promptly placed static magnets in the spacesuits and within the spacecraft and the problem was overcome. It's an effect known as the Hall Effect – blood-flow is stimulated by magnetic pads attracting electrically charged particles (positive and negative ions) in the bloodstream which, in turn, attract oxygen.

Many of us suffer a similar problem, albeit on a lesser level, even though we generally travel no further than to work and back.

Living in concrete cities, travelling in steel cars, buses, trains and planes, we are missing out on the health-giving benefits of natural magnetism, and so our circulation (and as a consequence, our entire body) is working under par.

In Japan, magnetotherapy is as mainstream as aspirin, and every businessman worth his yen has a magnetic therapy couch costing thousands of pounds in his penthouse. Even the humblest corner store boasts a range of magnetic products – from insoles to car-cushions, from back-massagers to mattresses. Now, the rest of the world is catching on: the FDA (the US Food and Drug Administration) had funded a symposium to review and explore the possible uses of electromagnetic field therapy and, so far, the conclusion seems to be that magnetotherapy will soon be a major complementary therapy, available to every doctor. Already, US doctors are seeing benefits and are starting to use magnetotherapy for low-back pain, shingles, diabetic neuropathy, degenerative joint disease, chronic fatigue, asthma and even sore throats. Some practitioners have even claimed that the use of magnetic products has enabled them to reduce their prescriptions of steroids and asthmatic medicine by 60–70 per cent.

The lowdown

Magnetotherapy, sometimes known as magnotherapy, may be a multi-billion pound industry, but it's one that is based on solid scientific research rather than marketing hype. Clinical trials and studies have shown that using magnetism can have wide-reaching beneficial effects: from general wellbeing (improving sleep, concentration and energy levels while alleviating stress and tension) through injuries (aiding recovery of torn muscles, ligaments and tendons, accelerating the healing of bone fractures, reducing swelling and bruising) to ameliorating serious medical conditions (improving mobility in rheumatic and arthritic conditions, easing migraine, restoring hormonal imbalance and helping in chronic fatigue).

Companies such as Nikken which enjoy a large slice of the Far Eastern magnetic market are now introducing their range of products to the UK. London's Hale Clinic has been trial-ling the magnetic therapy bed and, so far, the results have been encouraging. It has been found useful in cases of insomnia and low energy plus it gives relief, albeit temporarily, for slipped discs. Although it doesn't quite cure injuries, it certainly seems to speed up recovery. Patients also find interesting side effects. Jet lag seems to be diminished and hangovers seem to disappear. Some have discovered that they have mysteriously lost the desire to smoke, while many others have reported that a magnetic boost can *increase* other desires – it appears that magnetotherapy does wonders for your sex life.

Many doctors, both in Japan and the USA, see magnetism as a new force to be reckoned with in the medical field, and some researchers are even suggesting that magno-power might hold the secrets of anti-ageing and increased lifespan. And if magneto-therapy could allow us to keep going without keeling over by the wayside, then soon we'll all be queuing up for a little recharging as a matter of course.

The session

Before treatment at the Hale Clinic I was asked whether I was pregnant, had a pacemaker or active cancer, as the bed is not suitable for people with these conditions. I removed my shoes and jewellery, then laid down gingerly on the bed which looks like a cross between a sunbed and a space pod. It hums and whirs but you don't really feel anything – certainly no weird force-fields. After a few minutes, my feet began to tingle, and as I reached the fifteen minute cut-off point, the machine was starting to warm up considerably. The optimum period of treatment is once a day for ten days, but most people tend to test the bed and, if they like the effect, they usually buy products for home use. The inner soles, which are supposedly particularly good for improving circulation and sparking up energy levels, take some getting used to – they're not particularly heavy, but as they also aim to stimulate acupressure points on your feet, it feels somewhat like walking with a handful of small pebbles in your shoes. The car-seat is decidedly itchy and the mattress gives you a fair approximation of sleeping on Brighton beach. But these are minor considerations if you're sleeping better, feeling livelier, more focused and generally healthier.

SOUND THERAPY

WHAT IS IT?   The use of sound as a healing agent – by listening to certain sounds, making certain sounds yourself or having a therapist direct healing sound at your body.

USED FOR   Stress relief; headaches and migraine; increased energy. In the future, it is believed that sound healing will have a far wider range of applications.

SUITABLE FOR   Everyone. People who feel they can't use their voice would, in fact, benefit enormously from experiential workshops.

NOT SUITABLE FOR   No contraindications.

PERFORMED   Fully clothed.

ANYTHING TO TAKE ORALLY?   No.

STRESSBUSTER   Yes, very much so.

COST   Varies. Workshops are usually quite reasonable. Individual sessions are in the medium-priced range.

NUMBER OF SESSIONS REQUIRED   No set amount prescribed. One workshop can set you up for DIY practice.

DIY   Yes, there are workshops, books and tapes available.

IF YOU LIKE THIS, TRY   Therapies that also think in terms of vibrations include ELECTRO-CRYSTAL THERAPY, RADIONICS and HEALTH KINESIOLOGY. COLOUR THERAPY might also appeal. But there is nothing to compare to the sound of your own liberated voice.

When we were children, we sang for joy. We yelled if we were angry and we wailed if we got hurt. And yet, as adults, we rarely use a fraction of our voices. We learn not to cry or groan; we hate having to speak in public and if, for any reason, we have to sing, most of us squeak like mice or simply mouth the words.

And yet a growing band of researchers believe that by refusing to vocalize we are missing out on a simple, free and easy way to release stress, improve our moods and even heal ourselves.

'Our voice is unique,' says Susan Lever, who teaches people how to rediscover their natural voice. 'It says so much about who we are, it's so personal that often people try to distort it. So many people try to copy other people's voices, have "telephone" voices or try to get rid of dialects. They do it because often they have been given a lot of early messages that it's not OK to be who they are.' A false voice is a stressed voice and, if we are straining our speaking voice, we are often massacring our singing voice.

The history

In earlier times, singing was a natural part of daily life: our predecessors sang as they worked, sang as they worshipped and sang for pleasure. They probably never realized that they were following an age-old tradition of using the power of therapeutic sound. The ancient esoteric schools of India and Tibet, Greece and Egypt all taught the importance of the power of sound: vibration was held to be the basic creative force of the universe. The Bible teaches the same thing: 'In the beginning was the Word.' The occult science of Quaballah, the hidden teachings of Judaism, places precise and great importance on sounds. And it's no coincidence that, in Ancient Greece, the god Apollo was responsible for both music and medicine: healing temples brought about cures purely by harmonizing both body and spirit through the power of music.

The Greek philosopher Pythagoras formulated the idea that the universe behaved like a vast instrument fitted with a single string which stretched from spirit to matter. He was better known for his theory of the 'music of the spheres', that as the planets moved through the universe they created differing, but harmonically linked, sounds. It sounds delightfully fanciful until you realize that scientists have recently equated different sounds with different planets – and, yes, they are harmonically related, just as Pythagoras said.

But Pythagoras wasn't content just to listen to the music: he healed with it. Pythagoras had a school where he taught his wisdom on three levels: in the first level, pupils learned about the proportions in music and became conversant with the harmonics in a chord; the second level dealt with the mathematics of music as well as individual purification and mental self-control. The third, and highest level was where pupils were taught the secrets of healing with sound and music.

Such knowledge was subsequently lost or went underground, and the science of healing through sound all but vanished for centuries. However, the twentieth century has seen a huge increase in interest in the mathematics and science of sound. In the 1920s a German scientist called Hans Kayser became intrigued with harmonics and worked out number ratios linking harmonics with a vast series of sciences: from chemistry and physics to astronomy and architecture. Meanwhile Dr Hans Jenny, a Swiss scientist, took the understanding of the intrinsic relationship between sound and form a huge leap forward. He put various substances (sand, dust, paste, water and other liquids) on steel plates and then vibrated the plates at different frequencies. An amazing thing happened: the blobs of paste or water began to move, not randomly, but as if given form.

A fascinating sideshoot of this is something I have never seen but have heard reported many times: if the sound of the mantra Ohm is vibrated round a dish containing sand, the sand is said to move into the shape of a mandala or sacred geometric pattern.

298

The lowdown

Simply making different sounds can affect your mind in minutes. As Susan Lever explains, 'If you feel low and you make happy sounds, it will lift you without a doubt. Your breathing will automatically change and so will your physiological state. You will find you have a lot more energy, a lot more confidence and that you have a lot less stress.'

Singing in the bath will help no end, but researchers are now going even further: some believe that sound could be, quite literally, the medicine of the future.

'Disease is simply part of our body vibrating out of tune,' says Jonathan Goldman, pioneering sound-therapist and author of *Healing Sounds* (Element). 'Every organ, bone, tissue and other part of the body has a healthy resonant frequency. When that frequency alters, that part of the body vibrates out of harmony and that is what is termed disease. If it were possible to determine the correct resonant frequency for a healthy organ and then project it into that part which is diseased, the organ should return to its normal frequency and a healing should occur.'

He believes that, by creating sounds which are harmonious with the 'correct' frequency of the healthy organ, we could all learn how to heal ourselves, bringing our bodies back into balance. He and other sound researchers have been focusing most of their attentions on the sacred chants of varying traditions, believing that the high-frequency harmonics which most of them share, could be having profound effects on both the mind and body.

Dr Alfred Tomatis, a French physician and sound researcher, believes that Gregorian chants could actually have a neurophysiological effect which charges the brain. On researching sacred chanting round the world, he discovered that many of the chants were employing very high frequencies (around 8,000 Hz) which were capable of stimulating the central nervous system and the cortex of the brain. Dr Tomatis himself says that he manages with less than four hours of sleep a night purely as a consequence of listening to four hours a day of harmonic sounds. Dr Mark Ryder of the Southern Methodist University in the USA discovered more benefits. By merely *listening* to music that was high in harmonic content his subjects reduced respiration and heart rate, calming and relaxing the entire brain and body. If you actually *make* the sounds yourself, the effects are even greater.

How does it happen? Goldman believes that when sound healing is taking place a process called 'entrainment' occurs: everything within the body that has a rhythm (the heartbeat, respiration, brain-waves, movement in the intestine etc.) starts to change in order to synchronize with the rhythm of a more powerful body – the healer.

The session

I have not experienced individual sound therapy myself, but what happens in a session is that the healer directs specific sounds at certain parts of the body. Journalist Jane Merer, writing in *The Independent* of her experience with Jonathan Goldman describes a session this way. She was asked to stand with her back to a wall with her eyes shut while Goldman made 'loud, strange noises directed at various parts of my body'. He sounded, she says, like a Buddhist monk. 'I start to feel some odd sensations,' she continues, 'an echoing hum in the bones and, finally, what feels like a small explosion in the centre of my forehead. I open my eyes and Mr Goldman is sitting on the floor shouting into my feet. Surprisingly, the headache that has accompanied me all day has gone.'

Jonathan Goldman has set up a sound healing centre in New York and is planning more but, at present, there are very few people who actually use sound directly as a healing mechanism. That will surely change and change quite quickly. However, for the time being, there are plenty of workshops that will teach you how to get back to using your voice, or you can take one-to-one lessons if you're shy about unleashing your voice in public. In practice, inhibitions tend to fly out of the window. Remember, the aim here is not to sing a perfect aria but to make sounds with a healing vibration. Anyone, however tone-deaf, can do the latter.

This is one area where you can do a lot on your own. Susan Lever suggests you start off by finding your natural voice and relearning how to speak and sing without strain or effort. Often, that involves relaxing and teaching yourself to let the voice come naturally from the whole body, rather than holding it tight in the throat. Learn to resonate. Once this happens, she warns, you might find some surprising side effects. 'Often it starts to release long-standing blocks and tensions,' she says. 'If you have always spoken or sung from your throat, it is probably a protection mechanism. Start singing from your heart or your abdomen and you might find something else coming up – old grief, hurt, anger . . .'

Tapes of harmonic singing and overtone chanting are readily available by mail order and, although they take a bit of getting used to, they certainly have an interesting effect on your energy levels. Jonathan Goldman's book and DIY tape are also a very useful introduction. I tested out his tape *Harmonic Journeys* (Spirit Music) sitting at my desk, wide awake and insomniac late at night, in a highly analytical (and somewhat sceptical) mood. I followed his instructions and joined him in toning different vowel sounds, imagining the sound coming from varying parts of the body. It started with a deep 'uuh' sound, resonating at the base of the spine, and moved right through the body, ending with a high 'iiiii' from the top of the head. Within minutes, I was deeply relaxed and it soon began to feel as though the sound was resonating *me* rather than I resonating the sound. I'm not sure how long the tape lasted because I totally lost track of time but, having finished it, I went straight to bed and had the best night's sleep I'd had in months.

'Sound is vibration,' says Goldman, 'and everything in the universe is in a state of vibration.' You can break a glass by matching its vibration and bring down a bridge by stamping out a rhythm over it, so he reasons that, if you can destroy with sound, then there is no reason why you can't heal as well. Start with the odd hum, a few rounds of Bruce Springsteen in the bath and see where it ends. You could find yourself tuning up your whole life.

Hum yourself happy: sing yourself sane – DIY sound techniques

- Humming is a good way of calming yourself. If you're feeling stressed, anxious or nervous, just sit quietly and hum very gently. Feel the hum resonating through your body. Where can you feel it? Does it change if you alter the note of the hum?
- Exaggerated yawning is ideal if you're feeling tired. We hold

a lot of tension in our jaws and mouths and stretching the mouth releases tension. Give a good stretch as well to really wake up the whole body.

• If you're feeling irritable and tense, try an elongated, noisy sigh. Chris James, the Australian workshop leader, recommends deep groaning as well to release any negative emotions. The key is to forget about being polite and really let go.

• Take every opportunity to sing. Sing along with the radio, while you're doing the housework, while you're in the bath or, even better, while you're driving in your car. Don't worry about what your voice sounds like, simply enjoy really belting it out.

• Try singing the different vowel sounds – uuuh, ooo, oooh, aaah, eeeh, iiii. Where do you feel them in your body? How do they make you feel?

• Play with mantras. You don't need to do 'Ohm' or anything spiritual – simply try singing positive statements, repeating them with different tunes. If you're feeling tense, try singing 'I'm calm, I'm calm'; if you need to feel more assertive, try 'I've got a right to be heard.'

• Experiment with listening to different music and work out what effect it has on your moods. Try listening to some of the sacred chants available on tape for deep relaxation and a profound sense of peace.

LIGHT THERAPY

WHAT IS IT? The use of full-spectrum lighting to treat both physiological and psychological problems.

USED FOR A wide variety of ailments – from SAD (seasonal affective disorder) and depression, joint problems to infertility and PMS.

SUITABLE FOR Those who spend most of their time indoors; particularly useful for those who suffer SAD or winter blues.

NOT SUITABLE FOR No contraindications.

PERFORMED Without eyewear; you can take off clothing or leave it on as you choose.

ANYTHING TO TAKE ORALLY? No.

STRESSBUSTER Not specifically, but relieves stress when combined with reflexology.

COST Medium.

NUMBER OF SESSIONS REQUIRED Depends on condition and time of year. Most usually one a week.

DIY Everyone should try to get natural daylight each day. Home units are available.

IF YOU LIKE THIS, TRY COLOUR THERAPY for light with a difference; MAGNETOTHERAPY might appeal – more state-of-the-art machinery.

A dose of spring sunshine, and the whole world seems to smile. When the sun comes out, spirits lift and energy levels bubble higher. Even our health seems to improve – it's as if someone had waved a miraculous magic wand. It may seem like magic, but the effect is certainly not merely in our minds. Research now clearly shows that the pure clear sunlight of spring can have measurable, highly beneficial effects on our health, both physiological and psychological.

Unfortunately, few of us take enough of this essential 'medicine'. 'We spend more and more of our time indoors,' says Dr Damien Downing, the leading UK exponent of the healing power of sunlight. 'The only time we see the sun is when we follow outdoors pursuits such as sport or gardening or go on holiday.'

It's a change that has come about over the last couple of hundred years with the shift from working on the land to working in factories and offices. An office may be warmer and drier and more comfortable than the average British field, but it is certainly darker. Dr Downing points out that our offices are lit at between two hundred and one thousand lux (the measurement for light) when, in reality, we need levels around ten times brighter. 'We keep ourselves for most of our lives in perpetual twilight,' he says. 'Nowadays we live, without realizing it, in self-imposed dungeons.'

The most common result is the well-documented syndrome of SAD (seasonal affective disorder), but Downing reckons this is the tip of the iceberg: around 60 per cent of the population suffer in a less dramatic way. Lack of light can cause depression and lethargy, disturbed sleep patterns and plummeting energy levels. Our metabolism can suffer, so can our hormone levels. Even conditions like osteoporosis and asthma worsen without regular doses of light. It's bad enough for pale-skinned Celts who have spent thousands of years adapting to deal with the low levels of sunlight in

Britain, but dark-skinned people fare particularly badly. Dr Downing says we are now seeing the recurrence of rickets in some black children – not because their diets are deficient but simply because they are not getting enough daylight.

The history

'Let there be light,' said God, and the world began. Since time immemorial, people have understood the healing energy of light. In ancient cultures they recognized the importance of light far more than we do: they knew that without the light their crops would not grow and they would not eat. No wonder they worshipped the sun. From the earliest writings we know that, amongst others, the Egyptians, the Greeks, the Romans and the Arabs all recognized the healing powers of sunlight.

However, the modern history of light therapy as such starts in the nineteenth century. Natural sunlight was used as a cure for all kinds of ailments, from paralysis to tuberculosis. Towards the end of the century, the use of colour started to become known. General Pleasanton, an early light-researcher, praised the healing qualities of blue light – stating that both animals and humans benefited from bathing in blue. He found that blue light regulated the hormones, increased growth and elevated fertility. By 1877, it became clear that sunlight was an effective killer of bacteria and, in 1878, Dr Edwin Babbitt published his study on the effects of light and colour called *The Principles of Light and Color*. He used various methods for healing: including potentizing water with sunlight and beaming coloured light through filters onto specific parts of the body. He frequently treated seemingly incurable diseases with great success and was considered something of a miracle-worker.

Much research followed, but the next great breakthrough was in 1933 when Dinshah Ghadiali produced the *Spectro-Chrometry Encyclopedia*. He pointed out that there were clear links between colours and the elements in the body. He believed that pure white light contains all the colours of the spectrum in harmonious balance. However, as soon as we alter the body's spectral balance by adding a chemical of the 'wrong' colour, the body cannot keep its equilibrium. The result is, at first, merely imbalance; finally sickness.

His work wasn't just theory: he developed a mathematically precise set of colour filters (red, orange, yellow, lemon, green, turquoise, blue, indigo, violet, purple, magenta, and scarlet) through which light could be shone directly on to specific areas of the body. No-one has ever scientifically proven his theories, but the method seemed to have great success for all manner of quite serious conditions – from heart problems to paralysis, from bleeding to fertility.

Around the same time, Dr Harry Riley Spitler was developing Syntonics. He found that by altering the colour of light that enters the eyes, he could alter a person's behaviour and physiology. He started to treat people according to their emotional make-up rather than purely their physical condition.

It's amazing, with this long history, that light therapy and colour therapy (see next chapter) are not more widely accepted. The natural inclination is to chuckle when we read that certain colours can cause insomnia while others can lower or raise blood pressure. Yet the evidence is quite clear. A study at the New England State Hospital in the USA showed that when people with normal blood pressure were bathed in blue light their blood pressure dropped; when they went into red light it increased. The effect didn't last long but, even more amazingly, the subjects were subsequently able to raise or lower their blood pressure at will, merely by imagining the colour.

The lowdown

To understand how light therapy works we need to take a look at the pineal gland. Located deep in the brain, it is a mysterious organ which has been venerated through history as the 'third eye'. It regulates our hormones and influences our moods; sends us to sleep and wakes us up. It also acts as the body's light meter, keeping us in sync with the outside world. It rhythmically secretes the hormone melatonin throughout the day – more so at night, less during the daylight hours.

Strangely enough, the melatonin/light connection was not fully realized until 1980 when Dr Alfred Lewy and Dr Thomas Wehr discovered that bright lights suppressed the normal night time secretion of melatonin. They figured that by shining bright artificial light on a patient, they could suppress melatonin and trick the brain into thinking it was spring. Their subsequent experiments were a breakthrough for the millions who suffered SAD (seasonal affective disorder), for whom bright full-spectrum light gave significant improvement. Patients felt as if they had been released from a long enforced hibernation.

But light therapy can treat far more than SAD. Natalie Handley, who practises light therapy at the Hale Clinic in London and Champneys health spa, sees people with a huge cross-section of needs: some simply want to increase their energy levels; some want help with serious depression or arthritic conditions. Just twenty minutes of light therapy, she says, can lower blood pressure for up to a week and also reduce blood-cholesterol levels. It balances hormones and so can be used as an alternative to HRT (hormone replacement therapy) and also to help fertility (incidentally, Dr Downing points out that sunlight can increase libido – the sun actually does make us sexier). The full-spectrum light can kill bacteria and accelerate wound healing. And, because exposure to the lights increases the production of vitamin D in the body which, in turn, aids the absorption of calcium, phosphorus and magnesium, it is useful in cases of arthritis, osteoporosis and dental caries.

There's still more. Because daylight suppresses the production of melatonin, light therapy can be used to treat sleep disorders and jet lag with great success. In short, says Natalie Handley, there really isn't anyone who wouldn't benefit from some light therapy – especially during dark and gloomy winters.

The session

The day I visited Handley was the archetypal winter day: gloomy, cold, dark – and wet. Summer – and sunlight – seemed a million miles away. But Handley was bright and cheerful, beaming with good health and vitality: she's a shining endorsement of her treatment. She regularly combines the light treatment with reflexology because, she explains, the combination will treat more or less anything.

First of all, she took a detailed medical history from me. The lights, she promises, are totally safe and completely without side

307

effects. In particular, she assures, they will not tan nor will they cause any damage to the skin. The case history, however, is necessary for reflexology so that she can tailor the treatment to your needs. Then she invited me to take off my shoes and as much clothing as I liked and get on the couch. Any glasses or contact lenses are taken off or out because, she explains, the light can only reach the pineal gland (essential for hormonal balance) through the eyes.

The lights are mounted in a panel above the couch several feet above your body. They look much like a sunbed except that the centre tubes are a beautiful shade of blue. For best effects, you keep your eyes open (although you don't have to look directly at the light) for the first twenty minutes.

The combination of the warm clear light and the firm but soothing touch of the reflexology were, I had to agree, a delightful combination. Without the reflexology I might have become a bit bored just lying in the light, but the two together were like snoozing in the garden on a soft summer's day with your feet being cradled in a lap, gently being massaged. It was total bliss.

After an hour, I slid off the couch with a broad smile. My skin felt warm and soft and a slight grumble in my lower back had been much eased. But, most noticeable, was the increase of energy that steadily rose throughout the day. Several hours after the treatment I felt as if I had been given a happy pill: I was bright and bubbly, several light years away from the tired, slightly gloomy person who had greeted another winter's day with a wince. I think I've seen the light.

Bright ideas to bring sunlight into your life

Lightbathing, says Dr Downing, stimulates the circulation, tones muscles, detoxifies the body and boosts production of vitamin D and hormones.

• During autumn and winter, when the danger of burning is very low, get as much natural daylight as you can. You don't have to lie exposed to the sun – gardening, dog-walking or even just walking outside in your lunch-hour can help.

• As the sun gets brighter you need to adjust the amount of sun you take to suit your skin type. Dr Downing insists that it is burning that causes skin cancer, not sensible exposure. As a rough guide, you need to stay out for half the amount of time that you can safely be in the sun before burning: for very fair skin that will be around ten minutes in very bright sunlight, through to an hour for very dark skins.

• Dr Downing recommends that you don't use creams or blocks when lightbathing – they block out the useful UV rays. Providing you limit your exposure strictly in line with the time limits recommended above, the more of your skin that is exposed to the light the better.

• Glasses, sunglasses and contact lenses all filter out the light. Wearing dark glasses all the time, says Handley, will tend to make you depressed or irritable – use a hat instead to shield you from glare.

Note: The above information is based on the principles of light therapy. It is not a recommendation for exposing yourself to the sun for long periods without suitable protection. Remember, moderation is the key. So, don't overdo it, and always err on the side of caution, particularly if you have a fair or sensitive skin.

COLOUR THERAPY

WHAT IS IT?   The use of colour, often in the form of coloured lights, to promote healing.

USED FOR   Psychological and behavioural problems; infertility; high and low blood pressure; allergy-driven complaints; digestive problems; insomnia and memory loss. Under medical supervision, some therapists use the therapy in the care of people with cancer, AIDS and angina.

SUITABLE FOR   Seems to attract people who want an element of personal development in their therapy. Some brands of colour therapy ask for your own intuitive input.

NOT SUITABLE FOR   No contraindications, but some of the colour therapy methods may seem a little too weird for some people.

PERFORMED   Generally fully clothed.

ANYTHING TO TAKE ORALLY?   Not usually. However some colour therapists advise you to adapt your diet to include or avoid foods of certain colours.

STRESSBUSTER   Yes, certain colours can ease stress.

COST   Medium.

NUMBER OF SESSIONS REQUIRED   Varies enormously. From once a week to once a month in most cases.

DIY   Yes, you may be given colour 'homework', asked to wear certain colours, eat food of certain colours or use specific colour products.

IF YOU LIKE THIS, TRY   For healing via a different sense, why not try SOUND THERAPY. FLOWER AND GEM REMEDIES may also appeal. ELECTRO-CRYSTAL THERAPY will allow you to see the full colours of your aura and *chakras*.

When I moved to a new house I took over what used to be the spare bedroom for my study. It was papered with a busy print of pink and red flowers; the ceiling was pink and so was the carpet. Every day I sat down to work and every day it was a battle. Then I decided to overhaul the room and painted it a cool pure blue. Suddenly, I found myself working coolly and calmly through each day. In addition, I added a small multi-faceted crystal which hangs in the window. When the sun shines, the light hits the crystal and sends small mini-rainbows of light bouncing round the room. There is nothing quite like it to give an instant lift.

Colour therapy, however, is one of the most ephemeral of the supertherapies. Despite the fact that the healing power of colour has been well documented through the last century (*see* the history section of LIGHT THERAPY), somehow colour therapy nowadays seems to be regarded as beyond the fringe, a bit of a hippy-dippy pale and watery therapy. It's a shame because, in the right hands, it can be strong medicine. However this is one supertherapy which everyone can use to one degree or another. After all, we can all choose the clothes we wear, the colours we surround ourselves with in our homes, even the colour food we eat.

The history

Some imaginative souls say that the history of colour therapy goes right back to the mythical culture of Atlantis where the true power of the sun and of coloured light was appreciated and utilized. Channelled information (given to sensitives in trance) reports that sick people were placed in healing rooms constructed of crystals angled so that the sunlight would diffuse through them to give beams of rainbow light. The patient would be positioned so that the correct colour of light could reach him or her.

Slightly more conventionally documented is the use of colour in the ancient world. The healing temples in ancient Greece knew of the therapeutic value of colour. In ancient Egypt they too had what were known as the Healing Temples of Light and Colour. And the great healing systems of India and China have also testified to the power of different colours. The chronology of modern colour therapy is outlined in the preceding section, LIGHT THERAPY.

The lowdown

Our whole bodies are sensitive to colour. Research in Russia even showed that many people can be trained to feel colour with their fingertips. Possibly what they feel is the vibration of the colour. Just as sound has a vibration and different sounds give out different vibrations, so different colours have varying vibrations. Our bodies, too, vibrate at varying frequencies.

Many colour therapists use the Indian concept of the *chakras*, the energy centres of the body, as a focus. From ancient times each *chakra* has been linked with a certain form of energy, with certain organs or bodily systems and, if imbalanced, with certain diseases.

• The base *chakra* is located in the sacral region of the body, and its role is to regulate the vitality of the body and to promote fertility. The colour associated with the base *chakra* is red. So, a colour therapist might well use red to treat conditions like severe fatigue, where the vitality of the body is being compromised.
• The spleen *chakra* is associated with circulation and assimilation in the body. When it is out of balance it tends to create disorders of the kidneys and problems with the lungs. Its colour is

orange. Asthma, bronchitis and emphysema have benefited from orange light therapy.

• The solar plexus *chakra* concerns the intellect, and imbalance causes disorders of the stomach, liver and pancreas. Its colour is yellow. Yellow can help ease stress-related disorders such as ulcers and can also ease indigestion and stomach problems.

• The heart *chakra* deals with inner harmony. Its diseases of imbalance are heart disease and hypertension. Its colour is green.

• The throat *chakra* deals with self-expression, willpower and communication. It is connected with imbalance of the thyroid and problems with the larynx. Its colour is blue. Blue can help you verbalize what is hard to say and, on a more physical level, can ease sore throats and laryngitis.

• The brow *chakra* deals with vision and when imbalanced can cause disorders of the eyes. Its colour is indigo. It is also called the third eye centre and is connected with psychic powers, intuition and clairvoyance. Indigo can help with problems of all the senses.

• The crown *chakra* has the energy of the higher mind, the super consciousness and, when disturbed, can cause nervous and mental disorders. Its colour is violet. Interestingly, Leonardo da Vinci said that the indigo beloved of stained glass windows in churches actually increased the meditative qualities of the church tenfold. Violet can also help relieve headaches, neuroses and a huge array of mental and nervous disorders.

The session

There is no typical colour therapy session. There are as many methods for treating with colours as there are colours in the rainbow. However, most colour therapists rely a lot on intuition and many are also quite clairvoyant. You may well find your therapist gazing vaguely at you as if he or she had become bored with the whole session. More likely, he or she would be scanning your aura to see which colours are lacking. If your therapist is gifted in this way, that may be all that is needed for diagnosis. Some now use a specific kind of camera that records the aura on polaroid film. The aura can be a clear indication of health and wellbeing. If you are feeling well and happy, the colours will be bright and clear; if you're depressed or sad, the colours will grow dimmer and duller.

However, I must say that my experiences of aura readings and photographs have been less than convincing. Often the information seems very vague and I would not rate it as a first-rate diagnostic tool unless in very skilled hands. The only really effective readings I have had were with Harry Oldfield's PIP scan equipment (see ELECTRO-CRYSTAL THERAPY).

Other colour therapists, however, may rely on more pragmatic means: a full medical history; details of symptoms; information on your personality and emotions. They will all be interested in how you fare throughout the day, whether your condition gets better or worse at certain times; how your energy fluctuates during the day. Often you will be asked to pick out the colours that appeal to you. Many therapists believe that, on a deep level, our bodies know what healing we need and that we will automatically pick out the right colours. A clear example of this is the Aura Soma remedies, jewel-like bottles of coloured water and oil – mostly with two colours in each bottle. You simply browse through the bottles and choose the one that jumps out at you. Then you use the liquid either directly onto the body or splashed around your aura. It seems pretty haphazard and rather New Age, but it is not without scientific precedent. For many years, it has been clear that the colours you are drawn to reflect aspects of your personality and, by extension, your health. The Luscher colour test has been used since 1947 and some colour therapists still use it today. You simply put eight colours in order of preference and, in so doing, you give away precise details of your conscious and unconscious mind, areas of stress, imbalances in your glandular system and even potential illnesses.

How you are treated depends very much on the individual practitioner. Perhaps the most clinical treatment is with coloured lights. You sit or lie under a stand, generally wearing a white robe. Two colours are set in the machine – the colour you need and its complementary colour. Each will normally be beamed out through a specific shape, as certain shapes are said to enhance the power of each colour.

An interesting alternative is a bath that beams light into your whole body while you lie immersed in water. Any combination of colours can be set in the unit, but most usually they are set with a combination of blue and its complementary colour, orange, to reduce stress, ease insomnia and release muscle tension.

You may be asked to stick to a colour diet – eating either food that is balanced in colours or allowing yourself a predominance of one colour to balance your body.

Many therapists also use a technique called Colour Breathing. Again, it sounds pretty batty, but remember those people who were able to raise and lower their blood pressure merely by thinking about either red or blue? Try it for yourself, it might just have some interesting effects.

Colour breathing

Lie down or sit in a comfortable chair and make yourself feel calm and relaxed. Breathe comfortably and deeply keeping the rhythm of your breathing natural and relaxed.

Now imagine yourself bathed in the colour you choose. As you breathe in, imagine the colour entering your body through your solar plexus (just above your abdomen) and spreading throughout your body. As you breathe out, visualize the complementary colour suffusing and leaving your body.

DIY colour tips

You can also use these colours to wear or to incorporate into your food:

- RED gives energy and vitality; it increases your strength and also your sexuality. Use red when you're lacking in energy, when you're so exhausted you can't even think. Its complement is TURQUOISE.
- ORANGE is for fun, for happiness and sheer joy. If you are feeling dull and gloomy or fed up with your work, choose orange. Its complement is BLUE.
- YELLOW is a wonderful colour for studying and concentrating, as it stimulates your intellectual and mental powers and increases your ability to be objective. It increases detachment and helps if you are feeling oversensitive or controlled by other people or when you can't let go. Its complement is VIOLET.
- GREEN is the great healer. Use it to cleanse, to balance and to purify your system. It is useful if you continually take your work

home with you, or conversely take your home worries to work. It helps you to keep thoughts in balance. Its complement is MAGENTA.

• TURQUOISE calms and soothes; it strengthens the immune system and can help feverish conditions and inflammations. Use turquoise if you feel dominated by other people or always give in to their thoughts and ideas. Its complement is RED.

• BLUE relaxes and brings peace. Visualize blue when you can't get to sleep – it's great for insomnia. Use it also when you can't stop and think calmly. Its complement is ORANGE.

• VIOLET is the colour of dignity and self-respect. Breathe it in when you feel lacking in self-esteem. Use it also when you find you are putting yourself down or start to feel that, no matter how hard you try, you will never do as well as others. Its complement is YELLOW.

• MAGENTA is the great releaser. Breathe magenta when you need to let go of the past, of old thoughts and obsessions. It's wonderful as a help in change, of whatever kind. It also brings out your spiritual energies. Its complement is GREEN.

HEALING

WHAT IS IT?　Used to bring the body back into energetic balance by either the laying on of hands or mentally transferring healing energy.

USED FOR　Any condition might respond to healing. Most often used as a last resort, where other therapies have failed.

SUITABLE FOR　All ages. Healing is very gentle and non-invasive. The elderly and terminally ill often find great comfort from it.

NOT SUITABLE FOR　No contraindications. Some pragmatic people might find it too spiritual. Some healers see the powers as coming from a specific godhead which some people might find offputting.

PERFORMED　Fully clothed. Some healers will perform absent healing where you don't even need to be present.

ANYTHING TO TAKE ORALLY?　No.

STRESSBUSTER Not specifically, although many people find healing very relaxing.

COST Varies enormously. Some healers treat for free; others charge very high amounts. Generally speaking, you should expect to pay for healing – around the low to medium bracket.

NUMBER OF SESSIONS REQUIRED Sometimes it only takes one session; some people have regular weekly or monthly sessions.

DIY Many healers will ask you to take control of your own health and advise you to follow healthy eating and exercise patterns. There are many books and tapes giving self-healing exercises.

IF YOU LIKE THIS, TRY REIKI is a specific form of Japanese healing. METAMORPHIC TECHNIQUE is gentle and transformative. If you would like to try something more structured and scientific, try ELECTRO-CRYSTAL THERAPY.

We can all heal. As Jesus said in the Bible, 'These things that I do, so can you do and more.' Unfortunately, few of us take it seriously. And yet many of us might be healing every day, without even knowing it. Some would say that every time a doctor or nurse touches a patient with care and concern they are performing a kind of healing. A parent does the same when she or he cuddles their child, when they lay a soothing hand on the forehead or give a loving squeeze of the hand. Even total strangers can give the healing touch: some people simply shake your hand or put a hand on your shoulder and you can almost feel their energy leaping out at you.

Healing can be simple: the mere touch of hands. Or it can be clothed in ceremony with recitations of prayers or the chanting of mantras. Which form you pick is up to you.

The history

Healing didn't begin in the Bible. Like so many other super-therapies, healing was a part of most ancient cultures. Documentation exists which shows that the Chinese were practising it 5,000 years before Christ. The ancient Egyptians used it; so did the Greeks and Romans. In many cultures the art of healing by the laying on of hands has continued in a straight line from antiquity: the Native American culture and the Australian aborigine cultures still practise healing in the ancient way.

However, in the Western world, healing became entangled with the Church, and the situation became muddled. Healing became the province of the established Church, and anyone who performed healing who was not a member of the clergy was liable to be dubbed a witch and hounded to death. Amazingly, the witchcraft laws were still on the statute books up until 1953. Even now, many Christian fundamentalists still decry healing, saying that any healing which is not carried out by the clergy is the work of the devil. It's a curious situation because, ironically, the church is generally rather embarrassed by miracles and often seems as if it wishes healing could quietly be swept under the carpet.

However, healing is now gaining credibility again. In 1956 the British Medical Association published a report entitled 'Divine Healing and Co-operation between Doctors and Clergy'. It stated quite clearly that 'through spiritual healing, recoveries take place that cannot be explained by medical science.' At the forefront of the new wave of healing is the National Federation of Spiritual Healers who have been tirelessly working for the last thirty years to establish bona-fide healing. They are non-denominational and bound by a strict code of ethics. Many hospitals now happily accept them into their wards when a patient asks for their services.

The lowdown

Healing seems so simple – the healer either just touches the patient or hovers their hands above him or her. Some simply sit and think about the patient getting well – even though the patient is many miles away. How can it work? Many healers say that they are bringing their patients into a higher level of being, where they are in touch with the healing power of God or some higher force.

Others think in more prosaic terms and say they are using a bio-magnetic or bioelectrical energy and bringing the body into balance. However they describe it, what seems to be happening is much the same as in most other forms of therapy – the energetic system of the body is being balanced.

Many healers will insist that they do not heal, they merely open up the body so that it can perform its own healing. The healer is merely there as a catalyst. This is one reason why it is important for the patient to have some form of faith in the process. Healers recognize the enormous untapped power of the mind and believe that if the mind desires healing, then the body will follow suit. Hence many will use creative visualization or encourage their patients to take responsibility for their own health, instigating changes in diet, exercise, mental attitude, stress relief and so on.

However, there is no doubt that some people do seem to be 'tapped in' to some enormous fund of energy. They're a bit like live wires, literally buzzing with vital force. Kirlian photographs of healers' hands show bright darting shoots of energy. And the PIP scanner used in electro-crystal therapy has filmed a healer working on a patient – as she put up her hands, clear shooting energy flew from her hands to the patient's body. Generally, however, healers will say that they are simply tapping in to the universal store of energy that is open to us all. Many will say that it is God-given. The spiritual element of healing can sometimes be offputting in this modern, prosaic world and many people feel uncomfortable having God or Spirit pulled into their everyday lives.

However, healers just say openly what most supertherapists know: that often, in order to cure body and mind, you need to heal the spirit as well. Healing often has a deep and lasting effect on people's lives. Many people only turn to healers as a last resort and I often feel sorry for the healers: they seem to get the cases no-one else manages to help. They don't complain and they never promise miracles, but extraordinary things can and do happen. Even if someone is dying, healing can have an enormous effect, improving the quality of life and gently allowing people to die with more dignity and courage.

However, often healing does avert disease. It is generally most successful when it prompts changes in the patient's life.

Frequently, people find that, in the healing process, they start to question their lifestyles and discover better ways to live. They learn new values and decide on fresh paths in life. Healing often totally transforms lives.

The session

There is no typical healing session. My first bout of healing came at the annual Festival of Mind, Body and Spirit many years ago. The National Federation of Spiritual Healers had a large stand with a bevy of white-coated healers. I had a terrible headache and so went in. I was asked to sit on a chair while the man held his hands over my head and shoulders. To be brutally honest, my headache didn't vanish, but then the heavy incense floating from a nearby stall might have had something to do with it.

Years later I visited a healer for a 'proper' session. First of all, we just sat and talked for a while. All the time she looked at me slightly vaguely, as if she were only half-listening to what I was saying. It seemed pretty irritating until I realized that she was scanning my aura, looking for the energy field surrounding me. She announced I was utterly depleted, my energy stores virtually wiped out. It didn't come as a surprise – I could hardly keep myself awake during the day. She also informed me that my heart *chakra* was wide open and that I was leaking energy like an old boat. It all sounded rather nerve-racking but she seemed confident that she could patch me up. Taking off my shoes and jewellery, I hopped up onto her couch and let her start work.

Healing is a pretty inert therapy somehow: I just lay there while she moved her hands about a foot or so above my body. As she worked, she asked questions about my life, my health and my relationships and came up with some uncannily accurate insights. She taught me some simple visualization exercises to help keep my energy contained and to ward off the negative energy of other people which, she said, was affecting my health.

To be honest, I didn't feel that much different as I left. A week later I had another session and again, although it was very relaxing, I couldn't swear it changed things. Personally, I haven't yet felt the real power of healing, but I know enough people who swear by it to keep a very open mind.

Shamanic healing – the Egyptian way

If you really want to experience some weird magic, find yourself a shamanic healer. Most native cultures have shamans – people who have the power to tread between the worlds of matter and spirit. Shamanism is growing in popularity and now it's not uncommon to find Western healers who call on the powers of ancient deities or animal allies to help with healing.

One such is Nicki Skully who works with the gods and goddesses of ancient Egypt. Skully insists that the animal archetypes of Egyptian lore are neither imaginary nonsense nor occult demons – they are simply unexplored parts of our own psyche. 'The deities are really aspects of ourselves,' she explains, 'parts of our own consciousness that we can develop.' Take Sekhmet, the lioness goddess who represents both the destroyer and the passionate healer. By contacting the lion part of yourself, you can walk more powerfully and confidently through life and its confrontations. 'When we find that part of ourselves,' says Skully, 'we get taller and stronger and can move more easily into situations in life which seem very challenging or frightening or difficult.' As Skully talks about Sekhmet, you can almost see her *become* the lioness: her shoulders move back and her head seems to stand more proudly; her eyes look directly and searchingly at you and her voice almost imperceptibly deepens. She virtually growls.

Whatever aspect of yourself you want to develop, there is almost certainly an animal totem to help. The eagle helps you see situations from a fresh, clearer perspective; the crocodile allows you to regain balance; the snow leopard conquers fear; and the cat teaches love of self. But when Skully works, she most commonly calls on Sekhmet herself or another powerful, if frightening ally, the cobra. Recently, a man contacted Skully over the telephone: he was riddled with cancer, in great pain and begged her for help. Skully says she introduced him to the cobra, guiding him until he was able to visualize the creature and feel its power. Then, she says, 'he invited the cobra inside himself where it enjoyed a meal of one of his tumours. Now they have worked out a relationship: he goes into meditation every day and connects with that form, not only visually but also actually *feeling* it working with him to reduce his pain.' The man's state is terminal, and Skully honestly admits the process is unlikely to cure him. However, she points out, at least the pain is diminished and he feels more in control of his life.

Skully has faced cancer herself – and won with the help of the cobra. Suffering from breast cancer and undergoing the severe effects of chemotherapy, she put her preachings into practice and sent her cancer into what appears to be permanent remission, much to the surprise of her doctors.

Basically, she promises, we all have the power to heal. 'I don't feel I am special or extraordinary or particularly gifted,' she says, 'I think anyone can do it. I really believe that we have considerable natural inherent abilities that have simply atrophied through lack of use. It's time we took the power back.'

To demonstrate, Skully says she will 'open the eyes in my hands' for use in healing. Holding my hands out in front of me, she rubs the centre of my palms in a circular motion and then moves her hands away as if she were drawing something out of me. She then asks me to direct healing at her back and, surprisingly, I can feel a distinct column of heat emanating from my palms. Fine-tune this energy, she promises, and you can help people around you and even those separated by great distances.

Once, she recalls, a woman several hundred miles away asked Skully to help her daughter who was facing surgery for a tumour on her kidney. She told the woman the time she would work on her child and then asked the Egyptian god of wisdom Thoth for help. In her mind's eye she watched the figure throw a bolt of lightning out of his staff towards the direction of the child. The mother called back in complete amazement. Her daughter didn't need surgery, the tumour had gone and the doctors were totally baffled.

Shamanism appeals, not just to people who are seeking health but also to those who want to work on their personal growth. They are looking to get in touch with their inner power; they want to sort out difficulties in their lives; they are looking for new jobs, new relationships, for a fundamental change. And, Skully promises, the Egyptian archetypes really can help in very practical ways. 'The totemistic animals appear very metaphysical but they are very directly related to day to day applications. Take Sekhmet again: when you take on the attributes of the lion you learn how to move efficiently in life, how to be more effective in whatever you are looking for – whether it is gaining information, targeting a new business, getting a new relationship.'

Skully takes people on inner journeys in which they meet the Egyptian archetypes and learn to incorporate these subconscious aspects into their conscious life. She teaches how to walk through the world feeling taller, stronger, more powerful and more at ease with yourself. And she teaches healing. 'Once you turn on that inner healing power it's there for life, it's turned on,' she laughs. 'You can use it to help anything – if your plants are drooping or your pet seems off-colour or if your friend has a headache. And the beautiful thing is that, the more you use it, the more it helps you. The more energy you offer into the world, the more healing energy is given back to you.'

REIKI

WHAT IS IT?   A form of spiritual healing where practitioners channel universal life energy to the recipient for the purpose of healing body, mind and spirit.

USED FOR   General wellbeing; relaxation; accelerating the body's ability to heal itself; opening the mind to the causes of any disease and pain; helping the recipient to take responsibility for their life.

SUITABLE FOR   Everyone.

NOT SUITABLE FOR   No contraindications, but not great for those who want precise, measured results. Diabetics and anyone on medication should be carefully monitored, as often dosages need to be lowered following treatment.

PERFORMED   Fully clothed.

ANYTHING TO TAKE ORALLY?   No.

STRESSBUSTER   Most people find Reiki remarkably stress-reducing.

COST   Varies. Usually low, sometimes even free.

NUMBER OF SESSIONS REQUIRED   Varies. No set amount prescribed.

DIY   None, although many people choose to learn Reiki at workshops to practise on family, friends and pets.

IF YOU LIKE THIS, TRY   Other gentle techniques such as ZERO BALANCING, METAMORPHIC TECHNIQUE, CRANIAL OSTEOPATHY and CRANIO-SACRAL THERAPY.

They say that when you are ready for Reiki you will be drawn to it as irresistibly as a thirsty horse to water. But if the time is not right, you can walk right past it without even registering its existence. Reiki, the Japanese art of spiritual healing, is as mysterious and inscrutable as its country of origin.

Contradictions abound. Some practitioners call it 'relaxation therapy'; others insist it can be far from relaxing. Although it is known as 'healing', its exponents freely admit that sometimes it chooses not to heal.

It all sounds very vague and, to be honest, smacks somewhat of New Age waffle – airy references to creating balance, activating the body's natural capacity for healing, healing mind, body and spirit. Practitioners meditate on mystic symbols to initiate a downpouring of energy. They call themselves 'transformers' that simply allow the healing energy to pass through from the universe to the client. And yet, despite the arcane nature of this form of healing, Reiki is becoming very popular, and even hard-nosed scientists are admitting it certainly seems to do something remarkable.

The history

A leap of faith heralded the birth of Reiki. It was 'discovered' around the turn of the century by a Japanese man called Mikao Usui. Usui was a devout Christian and the principal of a missionary school for boys. One day, he was challenged by two boys who asked whether he really believed that Christ could heal. 'Yes, of course,' answered Usui. Did he then believe Jesus when He said

'What I can do, you can do'? He nodded. So, with implacable logic, the boys asked him if he could show them how to heal. Usui realized that he could not and, convinced his faith was not strong enough, resigned from the school and commenced a fourteen-year search for the secret of physical healing.

The quest took him to America and eventually back to Japan and a Zen monastery where, after learning Sanskrit, he found 'the answer' in an ancient sutra or sacred text. In the manner of all the best yarns, no-one since has been able to rediscover the precise text, but it led him to meditate on a mountain where he was shown a vision of four symbols which could be used for healing. Coming down the mountain he stumbled and hurt his toe. As he placed his hand on the foot, the injury healed – and he realized his quest was over.

The lowdown

Reiki practitioners explain that Reiki is more than just a system of healing. When practised in its true sense, it is a profound spiritual path. The word Reiki can be split into two – *ki* means life-force, the Japanese equivalent of the Chinese *chi* that flows through the meridians. *Rei* means spiritually guided. So, practitioners say, it's a case of non-matter coming into matter and being balanced; the spiritual affecting the physical. To accept Reiki you have to abandon the world of neat equations and solid reason. It's like a leap of faith.

However, the physical part of the Reiki system is very simple. Consisting of twenty 'holds', it can be learned in a weekend. There is no need to learn anatomy or physiology; students aren't expected to even study basic psychology. The key is in the spiritual symbols which are 'transmitted' to the trainee healer. Then, it seems, the force is free to flow through.

Practitioners insist it is not *they* who are healing; it is not even the Reiki which is healing: it is the individual who is being treated who *decides* how much of the healing energy to take and use. Or rather, it is their subconscious which decides. For example, someone might arrive for a session complaining of a sore knee and will leave, still with a sore knee. But maybe a deep-seated phobia has vanished or a depression has lifted. It's not the best therapy for people who want definitive results because there is no guarantee what will happen. Reiki is decidedly unpredictable.

And yet the few studies that have been carried out on Reiki have shown surprisingly clear results. One experiment compared how quickly injured rats recovered. A control group which was left to its own devices took ten days to heal. The same thing happened with a group which was picked up daily and stroked by laboratory staff. And yet a further group which was 'healed' each day with Reiki mended in just four days. Practitioners will make no claims for Reiki and yet there are endless reports of Reiki 'miracles' – tumours disappearing, wounds healing, illnesses vanishing, long-term depression lifting. People with ME, skin diseases, bad asthma, tinnitus, irritable bowel syndrome have all improved or recovered although, to be fair, nearly all have been undergoing some other form of therapy – whether orthodox or complementary – at the same time.

At Stanford University in the USA Reiki has been involved in a five-year project with cancer. Around three hundred people with terminal cancer who had been given less than three months to live were given Reiki alongside their traditional treatment. After two and a half years, over half of them are still alive. This amazed the doctors, but what impressed them even more was the extent to which their quality of life had improved.

Slowly, Reiki is beginning to be used in hospitals for pain relief – patients find that after half an hour of treatment they can sleep for the night because the pain has gone. In Holland, Reiki is used a lot in hospices, especially for people with cancer. Sometimes people go into remission; sometimes they die. But if they do die, at least they seem to die in peace – without pain, without fear and feeling clear and accepting.

Practitioners say that there is always a purpose behind Reiki – even when it chooses not to heal. One practitioner explains how she uses Reiki for injuries: 'If I sprain my ankle I can immediately put my hand on it and nine times out of ten there will be no sprain within five minutes, simply no pain or swelling. But then the tenth time it won't work and I can normally see why. Maybe I need a couple of day's rest or something.'

Many people who choose to learn Reiki for themselves look on it as a tool for personal growth. For many, it takes the place of psychotherapy, bringing up all the suppressed hurts and wounds. Although Reiki is very gentle and practitioners insist it won't bring up anything you cannot handle, it can be a very powerful technique in this field, and devotees all say it can be quite challenging.

The session

At the time I visited Margaret-Anne Pauffley, a Reiki master who both practises and teaches, I had no specific ailments nor, so I thought, any particular emotional traumas to unburden. However, I was keen to find out how the Reiki experience felt. I was surprised to find that Pauffley did not ask me specifically how I felt or what I wanted to achieve. If I wanted to talk, she said, that was fine; if I wanted to stay quiet, that was equally fine. However, she did check whether I was on insulin or on any other medication. The reason, she explained, is that diabetics need to be carefully monitored after Reiki because sometimes the amounts of insulin they need decline sharply. The same can be true for levels of other medication.

As I lay fully clothed on a massage table, with soft Oriental music playing in the background, Pauffley began by gently but firmly touching my head with her fingers. Her hands felt cool on my brow and I started to relax. After several minutes she lifted one hand and touched another part of my head, then the other hand followed.

So it continued as she worked down my body. Time started to shift and wander as I became more relaxed and distinctly drowsy. At one point I saw scenes from my childhood float past my eyes, as if I were watching an old home movie. It was very vivid, very detailed – full of incidents I had completely forgotten. I even revisited the time when my father died – but without feeling any pain. Her hands were now on my chest and they felt very warm. Suddenly my feet involuntarily convulsed in a brief spasm. The pictures faded and I travelled off into a wonderful calm, warm, safe place where time simply didn't exist. I had no idea whether I had been lying on the couch for minutes or hours.

Then came the most curious sensation. I suddenly realized that I didn't know where Margaret-Anne's hands were on me. My conscious mind struggled with the problem and then decided it really

329

didn't matter and let it go. When I sat up after what was apparently an hour, I felt absolutely wonderful: totally relaxed, quietly peaceful, as if something ineffable had smiled and said, 'You're just fine. Let go.'

My experience isn't unusual: some people even see brilliant colours or feel a burning sensation from the hands. Others feel nothing at all. Some people are taken by surprise by the emotions that arise and find themselves crying. Other will find anger or laughter emerging instead.

Frankly, I was impressed by Reiki. It makes no grand claims, does not puff itself up or promise miracles. Many of its practitioners are even unhappy about charging for their services. And yet its effects continue long after the session ends and the hands have been lifted. In some strange way you feel touched by something very awesome yet infinitely loving. Perhaps it really is a divine blessing.

METAMORPHIC TECHNIQUE

WHAT IS IT? Practitioners insist this is not a therapy or a healing but simply a catalyst that provides the person with the freedom to make any changes necessary in their lives. It employs a very gentle technique of massaging predominantly the feet but also the hands and head.

USED FOR Transformation and realization of your true potential.

SUITABLE FOR Anyone who wants to change for the better. Very useful for children with learning difficulties.

NOT SUITABLE FOR No contraindications.

PERFORMED With bare feet.

ANYTHING TO TAKE ORALLY? No.

STRESSBUSTER Can have a stress-reducing effect – if this is the change your body wants!

COST Low.

NUMBER OF SESSIONS REQUIRED   Varies immensely. Many people have one a week; some only every so often or when they feel the need.

DIY   Yes, many people take short courses to practise on friends and family. Parents especially will often be taught how to touch their children.

IF YOU LIKE THIS, TRY   If you love having your feet touched in a gentle way try MORRELL REFLEXOLOGY. REFLEXOLOGY in general will have a much firmer touch – try this if you would like something more substantial. Still on the foot theme, take a look at CHAVUTTI THIRUMAL, an all-over body massage which is performed with the masseur's feet! Those who like the none-invasive gentle healing aspect of Metamorphic would probably love REIKI.

The Metamorphic Technique is neither a therapy nor a massage, it's not healing and, its practitioners insist, it's not even a treatment. Of all the practices in complementary medicine this is perhaps one of the most mystical and unexplained. Much like Reiki, it asks for a suspension of belief, a casting off of logical explanations, and invites you to put your trust in your own inner life-force.

Nebulous though it may appear, thousands of people who have experienced the technique affirm that life is never the same once you step onto the Metamorphic path. As its name suggests, the main aim of Metamorphic is transformation, and people often find that, following a session or series of sessions, their lives really do change, often in quite radical and far-reaching ways. Practitioners say that the very fact you have chosen to take a session indicates that you are acknowledging an underlying need for change in your life. Many people request sessions at difficult periods of their lives – times of bereavement, moving, divorce and so on – and fans of the technique say it allows them to shift from feeling a victim of circumstance to becoming clear about what they want and need, able to initiate definite changes in their lives. The main changes tend to be emotional or psychological, although a few people with physical disabilities do become more mobile or find they are able to make more positive use of other treatments, such as physiotherapy, which in turn leads to greater mobility.

The history

The technique was developed in the 1960s while naturopath and reflexologist Robert St John was working in a school for mentally handicapped children. Although his work did seem to be helping the children, the changes were, to his mind, not deep or lasting enough. He wanted something that would change the children for the better – permanently. While practising reflexology, he came to the conclusion that not only are all the parts of the body represented in the foot (as reflexology teaches) but that our passage through the womb, from conception to birth, is also mapped out on the side of the foot, along the points reflexologists call the spinal reflexes. The finding, in itself, would be merely a curiosity were it not for the fact that St John also came to believe that the ailments we suffer and the characteristics we carry through life are established during the gestation period, in our mothers' wombs. By working on the feet with a particular light touch, he found he could release blocks and facilitate 'transformations' both on a physical and an emotional level.

One case in particular made him realize he had stumbled on something very important. A woman came to him with a six-week-old baby with severe Down's Syndrome. St John taught the technique to the baby's mother and, after a year of sessions both from St John and the mother, the child had become totally normal. The extra chromosome had not disappeared but it was simply no longer operative.

Gaston Saint-Pierre learnt the metamorphic technique from St John, and in 1979 he set up the Metamorphic Association as a registered charity to promote the work worldwide. Despite a pile of testimonials from both orthodox doctors and complementary practitioners, clinics, schools and institutions, he is insistent that it is not the technique itself nor the practitioner which brings about such results, it is the life-force working inside the person. 'It is not the touch itself,' he insists, 'nor we as practitioners. We are merely the catalyst. It is a case of loosening a structure to enable the power of life to take over.'

The lowdown

Getting to grips with how the Metamorphic Technique actually works is like trying to build a house out of running water. Saint-Pierre likes to use metaphors, almost parables, to explain the principles. He says we are all like seeds which have, inside us, the blueprint of a plant or a tree. We need a catalyst, the earth, in order to grow. However, it is not the earth which makes us grow but our own inner life-force. With a little gentle prodding, he suggests, we can all become oak trees or, in another Saint-Pierre metaphor, we can leave behind our caterpillar existences and fly free as butterflies. Cut away the allegory and Metamorphic goes something like this: by manipulating the feet it is possible to release energy blockages established during the prenatal period, while we were in the womb, by working along the spinal reflex points of the foot.

Those who practise the technique are taught that every cell in the human body contains a full knowledge of every other cell and therefore of our whole being, not just in the present but also with a recollection of the past. So when the Metamorphic touch works along the reflexes of the spine (in the foot, the hands or the head) it can focus on precise moments in the past, on those thirty-eight weeks of gestation when, they say, all our physical, mental, emotional and spiritual characteristics are formed. By loosening the structure, the practitioner can 'free up' the person and allow them a choice to change. Metamorphic practitioners say that working on the feet brings about a movement of change in the person; working on the hands allows the person to handle the changes that will take place; while working on the head helps the person to understand and make sense of what is happening in his or her life.

St John made some quite bizarre discoveries. He found that when hard skin formed around the heel it was an indication that the person was not very grounded – they would tend to be 'spaced out' and rather ethereal. If there was hard skin on the side of the big toe it was a good indication that there was resistance to authority – whether to one's parents, one's boss, or even God. It also indicated an inability to deal with our own internal authority – the classic case of the 'victim'. And he found that, as the person

334

began to take more authority or expressed their own needs, the hard skin would go.

Because practitioners merely act as catalysts, they are not interested in symptoms or case histories. Although they will listen with compassion and understanding, they remain detached and, within time they say, the patient him or herself becomes less concerned with the symptoms.

The Metamorphic Technique is still used a great deal in work with both physically and mentally handicapped children and adults, and Metamorphic practitioners also work on a voluntary basis in hospitals, in schools for children with learning difficulties and even in jails. A host of testimonials (some frankly amazed) from doctors and care workers testify to its success, particularly in the field of mental health. More recently the technique has been given to people with HIV and AIDS and taught to their friends and family. It is, says Saint-Pierre, a wonderful way to help without interfering.

Although he and a large network of practitioners all over the country will give private sessions, they really hope that people will learn the technique themselves to practise on their families and friends. Even though the philosophy of Metamorphic is so esoteric, the practice is remarkably simple. It can be learned over a weekend (the basic touch can be taught in five minutes), and Saint-Pierre believes anyone can learn it. It does not require deep meditation – you can even talk or watch television while you are doing it.

The Metamorphic Association is particularly keen to teach it to parents, since it believes it can help to bond families together and allow them to move and transform as a unit. However, it is important that the whole family has sessions – if just one member changes, the whole dynamic of the family could alter.

If the technique is given during pregnancy and particularly during labour, it can apparently even ease the birth. Frequently, women find it creates a quick and simple birth – an hour to an hour and a half from the first contraction to the appearance of the baby. Many midwives are learning the technique, not just to ease childbirth but also because a few simple touches to the newborn baby's feet will instantly calm the baby.

'It is revolutionary work,' says Saint-Pierre. 'We can never predict what is likely to happen because we do not know what the life-force has got in store for each person.'

It's hard to see how such a simple technique can instigate profound changes, but people swear it has transformed their lives. Some find new relationships or end outdated ones; some move house or change their jobs; others are prompted to pursue a healthier lifestyle or to seek medical advice. Some simply find they suddenly seem to have more time or are able to accomplish all they need to do with greater ease. Often, Saint-Pierre says, it nudges people to seek the help they really need.

The session

Saint-Pierre is a still quiet man with a twinkle of humour in his eyes. He's the kind of person you would trust with your soul. Yet he does not ask for any details about your life and takes no case history. Instead, he simply invites you to take off your shoes and socks and lie or sit on a large window seat liberally scattered with cushions. Placing my foot on his lap, I lay back and closed my eyes while he started to work. His touch is light and fluid; sometimes I felt as if he were gently polishing my foot; at others as if he were almost searching for something. Occasionally, he would yawn. This, he explained, was not because he was bored or tired but because blockages were passing through his hands into his body. Yawning, sneezing or even burping apparently allows the blocks to disappear harmlessly into the air.

Some people report that during a session they 'see' scenes from their lives or that they can re-experience emotions from the womb. Nothing like that happened to me, but the whole experience was very enjoyable and I found myself in a strange half-dozing, half-waking state. After about half an hour, Saint-Pierre worked on my hands and then finally on my head, leaving me feeling very relaxed yet surprisingly energized.

336

FINDING A SUPERTHERAPIST

THE BASICS

Good food

WEIGHT LOSS

• Many of the supertherapies will aid weight loss as part of their programme. This book does not go into the purely psychological approaches to weight loss, but if you feel a psychotherapist could help, contact the **British Association of Psychotherapists**, 37 Mapesbury Road, London NW2 4HJ.

• The British Association for Counselling has compiled a list of specialists in different fields, including eating problems. For information send an SAE (148 x 210 mm) to the **British Association for Counselling**, 1 Regent Place, Rugby, Warwicks CV21 2PJ.

CHINESE HERBS

• Chinese herbs for cookery can be obtained by mail order from **East West Herbs**, Langston Priory Mews, Kingham, Oxon OX7 6UP (tel: 01608 658862).

DETOXING

• For information on Stop the World's detox breaks in Somerset, contact **Stop the World**, Hornblotton House, Hornblotton,

Shepton Mallet, Somerset BA4 6SB (tel: 01963 824100). Please enclose an SAE.

FASTING
• For details on safe fasting contact **The Purist Foundation**, Goddards Green Stable, Angley Road, Cranbrook, Kent TN17 3LR (tel: 01580 715851). Please enclose an SAE.

Good exercise
• Check out Yellow Pages for sports centres and gyms in your area. Local education authorities also often run classes as part of their adult education programmes.

WALKING
• The National Register of Personal Fitness Trainers can put you in touch with a personal trainer who specializes in powerwalking. Contact the **National Register of Personal Fitness Trainers**, Thornton House, Thornton Road, London SW19 4NG (tel: 0181 944 6688). Please enclose an SAE.
• For information on race-walking, send an SAE to the **Race Walking Association**, Hufflers, Heard's Lane, Shenfield, Brentwood, Essex CM15 0SF.

YOGA
• A full range of yoga classes devised by Godfrey Devereux and his team are held at the **Life Centre**, 15 Edge Street, London W8 7PN (tel: 0171 221 4602). Most local authorities, sports centres or gyms also run more traditional yoga classes.

CHI KUNG
• Dr Malcolm Kirsch teaches Chi Kung at the **101 Clinic**, 101 Seymour Place, London W1H 5TG (tel: 0171 262 4507). Where possible, Dr Kirsh will try to recommend a Chi Kung teacher in your area. Send an SAE for details.

QI-NETICS
• For details of Qi-netics classes, individual sessions and Qi-netics retreats all over the world, contact **Qi-netics**, 206 Great Western Road, London W11 1BD (tel: 0171 221 5358). Please enclose a large SAE.

PSYCHOCALISTHENICS

• Sarah Birrell teaches Psychocalisthenics in Bury St Edmunds. For details of her classes phone 01284 810587.

• For details of registered teachers and courses in other parts of the country, contact **The London School of T'ai-chi Chuan**, 45 Blenheim Road, London W4 1ET (tel: 01426 914540). Please enclose an SAE.

• Lindsay Wagner's video can be ordered by phone on 01252 703539.

Stressbusting

MEDITATION

• Transcendental Meditation: there are around eighty teaching centres around the UK which all give free introductory talks. For details phone 0800 269303.

• For details of Jill Purce's voice workshops, contact **Inner Sound and Voice**, Flat 3, 117 Church Road, Richmond, Surrey TW10 6LS (tel: 0181 948 5161).

• The Sivananda Yoga Vedanta Centre runs a variety of classes and courses on yoga and meditation, and can also put you in touch with teachers around the UK. For details contact the **Sivananda Yoga Vedanta Centre**, 51 Felsham Road, London SW15 1AZ (tel: 0181 780 0160). Please enclose an SAE.

• For details of Zen Practice, send an SAE to the **Zen Practice Centre Trust**, 2 The Colonnades, 4 West Street, West Malling, Kent ME19 6QZ.

AUTOGENIC TRAINING

• Autogenic training is taught in small groups. To find a group in the London area contact the **Autogenic Training Centre**, 100 Harley Street, London W1N 1AF (tel: 0171 935 1811). Please enclose an SAE.

• For groups outside London, send an SAE to the **British Association for Autogenic Training and Therapy**, 18 Holtsmere Close, Garston, Watford, Herts WD2 6NG.

FLOATING

• The **South London Natural Health Centre**, 7a Clapham Common Southside, London SW4 7AA (tel: 0171 720 8817). Please enclose an SAE.

- For details of a float centre near you (many combine floating with mind machines, aromatherapy and other forms of healing) contact **The Floatation Tank Association**, The Lodge, Manor Farm, Wendover Dean, Aylesbury HP22 6QA (tel: 01296 696300). Please enclose an SAE.

Good sleep
- If you are concerned about your sleep and would like medical advice, call the **Sleep Matters Helpline** on 0181 995 8503. Run by qualified nurses, it can often put your mind at rest.

Good posture
- For details of a qualified Alexander Technique teacher in your area, send an SAE to the **Society of Teachers of the Alexander Technique**, 20 London House, 266 Fulham Road, London SW10 9EL.
- For a list of physiotherapists in your area, contact either the **Chartered Society of Physiotherapy**, 14 Bedford Row, London WC1R 4ED (tel: 0171 242 1941) or the **Organisation of Chartered Physiotherapists in Private Practice**, Suite 8, Weston Chambers, Weston Road, Southend-on-Sea SS1 1AT (tel: 01702 392124).
- Pilates is taught at **Natureworks**, 16 Balderton Street, London W1 (tel: 0171 355 4036).
- Barbara McCrea teaches the Feldenkrais Method at **The Open Centre**, 188 Old Street, London EC1V 9FR (tel: 0171 251 1504). For details of classes in your area send an SAE to **The Feldenkrais Guild UK**, PO Box 370, London N10 3XA.

THE COMPLETE SYSTEMS FOR TOTAL HEALTH

AYURVEDA
- Angela Hope-Murray practises Ayurvedic nutrition at the **Hale Clinic**, 7 Park Crescent, London W1N 3HE (tel: 0171 631 0156) and at The Old Chapel, Drury Lane, Mortimer, Berkshire RG7 2JN (tel: 01734 332135).
- Ayurvedic Living has a catalogue of books and tapes on Ayurveda and can also provide further information on practitioners and workshops around the UK. Send an SAE (148 x 210 mm) to **Ayurvedic Living**, PO Box 188, Exeter EX4 5AY.

TRADITIONAL CHINESE MEDICINE
• For a list of herbalists, send an SAE to **The Register of Chinese Herbal Medicine**, 21 Warbeck Road, London W12 8NS.
• The Council for Acupuncture represents various organizations within the field of acupuncture and TCM. For further information or to obtain a copy of the Directory of British Acupuncturists contact **The Council for Acupuncture**, 179 Gloucester Place, London NW1 6DX (tel: 0171 724 5756). A small fee will be charged for the directory.

NATUROPATHY
• **Tyringham Naturopathic Clinic**, Newport Pagnell, Buckinghamshire MK16 9ER (tel: 01908 610450). There is also a provision for outpatients.
• **The British Naturopathic and Osteopathic Association** has an outpatients clinic in London at 6 Frazer House, 6 Netherhall Gardens, London NW3 5RR. Phone 0171 435 7830 for details.
• For details of individual naturopaths in your area contact the **General Council and Register of Naturopaths**, 6 Netherhall Gardens, London NW3 5RR (tel: 0171 435 8728).

THE NUTRITIONAL AND HERBAL APPROACH

NUTRITIONAL THERAPY
• Some NHS health centres can refer you to a dietician or nurse within their practice. However, although they can advise on what makes up a healthy diet, they are not able to diagnose and treat illness through food and supplementation in the way a fully qualified nutritionist can. Some health centres do have nutritionists but generally, you will have to pay for the service.
• **Ultimate Health Clinic**, 24 Queens Road, East Sheen, London SW14 8PJ (tel: 0181 392 2777). Please send an SAE for details.
• To find a well-qualified practitioner in your area contact the **Society for the Promotion of Nutritional Therapy**, PO Box 47, Heathfield, East Sussex TN21 8ZX (tel: 01435 867007). Please enclose an SAE. A small fee will be charged for a copy of their register.

HERBALISM
- **The National Institute of Medical Herbalists**, 56 Longbrook Street, Exeter EX4 6AH (tel: 01392 426022). For a register send a large SAE and a first-class stamp.
- **The General Council and Register of Consultant Herbalists**, 18 Sussex Square, Brighton, East Sussex BN2 5AA (tel: 01243 267126). Please enclose an SAE. For a small charge they will supply a register of practitioners.

BODYWORKING

The manipulation therapies: working on the skeletal structure

OSTEOPATHY
- For a register of practitioners contact **The General Osteopathic Information Service**, PO Box 2074, Reading, Berkshire RG1 4YR (tel: 01734 512051). Please enclose an SAE. You can also ask your GP for a referral.

CRANIAL OSTEOPATHY
- Peter Bartlett and Corina Petter both practise at the **Hale Clinic**, 7 Park Crescent, London W1N 3HE (tel: 0171 631 0156).
- For a register of osteopaths send an SAE to **General Osteopathic Information Service**, PO Box 2074, Reading, Berkshire RG1 4YR. (You will have to check with individual osteopaths as to whether they use cranial techniques.)

CRANIO-SACRAL THERAPY
- Monica Anthony practises at Violet Hill Studios. For details contact **Violet Hill Studios**, 6 Violet Hill, London NW8 9EB (tel: 0171 624 6101 or 0171 232 2562). Please enclose an SAE.
- For a list of cranio-sacral therapists contact the **International Register of Cranio-sacral Therapists**, 160 Upper Fant Road, Maidstone, Kent ME16 8DJ (tel: 01622 729231). Please enclose an SAE.

CHIROPRACTIC
- **British Chiropractic Association**, 29 Whitley Street, Reading, Berks RG2 0EG (tel: 01734 757557). For a small fee you can obtain an information pack or register of practitioners. Please enclose an SAE (148 x 210 mm).

McTIMONEY CHIROPRACTIC

• Jacquie Thomas practises at **Life Centre**, 15 Edge Street, London W8 7PN (tel: 0171 221 4602 for appointments only).

• For further information on McTimoney and a director of practitioners throughout the UK, send an SAE to **McTimoney Chiropractic Association**, 21 High Street, Eynsham, Oxon OX8 1HE. A small fee will be charged for the directory of practitioners.

ZERO BALANCING

• Jeff Lennard can be contacted at **Nature Works**, 16 Balderton Street, London W1 (tel: 0171 355 4036 or 0181 723 9209).

• For details of certified Zero Balancers around the country, send an SAE to the **Zero Balance Association UK**, 36 Richmond Road, Cambridge CB4 3PU. Fritz Smith's book *Inner Bridges* is also available from them.

The manipulation therapies: working on the fascial structure

BOWEN TECHNIQUE

• For more details on the Bowen technique and practitioners contact Julian Baker at 6 Rowan Court, Frome, Somerset BA11 2SJ (tel: 01373 461873). A four-day introductory course teaches the technique for use on family and friends: for details contact the above address. Please enclose an SAE.

ROLFING

• For more details on Rolfing and a list of Rolfers, phone Jenny Crewdson on 0171 834 1493.

HELLERWORK

• For details on Hellerwork and a list of Hellerworkers, contact **Bodyworkers**, Suite 211, Coppergate House, 16 Brune Street, London E1 7NJ (tel: 0171 721 7833).

Re-educating reflexes

INTEGRATION THERAPY

• For more information contact the **Institute for Developmental Potential**, 6 Patna Place, North Road West, Plymouth, Devon PL1 5AY (tel: 01752 222188). Consultations take place in Devon and London.

The pressure point therapies

REFLEXOLOGY
- **The Association of Reflexologists**, 27 Old Gloucester Street, London WC1N 3XX (tel: 01273 479020). Send an SAE for a copy of their register.
- **The Reflexologists Society**, Membership Secretary, 127 Bullbrook Drive, Bracknell RG12 2QP (tel: 01344 429770). Send an SAE for a copy of their register.

MORRELL REFLEXOLOGY
- For more information and details of courses and practitioners in your area, contact either Sue Ricks, 15 Cropston Avenue, Loughborough, Leics LE11 0PR (tel: 01509 214373) or Patricia Morrell at Sedbury Park Lodge, Sedbury, Chepstow, Gwent (tel: 01291 621489). Please enclose an SAE.

ACUPRESSURE/SHIATSU
- **The Shiatsu Society**, 5 Foxcote, Wokingham, Berkshire RG11 3PG (tel: 01734 730836). Please send an SAE for a list of practitioners in your area.

JIN SHIN JYUTSU
- For more details on Jin Shin Jyutsu, contact Roselyn Journeaux, **Southsea Centre for Complementary Medicine**, 25 Osborne Road, Southsea, Hampshire PO5 3ND (tel: 01705 874748). There are frequent workshops around the UK which teach the technique. Send an SAE to the above address for details.

The massage therapies

AROMATHERAPY
- For a register of practitioners, send an SAE (148 x 210 mm) to the **International Federation of Aromatherapists**, Stamford House, 2–4 Chiswick High Road, London W4 1TH. A small fee is charged for the register.
- **International Society of Professional Aromatherapists**, The Annexe, Hinckley, Leics LE10 1AG (tel: 01455 637987). Send an SAE for information.
- **The Aromatherapy Organisations Council**, 3 Latymer Close, Braybrooke, Market Harborough, Leicester LE16 8LN (tel: 01858 434242). Send an SAE for information.

MANUAL LYMPH DRAINAGE
- Dee Jones practises MLD in London (tel: 0171 221 4602 or 0181 994 1816).
- For details of other practitioners around the UK, send an SAE to **MLD UK**, 8 Wittenham Lane, Dorchester on Thames, Oxon OX10 7JW.

CHAVUTTI THIRUMAL
- For more details contact Jessica Loeb at **Natureworks**, 16 Balderton Street, London W1 (tel: 0171 355 4036). Please enclose an SAE. For details of practitioners in Scotland phone 01896 822656 and for practitioners in the south west of England phone 01395 512355.

KAHUNA BODYWORK
- Rosalie Samet can be contacted at the **Hope House Healing Sanctuary**, 51 Benedict Street, Glastonbury, Somerset BA6 9NB (tel: 01458 834451). Please enclose an SAE. There are very few performers of the massage in the UK, but Rosalie Samet will try to put you in touch with the nearest.

INDIAN HEAD MASSAGE
- Narendra Mehta practises at **Natureworks**, 16 Balderton Street, London W1 (tel: 0171 355 4036).
- For details of weekend courses and practitioners around the UK, contact Narendra at the **Eastern Health and Beauty Centre**, 136 Holloway Road, London N7 8DD (tel: 0171 609 3590).

ENERGYWORKING

HOMEOPATHY
- For a list of classically trained homeopaths, contact the **Society of Homeopaths,** 2 Artizan Road, Northampton NN1 4HU (tel: 01604 21400).
- For a list of doctors who also use homeopathy, contact **British Homeopathic Association**, 27a Devonshire Street, London W1N 1RJ (tel: 0171 935 2163).
- Homeopaths who are GPs working within the NHS can refer patients to consultants at NHS homeopathic hospitals in London, Kent, Liverpool, Glasgow and Bristol.

BACH FLOWER REMEDIES

• For further details of the Ultimate Health Clinic's weight-loss programme, contact the **Ultimate Health Clinic**, 24 Queens Road, East Sheen, London SW14 8PJ (tel: 0181 392 2777). Please enclose an SAE.

• For details of mail order books on the Bach flower remedies and the remedies themselves, phone 0171 495 2404.

• For details of practitioners around the UK, contact the **Dr Edward Bach Centre**, Mount Vernon, Sotwell, Wallingford, Oxon OX10 0PZ (tel: 01491 834678). Please enclose an SAE.

AUSTRALIAN BUSH FLOWER REMEDIES

• Serena Smith can be contacted at the **London Personal Development Centre**, Lazenby House, 2 Thayer Street, London W1M 5LG (tel: 0171 935 8935 or 0171 431 6153). Please enclose an SAE.

• *Australian Bush Flower Essences* by Ian White (Findhorn Press) gives full details of how to self-treat using the essences.

OTHER FLOWER AND GEM REMEDIES

• The Yantra Centre for Vibrational Therapy has a mail order catalogue covering a wide range of essences: Bach; Australian Bush; Himalayan flower and tree essences; Shimara crystal, herb, flower and gem essences; Chakra essences; the Californian Flower Essence Society remedies and others. For a catalogue contact the **Yantra Centre for Vibrational Therapy**, 204 Kensington Park Road, London W11 1NR (tel: 0171 229 9646). Please enclose an SAE. A small fee is charged for the catalogue.

RADIONICS

• For more details on radionics and practitioners send an SAE to Keith Mason at The Mill House, Breamore, Fordingbridge, Hampshire SP6 2AF.

HEALTH KINESIOLOGY

• For more information on Health Kinesiology, practitioners around the UK, workshops and training courses contact Jane Thurnell-Read at 12 Castle Road, Penzance, Cornwall TR18 2AX (tel: 01736 64800). Please enclose an SAE. A simple form of Health Kinesiology is explained in *Cure Your Own Allergies In Minutes* by Jimmy Scott (Health Kinesiology Publications). It isn't generally available in bookshops but can be ordered from Jane Thurnell-Read at the above address.

ELECTRO-CRYSTAL THERAPY
• For details of electro-crystal therapy and a therapist in your area contact the **Yantra Centre for Vibrational Therapy**, 204 Kensington Park Road, London W11 1NR (please include an SAE). Or phone 0171 229 4781.

POLARITY THERAPY
• Rosamund Webster is based at **International School of Polarity Therapy**, 7 Nunney Close, Golden Valley, Cheltenham, Glos GL51 0TU (tel: 01242 522352). Please send an SAE for details of practitioners and training courses.
• For details of polarity therapists around the UK, contact The Secretary, **International Society of Polarity Therapists**, 54 Ashford Road, Topsham, Exeter, Devon EX3 0LA (tel: 01392 877015). Please enclose an SAE.

MAGNETOTHERAPY
• Magnetotherapy sessions are held at the Hale Clinic in London. Nikken magnetic products are also on sale via the clinic. The Hale Clinic also holds seminars on magnetotherapy: for details contact the **Hale Clinic**, 7 Park Crescent, London W1V 3HE (tel: 0171 631 0156 or 0171 637 3377).

SOUND THERAPY
• Susan Lever runs sound healing workshops and individual sessions. She also distributes Jonathan Goldman's book (*Healing Sounds*) and tape (*Harmonic Journeys*) together with other healing sounds tapes, and can give information on workshops run by Goldman. For details contact **Rainbow Express**, 4 Maldon Road, London W3 6SU (tel: 0181 992 5987).
• Jill Purce is another well-known workshop leader who specializes in the healing power of sound. For details of her workshops contact **Inner Sound and Voice**, Flat 3, 117 Church Road, Richmond, Surrey TW10 6LS (tel: 0181 948 5161).
• The Festival for Mind, Body, Spirit and the Healing Arts exhibitions generally include sound workshops. For more information and a free programme phone 0171 938 3788.

LIGHT THERAPY
• For more details on light therapy and Natalie Handley's light therapy and reflexology treatment, contact the **Hale Clinic**, 7 Park Crescent, London W1V 3HE (tel: 0171 631 0156). The clinic also runs seminars open to the public with Dr Downing and Natalie Handley. Portable light units for home use can be ordered from the above address.

COLOUR THERAPY
• For a register of practitioners, contact the **Institute for Complementary Medicine** (ICM), Box 194, London SE16 1QZ (tel: 0171 237 5165). Please enclose an SAE.
• The **International Association for Colour Therapy**, Brook House, Avering, Tetbury GL8 8NS (tel: 01453 832150) can also provide a list of practitioners. Please send an SAE.

HEALING
• For more information contact the **National Federation of Spiritual Healers**, Old Manor Farm Studio, Church Street, Sunbury-on-Thames, Middlesex TW16 6RG (tel: 01932 783164). Please enclose an SAE. For referral to healers in your area, phone the **National Healer Referral Service** on 01891 616080.
• Nicki Skully teaches occasional workshops in this country. Her book *The Golden Cauldron* describes how to get in touch with the animal archetypes; this and tapes of inner journeys with the cobra and other animals can be ordered by mail order. For details phone 01225 461687.

REIKI
• The Reiki Alliance can put you in touch with a practitioner in your area. Equally, you can attend workshops to learn Reiki for yourself. For details contact **The Reiki Alliance**, 27 Lavington Road, Ealing, London W13 9NN (tel: 0181 579 3813). Please enclose an SAE.

METAMORPHIC TECHNIQUE
• For details of workshops and practitioners of the metamorphic technique, contact **The Metamorphic Association**, 67 Ritherdon Road, Tooting, London SW17 8QE (tel: 0181 672 5951). Please enclose an SAE.

UMBRELLA ORGANIZATIONS

The following organizations can give advice and information on complementary healthcare in general and also have lists of practitioners. Please send an SAE with any enquiry.

• The **Institute for Complementary Medicine** (ICM), PO Box 194, London SE16 1QZ (tel: 0171 237 5165). Administers the British Register of Complementary Practitioners.

• The **British Complementary Medicine Association** (BCMA), St Charles' Hospital, 94 Exmoor Street, London W10 6DZ (tel: 0181 964 1205). Covers most major therapies except acupuncture, homeopathy and herbalism.

EXHIBITIONS

• The Festival for Mind, Body, Spirit and the Healing Arts exhibitions, held in London, offer a good chance to meet a wide variety of practitioners and sample different therapies via workshops and lectures. For more information and a free programme contact **New Life Promotions**, Arnica House, 170 Campden Hill Road, London W8 7AS (tel: 0171 938 3788).

FURTHER READING

Barnard, Neal D., *The Power of Your Plate* (BPC)

Baum, Glenda, *Aquarobics* (Arrow)

Bennett, Bija, *Breathing Into Life* (HarperSanFrancisco)

Bonds, Lilian Verner, *Discover the Magic of Colour* (Optima)

Brennan, Richard, *The Alexander Technique – Natural Poise for Health* (Element)

Campion, Kitty, *A Woman's Herbal* (Vermilion)

Chaitow, Leon, *Body Tonic* (Gaia)

Chopra, Deepak, *Restful Sleep* (Rider)

Davies, Dr Stephen and Steward, Dr Alan, *Nutritional Medicine* (Pan)

Dougans, Inge, *Reflexology – Foot Massage for Total Health* (Element)

Douillard, John, *Body, Mind and Sport* (Bantam)

Downing, Damien, *Day Light Robbery* (Arrow)

Gimbel, Theo, *The Book of Colour Healing* (Gaia)

Goldman, Jonathan, *Healing Sounds* (Element)

Harvey, Eliana and Oatley, Mary Jane, *Acupressure* (Headway)

Hay, Louise, *You Can Heal Your Life* (Eden Grove); *Love Your Body, Heal Your Life* (Eden Grove)

Holden, Robert, *Stress Busters* (Thorsons)

Howitt Wilson, Michael, *Thorsons Introductory Guide to Chiropractic* (Thorsons)

Hutchinson, Michael, *The Book of Floating* (Quill)

Ichazo, Oscar, *Master Level Exercise – Psychocalisthenics* (Sequoia Press)

Kit, Wong Kiew, *The Art of Chi Kung* (Element)

Liberman, Jacob, *Light – Medicine of the Future* (Bear & Co.)

Liechti, Elaine, *Shiatsu* (Element)

Lockie, Dr Andrew and Geddes, Dr Nicola, *The Family Guide to Homeopathy* (Hamish Hamilton); *The Women's Guide to Homeopathy* (Hamish Hamilton)

Lu, Henry C, *Chinese Systems of Food Cures* (Sterling Publishing)

Mansfield, Peter, *Flower Remedies* (Optima)

Mason, Keith, *Medicine for the 21st Century* (Element)

Morrison, Judith H., *The Book of Ayurveda* (Gaia)

Murray, Michael and Pizzorno, Joseph, *Encyclopaedia of Natural Medicine* (Optima)

Oldfield, Harry and Coghill, Roger, *The Dark Side of the Brain* (Element)

Rhyner, Hans H., *Ayurveda – The Gentle Health System* (Sterling)

Scheffer, Mechthild, *Bach Flower Therapy* (Thorsons)

Scott, Jimmy, *Cure Your Own Allergies in Minutes* (Health Kinesiology Publications)

Skully, Nicki, *The Golden Cauldron* (Bear & Co.)

Smith, Fritz Frederick, *Inner Bridges* (Humanics Ltd)

Stone, Dr Randolph, *Health Building* (CRCS Publications)

Straten, Michael Van and Griggs, Barbara, *Superfoods* (Dorling Kindersley)

Taylor, Allegra, *Healing Hands* (Optima)

Teeguarden, Ron, *Chinese Tonic Herbs* (Japan Publications, Inc.)

Vishnu-devananda, Swami, *The Complete Illustrated Book of Yoga* (Harmony Books)

Vogel, H. C. A., *The Nature Doctor* (Mainstream Publishing)

White, Ian, *Australian Bush Flower Essences* (Findhorn Press)

Worwood, Valerie Ann, *The Fragrant Pharmacy* (Bantam)

INDEX

BOLD numbers indicate main references to each therapy

Wagner, Lindsay 339
Walker, Mary 167
walking **51–6**, 338
   for lymphatic system 230
   posture 102
   safety 56
water therapies *see* aqua aerobics;
       baths; floating;
       hydrotherapy
Webster, Rosamund 288–9, 347
Wehr, Thomas 306–7
weight loss 42, 45–6, 59, 68, 148,
    234
   useful addresses 337, 346
   see also dieting
White, Ian 263, 266, 346
WHO *see* World Health
      Organisation

Winter, David 55
Wong, Lydia 63–6
Wood, Julie 282
World Health Organisation
      (WHO): diet and nutrition
      guidelines 27, 122

yin and *yang* 221
yoga 50, 56, **57–60**
   breathing (*pranayama*) 72–3, 235
   'Dynamis' 57–60
   for lymphatic system 230, 231
   in naturopathic treatment 131
   polarity yoga 289
   useful addresses 338, 339

Zen meditation 80, 339
Zero Balancing **171–6**, 184, 343
Zone Therapy 197

NOTES

NOTES

NOTES

NOTES

NOTES